P9-CQN-562

Nelson's English Series
General Editor—ERNEST BERNBAUM

MALORY TO MRS. BEHN

SELECTIONS FROM THE BEST PROSE FICTION

VOL. I. MALORY TO MRS. BEHN

MALORY TO MRS. BEHN

SPECIMENS OF EARLY PROSE FICTION

Selected and Edited by
ALBERT MORTON TURNER
Associate Professor of English
University of Maine
and
PERCIE HOPKINS TURNER
Formerly Assistant Professor of English
University of Maine

THOMAS NELSON AND SONS
NEW YORK
1930

PRINTED IN THE UNITED STATES OF AMERICA

CONTENTS

INTRODUCTION

THE present introduction attempts to give, for the benefit of the general reader, a very brief sketch of the English novel up to 1700. Only a few authors and works can be touched upon in the short space available, but the chief movements or currents in the development of English prose fiction are indicated and the position therein of the works from which the ensuing specimens are drawn.

In the middle ages, short tales existed in prose form, and collections of moral stories were written down, but the chief representative of fiction was the romance. Originally treated in verse, the great themes of medieval literature, both on the continent and in England, came eventually into prose versions. These romances center about the adventures and heroic combats of knights; they stress devotion to ladies and to the church; they revel in the supernatural. Three names stand preeminent among the authors of prose romance in medieval England: Malory, Caxton, and Lord Berners. Malory, in the later fifteenth century, compiled *Le Morte Darthur*, the noblest specimen of the genre in English. Caxton, the first English printer, not only published Malory's work in 1485 but himself rendered from the French numerous prose romances, albeit less eloquently. Lord Berners, finally, translated *Huon of Bordeaux* in the early sixteenth century. With the Renaissance, however, medieval romances waned in popularity and usually drew their readers from the lower social classes.

With the advent of the Elizabethan age, numerous influences affected English fiction. There had come down from the very late middle ages a popular literature consisting of anecdotes, domestic stories, and jests. In addition, the literature of Italy and Spain was brought to bear upon that of England: the Italian *novella*, a short story, often of thrilling nature; the romance of shepherd life with or without knightly adventures; the novel of rogues. Finally the old Greek romances began to affect fiction profoundly.

English prose fiction of the age may be roughly divided into the romantic and the realistic. A most important example of the former is Lyly's *Euphues*. Refined in its outlook on life and distinguished by a highly wrought but equally artificial style, this book enjoyed vast popularity and occasioned a swarm of imitations. Another most important work was Sidney's *Arcadia,* a romance combining shepherd life and knightly adventure, wholly independent of Lyly, but enjoying equal popularity.

Many other romances were produced in this age, some of them influenced by Lyly, whether in ideas, plot, or style; others reflecting the *Arcadia* or the Greek romances. Thomas Lodge's *Rosalynde,* his masterpiece, is of the school of Lyly and is so good a representative of what the Elizabethan romance strove for that it is printed in this volume complete. Robert Greene, a most active writer, turned out numerous romances, mirroring all these influences. The chief among them are the pastoral romances *Menaphon* and *Pandosto,* the latter the source of Shakespeare's *Winter's Tale.* Like many Elizabethan writers, Greene troubled himself little about reality. In his works, Bohemia enjoys a sea-coast; people send to the "isle of Delphos" to consult the oracle of Apollo; and one heroine is so eternally youthful that when she appears incognita after a long absence, her father, her husband, and her son, all fall desperately in love.

The realistic fiction of the Elizabethan age springs, in general, from the stream of popular literature coming down from the middle ages. A large part of this Elizabethan realism treated of the adventures of rogues and scamps, whether agreeable ones or not. Most important in this class of fiction is Nashe's *The Unfortunate Traveller* or *Jack Wilton,* the first English picaresque novel. Closely related to such stories are books descriptive of popular life but wanting a central plot. The fecund Robert Greene turned out several such pamphlets, purporting to reveal the tricks whereby rogues hoodwinked honest men. Later, in the first decade of the seventeenth century, Dekker produced similar works, depicting contemporary manners vividly. Another prominent realistic novelist, in conclusion, is Thomas Deloney, who treated the working classes rather than vagabonds, and portrayed Elizabethan life with vigor.

With the close of Queen Elizabeth's reign, prose fiction became much less important in England, though there was still some demand for certain Elizabethan favorites, notably Sidney's *Arcadia.* When fiction rose again in popularity, it was inspired by the French romance, a type which had gradually developed across the Channel. Gomberville's *Polexandre* (1637) has been considered the first fully developed example. Following in its wake, La Calprenède wove glittering fictions about the names of Cleopatra, Cyrus, and Darius; and Madeleine de Scudéry treated Solyman the Magnificent, Cyrus, and legendary Roman history. These French romances were often of immense length and were full of extravagances. The heroes were prodigious in their valor; the ladies monumental in their virtue. Love was the favorite theme, and the hero was torn between this passion and ambition. The style fitted the subject matter and became high flown and stilted. These French romances grew in popularity in England, and by 1647 a stream of translations appeared. Strange as it may seem, only a few original English works of this type were produced. The most notable was *Parthenissa* (1654-1659).

In general the French romance continued the most popular type of fiction in seventeenth century England till about 1660. After this date, realism began to raise its head once more. A picaresque novel, *The English Rogue,* was produced by the combined efforts by Head and Kirkman, two literary hacks, and was followed by several other even less remarkable examples of the genre. Bunyan's *Pilgrim's Progress* and *The Life and Death of Mr. Badman,* though primarily allegory, are akin to realistic fiction in their handling of character. In 1678, moreover, there were translated into English *The Letters of a Portuguese Nun,* influential for their open and detailed treatment of passion and for the letter form, which in the next century was to grow in significance.

More important than any of these, however, were the novels which, based originally on the Italian *novella,* showed the influence of French or Spanish treatment. More than half of these were taken from the French, and less than one quarter were a native English product. Some of these stories treat historical characters, often with a scurrilous touch; others are so-called biographies, many of them with elements of truth but others wholly fictitious; and still others are incipient novels of manners, depicting the life of the scandalous court set. Outstanding among the novels of this general type are *Incognita* by the famous dramatist, Congreve, and various works by Mrs. Behn. This authoress' best narrative, *Oroonoko,* is printed entire in this volume, both because it exemplifies this style of fiction and because it anticipates several future tendencies of the English novel.

One other realistic literary form much cultivated in the seventeenth century, the character, is akin to the novel. The character is a short and specific account of a person typical of his class. The class chosen may be more or less general:

"a child," "a baker," "a she precise hypocrite," "a drunken Dutchman resident in England." Both physical details and, even more, traits of personality enter in, but there is, of course, no plot. The character reached the height of its development after 1700 in the hands of Addison and Steele, at which time it could go no further without merging in the novel.

In the ensuing specimens, though modernizing spelling and punctuation, we have tried to follow the best texts available. Sometimes, as the notes indicate, we have used excellent modern editions; at others we have gone direct to very early editions which the Harvard Library has kindly placed at our disposal. To the officials of this library and that of the University of Maine we are most grateful for a generosity and helpfulness which have done much toward making this book possible.

SIR THOMAS MALORY

LE MORTE DARTHUR

Sir Thomas Malory's own career had the adventures and heroic vicissitudes appropriate to the author of *Le Morte Darthur*. We first hear of him about 1415 fighting in France with Richard Beauchamp, Earl of Warwick. Accompanied by a lance and two archers, he bore his part in the war against Joan of Arc and indeed was probably present at her burning since his master furnished the special guard in Rouen market-place on that occasion. Beauchamp himself was the ideal knight of his time, called the "Father of Courtesy," delighting in romantic tournaments, yet a patron of learning. With him Malory may even have gone to Rome. Certainly the earl's life and character must have impressed his young follower.

Malory came home from the wars in France to an England disturbed by civil unrest. In 1445 he was a member of the Parliament which ratified peace after the Hundred Years'

War. A few years later, began the series of his accusations, trials, and imprisonments which can be traced in the legal records although the real extent of Sir Thomas' guilt is hard to determine. At Nuneaton, August 23, 1451, Malory was ordered to find securities to guarantee his good behavior toward the Carthusian Priory of Axholme. Imprisoned thereafter by the sheriff, he broke out at night, swam the moat, and escaped. With a group of followers he is twice recorded as having robbed of money and jewels the Cistercian Abbey of Blessed Mary of Combe, but the two accounts may refer to the same affair. There were also other charges preferred against him.

Finally brought before the king by the sheriffs of London, Sir Thomas pleaded not guilty but was imprisoned in the Tower. He had wisely made over his property to his wife, (that Elizabeth for whom he named Tristan's noble mother,) so that his twenty years of confinement were doubtless as comfortable as a good income could make them. Although he produced the king's pardon for all transgressions before 1455, he spent the rest of his life in prison, at the Marshalsea and in Newgate. The latter was a fortunate location since from it Malory must have had access to the London Library, founded just across the road by Dick Whittington. In prison he wrote his own great book and died, probably of plague, in 1471, only a year or two after finishing it. He is buried in Grey Friars' Churchyard where his tombstone proclaims him a *valens miles.*

Le Morte Darthur gave new impetus to the interest in chivalric romances by putting into admirable form that great series of tales dealing with King Arthur. These had been so very popular in the middle ages that Malory found them an enormous and confused mass of material, much of it in English verse and much in French prose. It was divided loosely into a Launcelot, a Tristan, and a Merlin cycle, the whole full of the discrepancies and contradictions which naturally had resulted from its slow development at many hands. After making various additions of his own, he fused the cycles into a fairly consistent narrative, and the mass he reduced into a tenth of its original bulk. Moreover he adapted the tales to his own times. The wars, especially those in the last book, reflect the civil strife in the England of his own day. Furthermore, the whole story of Arthur and Gawaine, of Launcelot and Galahad was intended as a guide for the characters and careers of gentlemen. Above all, Malory succeeded in couching his long story in noble and resonant English prose.

MORTE DARTHUR

"Madam," said Sir Launcelot, "I allow your wit; it is of late come since ye were wise. And therefore, madam, at this time I will be ruled by your counsel, and this night I will take my rest, and to-morrow by time I will take my way toward Winchester. But wit you well," said Sir Launcelot to the queen, "that at that jousts I will be against the king, and against all his fellowship." "Ye may there do as ye list," said the queen, "but by my counsel ye shall not be 10 against your king and your fellowship. For therein be full many hard knights of your blood, as ye wot well enough, it needeth not to rehearse them." "Madam," said Sir Launcelot, "I pray you that ye be not displeased with me, for I will take the adventure that God will send me."

And so upon the morn early Sir Launcelot heard mass and brake his fast, and so took his leave of the queen and departed. And then he rode so much until he came to Astolat, that is Guildford; and there 20 it happed him in the eventide he came to an old baron's place that hight Sir Bernard of Astolat. And as Sir Launcelot entered into his lodging, King Arthur espied him as he did walk in a garden beside the castle, how he took his lodging, and knew him full well. "It is well," said King Arthur unto the knights that were with him in that garden beside the castle, "I have now espied one knight that will play his play at the jousts to the which we be gone toward; I undertake he will do marvels." "Who is 30 that, we pray you tell us?" said many knights that were there at that time. "Ye shall not wit for me," said the king, as at this time. And so the king smiled, and went to his lodging.

So when Sir Launcelot was in his lodging, and un-

armed him in his chamber, the old baron and hermit came to him making his reverence, and welcomed him in the best manner; but the old knight knew not Sir Launcelot. "Fair sir," said Sir Launcelot to his host, "I would pray you to lend me a shield that were not openly known, for mine is well known." "Sir," said his host, "ye shall have your desire, for meseemeth ye be one of the likeliest knights of the world, and therefore I shall shew you
10 friendship. Sir, wit you well I have two sons that were but late made knights, and the eldest hight Sir Tirre, and he was hurt that same day he was made knight, that he may not ride, and his shield ye shall have; for that is not known I dare say but here, and in no place else. And my youngest son hight Lavaine, and if it please you, he shall ride with you unto that jousts; and he is of his age strong and wight, for much my heart giveth unto you that ye should be a noble knight; therefore, I pray you, tell
20 me your name," said Sir Bernard. "As for that," said Sir Launcelot, "ye must hold me excused as at this time, and if God give me grace to speed well at the jousts, I shall come again and tell you. But I pray you," said Sir Launcelot, "in any wise let me have your son, Sir Lavaine, with me, and that I may have his brother's shield." "All this shall be done," said Sir Bernard.

This old baron had a daughter that time that was called that time the Fair Maiden of Astolat. And
30 ever she beheld Sir Launcelot wonderfully. And as the book saith, she cast such a love unto Sir Launcelot that she could never withdraw her love, wherefore she died, and her name was Elaine le Blank. So thus as she came to and fro, she was so hot in her love that she besought Sir Launcelot to wear upon him at the jousts a token of hers. "Fair damosel," said Sir Launcelot, "an if I grant you

that, ye may say I do more for your love than ever I did for lady or damosel." Then he remembered him he would go to the jousts disguised. And because he had never fore that time borne no manner of token of no damosel, then he bethought him that he would bear one of her, that none of his blood thereby might know him, and then he said, "Fair maiden, I will grant you to wear a token of yours upon mine helmet, and therefore what it is, shew it 10 me." "Sir," she said, "it is a red sleeve of mine, of scarlet, well embroidered with great pearls," and so she brought it him. So Sir Launcelot received it, and said, "Never did I erst so much for any damosel." And then Sir Launcelot betook the fair maiden his shield in keeping, and prayed her to keep that until that he came again; and so that night he had merry rest and great cheer. For ever the damosel Elaine was about Sir Launcelot all the while she might be suffered.

20 So upon a day, on the morn, King Arthur and all his knights departed, for their king had tarried three days to abide his noble knights. And so when the king was ridden, Sir Launcelot and Sir Lavaine made them ready to ride, and either of them had white shields, and the red sleeve Sir Launcelot let carry with him. And so they took their leave at Sir Bernard, the old baron, and at his daughter, the Fair Maiden of Astolat. And then they rode so long till that they came to Camelot, that time called Winches- 30 ter; and there was great press of kings, dukes, earls, and barons, and many noble knights. But there Sir Launcelot was lodged privily by the means of Sir Lavaine with a rich burgess, that no man in that town was ware what they were. And so they reposed them there till our Lady Day, Assumption, as the great feast should be. So then trumpets blew

unto the field, and King Arthur was set on high upon a scaffold to behold who did best. But as the French book saith, the king would not suffer Sir Gawaine to go from him, for never had Sir Gawaine the better and Sir Launcelot were in the field; and many times was Sir Gawaine rebuked when Launcelot came into any jousts disguised.

Then some of the kings, as King Anguish of Ireland and the King of Scots, were that time turned 10 upon the side of King Arthur. And then on the other party was the King of Northgalis, and the King with the Hundred Knights, and the King of Northumberland, and Sir Galahad, the haut prince. But these three kings and this duke were passing weak to hold against King Arthur's party, for with him were the noblest knights of the world. So then they withdrew them either party from other, and every man made him ready in his best manner to do what he might.

20 Then Sir Launcelot made him ready and put the red sleeve upon his head and fastened it fast; and so Sir Launcelot and Sir Lavaine departed out of Winchester privily and rode until a little leaved wood behind the party that held against King Arthur's party, and there they held them still till the parties smote together. And then came in the King of Scots and the King of Ireland on Arthur's party, and against them came the King of Northumberland, and the King with the Hundred Knights smote down 30 the King of Northumberland, and the King with the Hundred Knights smote down King Anguish of Ireland. Then Sir Palomides, that was on Arthur's party, encountered with Sir Galahad, and either of them smote down other, and either party halp their lords on horseback again. So there began a strong assail upon both parties. And then came in Sir Brandiles, Sir Sagramore le Desirous, Sir

Dodinas le Savage, Sir Kay le Seneschal, Sir Griflet le Fise de Dieu, Sir Mordred, Sir Meliot de Logris, Sir Ozanna le Cure Hardy, Sir Safere, Sir Epinogris, Sir Galleron of Galway. All these fifteen knights were knights of the Table Round. So these with more other came in together and beat aback the King of Northumberland and the King of Northgalis. When Sir Launcelot saw this, as he hoved in a little leaved wood, then he said unto Sir Lavaine, 10 "See, yonder is a company of good knights, and they hold them together as boars that were chafed with dogs." "That is truth," said Sir Lavaine.

"Now," said Sir Launcelot, "and ye will help me a little, ye shall see yonder fellowship that chaseth now these men in our side, that they shall go as fast backward as they went forward." "Sir, spare not," said Sir Lavaine, "for I shall do what I may." Then Sir Launcelot and Sir Lavaine came in at the thickest of the press, and there Sir Launcelot smote down Sir 20 Brandiles, Sir Sagramore, Sir Dodinas, Sir Kay, Sir Griflet, and all this he did with one spear; and Sir Lavaine smote down Sir Lucan le Butler and Sir Bedevere. And then Sir Launcelot gat another spear, and there he smote down Sir Agravaine, Sir Gaheris, and Sir Mordred, and Sir Meliot de Logris; and Sir Lavaine smote Ozanna le Cure Hardy. And then Sir Launcelot drew his sword, and there he smote on the right hand and on the left hand, and by great force he unhorsed Sir Safere, Sir Epino- 30 gris, and Sir Galleron; and then the knights of the Table Round withdrew them aback, after they had gotten their horses as well as they might. "O mercy Jesu," said Sir Gawaine, "what knight is yonder that doth so marvellous deeds of arms in that field?" "I wot well what he is," said King Arthur, "but as at this time I will not name him." "Sir," said Sir Gawaine, "I would say it were Sir Launcelot by his riding and his buffets that I see him deal, but ever meseemeth it should not be he, for that he beareth the red sleeve upon his head; for I wist him never bear token at no jousts, of lady nor gentlewoman." "Let him be," said King Arthur; "he will be better known, and do more, or ever he depart."

Then the party that was against King Arthur were well comforted, and then they held them together that beforehand were sore rebuked. Then Sir Bors, 10 Sir Ector de Maris, and Sir Lionel called unto them the knights of their blood, as Sir Blamore de Ganis, Sir Bleoberis, Sir Aliduke, Sir Galihud, Sir Galihodin, Sir Bellangere le Beuse. So these nine knights of Sir Launcelot's kin thrust in mightily, for they were all noble knights; and they, of great hate and despite that they had unto him, thought to rebuke that noble knight Sir Launcelot, and Sir Lavaine, for they knew them not; and so they came hurling together, and smote down many knights of North-20 galis and of Northumberland. And when Sir Launcelot saw them fare so, he gat a spear in his hand; and there encountered with him all at once Sir Bors, Sir Ector, and Sir Lionel, and all they three smote him at once with their spears. And with force of themself they smote Sir Launcelot's horse to the earth; and by misfortune Sir Bors smote Sir Launcelot through the shield into the side, and the spear brake, and the head left still in his side; when Sir Lavaine saw his master lie on the ground, he ran 30 to the King of Scots and smote him to the earth; and by great force he took his horse and brought him to Sir Launcelot, and maugre of them all he made him to mount upon that horse. And then Launcelot gat a spear in his hand, and there he smote Sir Bors, horse and man, to the earth. In the same wise he served Sir Ector and Sir Lionel; and Sir Lavaine smote down Sir Blamore de Ganis. And then Sir Launcelot drew his sword, for he felt himself so sore y-hurt that he weened there to have had his death. And then he smote Sir Bleoberis such a buffet on the helmet that he fell down to the earth in a swoon. And in the same wise he served Sir Aliduke and Sir Galihud. And Sir Lavaine smote down Sir Bellangere, that was the son of Alisander le Orphelin; and by this was Sir Bors horsed, and then he came with Sir Ector and Sir Lionel, and all 10 they three smote with swords upon Sir Launcelot's helmet. And when he felt their buffets and his wound, the which was so grievous, then he thought to do what he might while he might endure. And then he gave Sir Bors such a buffet that he made him bow his head passing low; and therewithal he raced off his helm and might have slain him, and so pulled him down, and in the same wise he served Sir Ector and Sir Lionel. For as the book saith, he might have slain them; but when he saw their visages, his 20 heart might not serve him thereto, but left them there. And then afterward he hurled into the thickest press of them all, and did there the marvelloust deeds of arms that ever man saw or heard speak of. And ever Sir Lavaine, the good knight, with him, and there Sir Launcelot with his sword smote down and pulled down, as the French book maketh mention, mo than thirty knights, and the most part were of the Table Round; and Sir Lavaine did full well that day, for he smote down ten knights of the Table 30 Round.

"Mercy Jesu," said Sir Gawaine to Arthur, "I marvel what knight that he is with the red sleeve." "Sir," said King Arthur, "he will be known or he depart." And then the king blew unto lodging, and the prize was given by heralds unto the knight with the white shield that bare the red sleeve. Then came

the King with the Hundred Knights, the King of Northgalis, and the King of Northumberland, and Sir Galahad, the haut prince, and said unto Sir Launcelot, "Fair knight, God thee bless, for much have ye done this day for us, therefore we pray you that ye will come with us that ye may receive the honour and the prize as ye have worshipfully deserved it." "My fair lords," said Sir Launcelot, "wit you well if I have deserved thanks I have sore
10 bought it, and that me repenteth, for I am like never to escape with my life; therefore, fair lords, I pray you that ye will suffer me to depart where me liketh, for I am sore hurt. I take none force of none honor, for I had liefer to repose me than to be lord of all the world." And therewithal he groaned piteously, and rode a great wallop away-ward from them until he came under a wood's side.

And when he saw that he was from the field nigh a mile, that he was sure he might not be seen, then
20 he said with an high voice, "O gentle knight, Sir Lavaine, help me that this truncheon were out of my side, for it sticketh so sore that it nigh slayeth me." "O mine own lord," said Sir Lavaine, "I would fain do that might please you, but I dread me sore and I pull out the truncheon that ye shall be in peril of death." "I charge you," said Sir Launcelot, "as ye love me, draw it out." And therewithal he descended from his horse, and right so did Sir Lavaine; and forthwithal Sir Lavaine drew the trun-
30 cheon out of his side, and he gave a great shriek and a marvelous grisly groan, and the blood brast out nigh a pint at once that at the last he sank down upon his buttocks and so swooned pale and deadly. "Alas," said Sir Lavaine, "what shall I do?" And then he turned Sir Launcelot into the wind, but so he lay there nigh half an hour as he had been dead.

And so at the last Sir Launcelot cast up his eyes

and said, "O Lavaine, help me that I were on my horse, for here is fast by within this two mile a gentle hermit that sometime was a full noble knight and a great lord of possessions. And for great goodness he hath taken him to wilful poverty and forsaken many lands, and his name is Sir Baudwin of Brittany, and he is a full noble surgeon and a good leech. Now let see, help me up that I were there, for ever my heart giveth me that I shall never die of
10 my cousin-germain's hands." And then with great pain Sir Lavaine halp him upon his horse. And then they rode a great wallop together, and ever Sir Launcelot bled that it ran down to the earth; and so by fortune they came to that hermitage the which was under a wood and a great cliff on the other side and a fair water running under it.

And then Sir Lavaine beat on the gate with the butt of his spear and cried fast, "Let in for Jesu's sake;" and there came a fair child to them and asked
20 them what they would. "Fair son," said Sir Lavaine, "go and pray thy lord, the hermit, for God's sake to let in here a knight that is full sore wounded; and this day tell thy lord I saw him do more deeds of arms than ever I heard say that any man did." So the child went in lightly, and then he brought the hermit, the which was a passing good man. When Sir Lavaine saw him, he prayed him for God's sake of succour. "What knight is he?" said the hermit. "Is he of the house of King Arthur, or not?" "I
30 wot not," said Sir Lavaine, "what is he, nor what is his name, but well I wot I saw him do marvellously this day as of deeds of arms." "On whose party was he?" said the hermit. "Sir," said Sir Lavaine, "he was this day against King Arthur, and there he won the prize of all the knights of the Round Table." "I have seen the day," said the hermit, "I would have loved him the worse because he was against my lord,

King Arthur, for sometime I was one of the fellowship of the Round Table, but I thank God now I am otherwise disposed. But where is he? Let me see him." Then Sir Lavaine brought the hermit to him.

And when the hermit beheld him, as he sat leaning upon his saddle-bow ever bleeding piteously, and ever the knight-hermit thought that he should know him, but he could not bring him to knowledge because he was so pale for bleeding. "What knight are 10 ye," said the hermit, "and where were ye born?" "My fair lord," said Sir Launcelot, "I am a stranger and a knight adventurous, that laboureth throughout many realms for to win worship." Then the hermit advised him better, and saw by a wound on his cheek that he was Sir Launcelot. "Alas," said the hermit, "mine own lord why lain you your name from me? Forsooth I ought to know you of right, for ye are the most noblest knight of the world, for well I know you for Sir Launcelot." "Sir," said he, "sith 20 ye know me, help me and ye may, for God's sake, for I would be out of this pain at once, either to death or to life." "Have ye no doubt," said the hermit, "ye shall live and fare right well." And so the hermit called to him two of his servants, and so he and his servants bare him into the hermitage, and lightly unarmed him, and laid him in his bed. And then anon the hermit staunched his blood, and made him to drink good wine, so that Sir Launcelot was well refreshed and knew himself. For in those days 30 it was not the guise of hermits as is nowadays. For there were none hermits in those days but that they had been men of worship and of prowess, and those hermits held great household and refreshed people that were in distress.

Now turn we unto King Arthur, and leave we Sir Launcelot in the hermitage. So when the kings were come together on both parties, and the great feast should be holden, King Arthur asked the King of Northgalis and their fellowship where was that knight that bare the red sleeve: "Bring him afore me that he may have his laud, and honor, and the prize, as it is right." Then spake Sir Galahad, the haut prince, and the King with a Hundred Knights: "We suppose that knight is mischieved, and that he is never like to see you nor none of us all, and that is 10 the greatest pity that ever we wist of any knight." "Alas," said Arthur, "how may this be? Is he so hurt? What is his name?" said King Arthur. "Truly," said they all, "we know not his name, nor from whence he came, nor whither he would." "Alas," said the king, "this be to me the worst tidings that came to me this seven year, for I would not for all the lands I wield to know and wit it were so that that noble knight were slain." "Know ye him?" said they all. "As for that," said Arthur, 20 "whether I know him or know him not, ye shall not know for me what man he is, but Almighty Jesu send me good good tidings of him." And so said they all. "By my head," said Sir Gawaine, "if it so be that the good knight be so sore hurt, it is great damage and pity to all this land, for he is one of the noblest knights that ever I saw in a field handle a spear or a sword. And if he may be found, I shall find him, for I am sure he nis not far from this town." "Bear you well," said King Arthur, "an 30 ye may find him, unless that he be in such a plight that he may not wield himself." "Jesu defend," said Sir Gawaine, "but wit I shall what he is, and I may find him."

Right so Sir Gawaine took a squire with him upon hackneys and rode all about Camelot within six or seven mile, but so he came again and could hear no word of him. Then within two days King Arthur

and all the fellowship returned unto London again. And so as they rode by the way it happed Sir Gawaine at Astolat to lodge with Sir Bernard thereas was Sir Launcelot lodged. And so as Sir Gawaine was in his chamber to repose him, Sir Bernard, the old baron, came unto him, and his daughter Elaine, to cheer him and to ask him what tidings, and who did best at that tournament of Winchester. "So God me help," said Sir Gawaine, "there were two
10 knights that bare two white shields, but the one of them bare a red sleeve upon his head, and certainly he was one of the best knights that ever I saw joust in field. For I dare say," said Sir Gawaine, "that one knight with the red sleeve smote down forty knights of the Table Round, and his fellow did right well and worshipfully." "Now blessed be God," said the Fair Maiden of Astolat, "that that knight sped so well, for he is the man in the world that I first loved, and truly he shall be last that ever I shall
20 love." "Now, fair maid," said Sir Gawaine, "is that good knight your love?" "Certainly sir," said she, "wit ye well he is my love." "Then know ye his name?" said Sir Gawaine. "Nay truly," said the damosel, "I know not his name nor from whence he cometh, but to say that I love him, I promise you and God that I love him." "How had ye knowledge of him first?" said Sir Gawaine.

Then she told him as ye have heard to-fore, and how her father betook him her brother to do him
30 service, and how her father lent him her brother's, Sir Tirre's, shield: "And here with me he left his own shield." "For what cause did he so?" said Sir Gawaine. "For this cause," said the damosel, "for his shield was too well known among many noble knights." "Ah, fair damosel," said Sir Gawaine, "please it you let me have a sight of that shield?"

"Sir," said she, "it is in my chamber, covered with a case; an if ye will come with me, ye shall see it." "Not so," said Sir Bernard till his daughter; "let send for it."

So when the shield was come, Sir Gawaine took off the case. And when he beheld that shield, he knew anon that it was Sir Launcelot's shield and his own arms. "Ah Jesu mercy," said Sir Gawaine, "now is my heart more heavier than ever it was
10 to-fore." "Why?" said Elaine. "For I have great cause," said Sir Gawaine; "is that knight that oweth this shield your love?" "Yea truly," said she, "my love he is; God would I were his love." "So God me speed," said Sir Gawaine, "fair damosel, ye have right, for an he be your love, ye love the most honorable knight of the world and the man of most worship." "So me thought ever," said the damosel, "for never or that time, for no knight that ever I saw, loved I never none erst." "God grant," said
20 Sir Gawaine, "that either of you may rejoice other, but that is in a great adventure. But truly," said Sir Gawaine unto the damosel, "ye may say ye have a fair grace, for why I have known that noble knight this four-and-twenty year, and never or that day I nor none other knight, I dare make good, saw nor heard say that ever he bare token or sign of no lady, gentlewoman, ne maiden, at no jousts nor tournament. And therefore, fair maiden," said Sir Gawaine, "ye are much beholden to him to give him
30 thanks. But I dread me," said Sir Gawaine, "that ye shall never see him in this world, and that is great pity that ever was of earthly knight." "Alas," said she, "how may this be? Is he slain?" "I say not so," said Sir Gawaine, "but wit ye well he is grievously wounded by all manner of signs and by men's sight more likelier to be dead than to be alive; and wit ye well he is the noble knight Sir Launcelot for

by this shield I know him." "Alas," said the Fair Maiden of Astolat, "how may this be, and what was his hurt?" "Truly," said Sir Gawaine, "the man in the world that loved him best hurt him so; and I dare say," said Sir Gawaine, "and that knight that hurt him knew the very certainty that he had hurt Sir Launcelot, it would be the most sorrow that ever came to his heart."

"Now, fair father," said then Elaine, "I require 10 you give me leave to ride and to see him, or else I wot well I shall go out of my mind, for I shall never stint till that I find him and my brother, Sir Lavaine." "Do as it liketh you," said her father, "for me sore repenteth of the hurt of that noble knight." Right so the maid made her ready and before Sir Gawaine, making great dole.

Then on the morn Sir Gawaine came to King Arthur, and told him how he had found Sir Launcelot's shield in the keeping of the Fair Maiden of 20 Astolat. "All that knew I aforehand," said King Arthur, "and that caused me I would not suffer you to have ado at the great jousts, for I espied," said King Arthur, "when he came in till his lodging full late in the evening in Astolat. But marvel have I," said Arthur, "that ever he would bear any sign of any damosel, for or now I never heard say nor knew that ever he bare any token of none earthly woman." "By my head," said Sir Gawaine, "the Fair Maiden of Astolat loveth him marvellously well; what it 30 meaneth I cannot say, and she is ridden after to seek him." So the king and all came to London, and there Sir Gawaine openly disclosed to all the court that it was Sir Launcelot that jousted best.

And when Sir Bors heard that, wit ye well he was an heavy man, and so were all his kinsmen. But when Queen Guenever wist that Sir Launcelot bare the red sleeve of the Fair Maiden of Astolat she was nigh out of her mind for wrath. And then she sent for Sir Bors de Ganis in all the haste that might be. So when Sir Bors was come to-fore the queen, then she said, "Ah, Sir Bors, have ye heard say how falsely Sir Launcelot hath betrayed me?" "Alas, madam," said Sir Bors, "I am afeared he hath betrayed himself and us all." "No force," saith the queen, "though he be destroyed, for he is a false traitor knight." "Madam," said Sir Bors, "I pray you say ye not so, for wit you well I may not hear such language of him." "Why, Sir Bors," said she, "should I not call him traitor when he bare the red sleeve upon his head at Winchester at the great jousts?" "Madam," said Sir Bors, "that sleeve-bearing repenteth me sore, but I dare say he did it to none evil intent, but for this cause he bare the red sleeve that none of his blood should know him. For or then we, nor none of us all, never knew that ever he bare token or sign of maid, lady, ne gentlewoman." "Fie on him," said the queen; "yet for all his pride and bobaunce there ye proved yourself his better." "Nay, madam, say ye never more so, for he beat me and my fellows and might have slain us an he had would." "Fie on him," said the queen, "for I heard Sir Gawaine say before my lord Arthur that it were marvel to tell the great love that is between the Fair Maiden of Astolat and him." "Madam," said Sir Bors, "I may not warn Sir Gawaine to say what it pleased him. But I dare say as for my lord, Sir Launcelot, that he loveth no lady, gentlewoman, nor maid, but all he loveth in like much, and therefore, madam," said Sir Bors, "ye may say what ye will, but wit ye well I will haste me to seek him and find him wheresomever he be, and God send me good tidings of him." And so leave we them there, and speak we of Sir Launcelot that lay in great peril.

So as fair Elaine came to Winchester, she sought there all about, and by fortune Sir Lavaine was ridden to play him, to enchafe his horse. And anon as Elaine saw him, she knew him. And then she cried aloud until him. And when he heard her anon, he came to her, and then she asked her brother how did my lord, Sir Launcelot. "Who told you, sister, that my lord's name was Sir Launcelot?" Then she told him how Sir Gawaine by his shield knew him. 10 So they rode together till that they came to the hermitage, and anon she alighted.

So Sir Lavaine brought her in to Sir Launcelot; and when she saw him lie so sick and pale in his bed she might not speak, but suddenly she fell to the earth down suddenly in a swoon, and there she lay a great while. And when she was relieved, she shrieked and said, "My lord, Sir Launcelot, alas why be ye in this plight?" and then she swooned again. And then Sir Launcelot prayed Sir Lavaine to take 20 her up, "And bring her to me." And when she came to herself Sir Launcelot kissed her, and said, "Fair maiden, why fare ye thus? Ye put me to pain; wherefore make ye no more such cheer, for an ye be come to comfort me ye be right welcome; and of this little hurt that I have I shall be right hastily whole by the grace of God. But I marvel," said Sir Launcelot, "who told you my name?" Then the fair maiden told him all how Sir Gawaine was lodged with her father: "And there by your shield he dis- 30 covered your name." "Alas," said Sir Launcelot, "that me repenteth that my name is known, for I am sure it will turn unto anger." And then Sir Launcelot compassed in his mind that Sir Gawaine would tell Queen Guenever how he bare the red sleeve, and for whom; that he wist well would turn into great anger.

So this maiden Elaine never went from Sir

Launcelot, but watched him day and night, and did such attendance to him, that the French book saith there was never woman did more kindlier for man than she. Then Sir Launcelot prayed Sir Lavaine to make aspies in Winchester for Sir Bors if he came there, and told him by what tokens he should know him, by a wound in his forehead. "For well I am sure," said Sir Launcelot, "that Sir Bors will seek me, for he is the same good knight that hurt 10 me."

Now turn we unto Sir Bors de Ganis that came unto Winchester to seek after his cousin, Sir Launcelot, and so when he came to Winchester, anon there were men that Sir Lavaine had made to lie in a watch for such a man, and anon Sir Lavaine had warning; and then Sir Lavaine came to Winchester and found Sir Bors, and there he told him what he was, and with whom he was, and what was his name. "Now, fair knight," said Sir Bors, "I require you 20 that ye will bring me to my lord, Sir Launcelot." "Sir," said Sir Lavaine, "take your horse, and within this hour ye shall see him." And so they departed and came to the hermitage.

And when Sir Bors saw Sir Launcelot lie in his bed pale and discoloured, anon Sir Bors lost his countenance, and for kindness and pity he might not speak but wept tenderly a great while. And then when he might speak, he said thus: "O my lord, Sir Launcelot, God you bless, and send you hasty re-30 cover. And full heavy am I of my misfortune and of mine unhappiness, for now I may call myself unhappy. And I dread me that God is greatly displeased with me, that he would suffer me to have such a shame for to hurt you that are all our leader and all our worship, and therefore I call myself unhappy. Alas that ever such a caitiff-knight as I am should have power by unhappiness to hurt the most noblest knight of the world; where I so shamefully set upon you and overcharged you, and where ye might have slain me, ye saved me; and so did not I. For I and your blood did to you our utterance. I marvel," said Sir Bors, "that my heart or my blood would serve me; wherefore, my lord, Sir Launcelot, I ask your mercy." "Fair cousin," said Sir Launcelot, "ye be right welcome; and wit ye well, overmuch ye say for to please me, the which pleaseth me not, for why I have the same ysought; for I would with pride have overcome you all, and there in my pride I was near slain, and that was in mine own default, for I might have given you warning of my being there. And then had I had no hurt, for it is an old said saw, there is hard battle thereas kin and friends do battle either against other, there may be no mercy but mortal war. Therefore, fair cousin," said Sir Launcelot, "let this speech overpass, and all shall be welcome that God sendeth; and let us leave off this matter and let us speak of some rejoicing, for this that is done may not be undone; and let us find a remedy how soon that I may be whole."

Then Sir Bors leaned upon his bedside, and told Sir Launcelot how the queen was passing wroth with him, because he wore the red sleeve at the great jousts; and there Sir Bors told him all how Sir Gawaine discovered it: "By your shield that ye left with the Fair Maiden of Astolat." "Then is the queen wroth," said Sir Launcelot, "and therefore am I right heavy, for I deserved no wrath, for all that I did was because I would not be known." "Right so excused I you," said Sir Bors, "but all was in vain, for she said more largelier to me than I to you now. But is this she," said Sir Bors, "that is so busy about you, that men call the Fair Maiden of Astolat?" "She it is," said Sir Launcelot, "that by no means I cannot put her from me." "Why should ye put her from you?" said Sir Bors. "She is a passing fair damosel, and a well beseen, and well taught; and God would, fair cousin," said Sir Bors, "that ye could love her, but as to that I may not, nor I dare not, counsel you. But I see well," said Sir Bors, "by her diligence about you that she loveth you entirely." "That me repenteth," said Sir Launcelot. "Sir," said Sir Bors, "she is not the first that hath 10 lost her pain upon you, and that is the more pity"; and so they talked of many more things. And so within three days or four Sir Launcelot was big and strong again.

Then Sir Bors told Sir Launcelot how there was sworn a great tournament and jousts betwixt King Arthur and the King of Northgalis, that should be upon All Hallowmass Day beside Winchester. "Is that truth?" said Sir Launcelot; "then shall ye abide with me still a little while until that I be whole, for I 20 feel myself right big and strong." "Blessed be God," said Sir Bors. Then were they there nigh a month together, and ever this maiden Elaine did ever her diligent labor night and day unto Sir Launcelot, that there was never child nor wife more meeker to her father and husband than was that Fair Maiden of Astolat; wherefore Sir Bors was greatly pleased with her.

So upon a day, by the assent of Sir Launcelot, Sir Bors, and Sir Lavaine, they made the hermit to seek 30 in woods for divers herbs, and so Sir Launcelot made fair Elaine to gather herbs for him to make him a bain. In the meanwhile Sir Launcelot made him to arm him at all pieces, and there he thought to assay his armour and his spear for his hurt or not. And so when he was upon his horse, he stirred him fiercely, and the horse was passing lusty and fresh because he was not labored a month afore. And then Sir Launcelot couched that spear in the rest; that courser leapt mightily when he felt the spurs; and he that was upon him, the which was the noblest horse of the world, strained him mightily and stably and kept still the spear in the rest; and therewith Sir Launcelot strained himself so straitly with so great force to get the horse forward that the button of his wound brast both within and without; and 10 therewithal the blood came out so fiercely that he felt himself so feeble that he might not sit upon his horse. And then Sir Launcelot cried unto Sir Bors, "Ah, Sir Bors and Sir Lavaine, help, for I am come to mine end." And therewith he fell down on the one side to the earth like a dead corpse. And then Sir Bors and Sir Lavaine came to him with sorrow-making out of measure. And so by fortune the maiden Elaine heard their mourning, and then she came thither; and when she found Sir Launcelot 20 there armed in that place, she cried and wept as she had been wood; and then she kissed him, and did what she might to awake him. And then she rebuked her brother and Sir Bors, and called them false traitors, why they would take him out of his bed; there she cried, and said she would appeal them of his death.

With this came the holy hermit, Sir Baudwin of Brittany, and when he found Sir Launcelot in that plight, he said but little, but wit ye well he was 30 wroth; and then he bade them, "Let us have him in." And so they all bare him unto the hermitage, and unarmed him, and laid him in his bed; and evermore his wound bled piteously, but he stirred no limb of him. Then the knight-hermit put a thing in his nose and a little deal of water in his mouth. And then Sir Launcelot waked of his swoon, and then the hermit staunched his bleeding. And when he might speak, he asked Sir Launcelot why he put his life in jeopardy. "Sir," said Sir Launcelot, "because I weened I had been strong, and also Sir Bors told me that there should be at All Hallowmass a great jousts betwixt King Arthur and the King of Northgalis, and therefore I thought to assay it myself, whether I might be there or not." "Ah, Sir Launcelot," said the hermit, "your heart and your courage will never be done until your last day, but ye shall do now by 10 my counsel. Let Sir Bors depart from you, and let him do at that tournament what he may. And by the grace of God," said the knight-hermit, "by that the tournament be done and ye come hither again, Sir Launcelot shall be as whole as ye, so that he will be governed by me."

Then Sir Bors made him ready to depart from Sir Launcelot; and then Sir Launcelot said, "Fair cousin, Sir Bors, recommend me unto all them whom me ought to recommend me unto; and I pray you 20 enforce yourself at that jousts that ye may be best for my love, and here shall I abide you at the mercy of God till ye come again." And so Sir Bors departed and came to the court of King Arthur and told them in what place he had left Sir Launcelot. "That me repenteth," said the king, "but since he shall have his life, we all may thank God." And there Sir Bors told the queen in what jeopardy Sir Launcelot was when he would assay his horse. "And all that he did, madam, was for the love of you be- 30 cause he would have been at this tournament." "Fie on him, recreant knight," said the queen. "For wit ye well, I am right sorry an he shall have his life." "His life shall he have," said Sir Bors, "and who that would otherwise, except you, madam, we that be of his blood should help to short their lives; but, madam," said Sir Bors, "ye have been oft-times displeased with my lord, Sir Launcelot, but at all times at the end ye find him a true knight;" and so he departed.

And then every knight of the Round Table that were there at that time present made them ready to be at that jousts at All Hallowmass, and thither drew many knights of divers countries. And as All Hallowmass drew near, thither came the King of Northgalis, and the King with the Hundred Knights, and
10 Sir Galahad, the haut prince, of Surluse, and thither came King Anguish of Ireland, and the King of Scots; so these three kings came on King Arthur's party, and so that day Sir Gawaine did great deeds of arms and began first. And the heralds numbered that Sir Gawaine smote down twenty knights. Then Sir Bors de Ganis came in the same time, and he was numbered that he smote down twenty knights; and therefore the prize was given betwixt them both, for they began first and longest endured. Also Sir
20 Gareth, as the book saith, did that day great deeds of arms, for he smote down and pulled down thirty knights. But when he had done these deeds he tarried not but so departed, and therefore he lost his prize. And Sir Palomides did great deeds of arms that day, for he smote down twenty knights, but he departed suddenly, and men deemed Sir Gareth and he rode together to some manner adventures.

So when this tournament was done Sir Bors departed, and rode till he came to Sir Launcelot, his
30 cousin; and then he found him walking on his feet, and there either made great joy of other; and so Sir Bors told Sir Launcelot of all the jousts like as ye have heard. "I marvel," said Sir Launcelot, "that Sir Gareth, when he had done such deeds of arms, that he would not tarry." "Thereof we marvelled all," said Sir Bors, "for but if it were you, or Sir Tristram, or Sir Lamorak de Galis, I saw never

knight bear down so many in so little a while as did Sir Gareth: and anon he was gone we wist not where." "By my head," said Sir Launcelot, "he is a noble knight, and a mighty man and well breathed; and if he were well assayed," said Sir Launcelot, "I would deem he were good enough for any knight that beareth the life; and he is a gentle knight, courteous, true, and bounteous, meek, and mild, and in him is no manner of mal engin, but plain, faithful, 10 and true."

So then they made them ready to depart from the hermit. And so upon a morn they took their horses and Elaine le Blank with them; and when they came to Astolat, there were they well lodged, and had great cheer of Sir Bernard, the old baron, and of Sir Tirre, his son. And so upon the morn when Sir Launcelot should depart, fair Elaine brought her father with her, and Sir Lavaine, and Sir Tirre, and thus she said:

20 "My lord, Sir Launcelot, now I see ye will depart. Now, fair knight and courteous knight, have mercy upon me, and suffer me not to die for thy love." "What would ye that I did?" said Sir Launcelot. "I would have you to my husband," said Elaine. "Fair damosel, I thank you," said Sir Launcelot, "but truly," said he, "I cast me never to be wedded man." "Then, fair knight," said she, "will ye be my paramour?" "Jesu defend me," said Sir Launcelot, "for then I rewarded your father and your brother full 30 evil for their great goodness." "Alas," said she, "then must I die for your love." "Ye shall not so," said Sir Launcelot, "for wit ye well, fair maiden, I might have been married and I had would, but I never applied me to be married yet; but because, fair damosel, that ye love me as ye say ye do, I will for

your good will and kindness show you some goodness, and that is this, that wheresomever ye will beset your heart upon some good knight that will wed you, I shall give you together a thousand pound yearly to you and your heirs; thus much will I give you, fair madam, for your kindness, and always while I live to be your own knight." "Of all this," said the maiden, "I will none, for but if ye will wed me or else be my paramour at the least, wit you well, Sir 10 Launcelot, my good days are done." "Fair damosel," said Sir Launcelot, "of these two things ye must pardon me."

Then she shrieked shrilly and fell down in a swoon; and then women bare her into her chamber, and there she made overmuch sorrow; and then Sir Launcelot would depart, and there he asked Sir Lavaine what he would do. "What should I do," said Sir Lavaine, "but follow you, but if ye drive me from you or command me to go from you." Then 20 came Sir Bernard to Sir Launcelot and said to him, "I cannot see but that my daughter Elaine will die for your sake." "I may not do withal," said Sir Launcelot, "for that me sore repenteth, for I report me to yourself, that my proffer is fair; and me repenteth," said Sir Launcelot, "that she loveth me as she doth; I was never the causer of it, for I report me to your son I early ne late proffered her bounté nor fair behests; and as for me," said Sir Launcelot, "I dare do all that a knight 30 should do that she is a clean maiden for me, both for deed and for will. And I am right heavy of her distress, for she is a full fair maiden, good and gentle, and well taught." "Father," said Sir Lavaine, "I dare make good she is a clean maiden as for my lord Sir Launcelot; but she doth as I do, for sithen I first saw my lord Sir Launcelot, I could never depart from him, nor nought I will and I may follow him."

Then Sir Launcelot took his leave, and so they departed, and came unto Winchester. And when Arthur wist that Sir Launcelot was come whole and sound, the king made great joy of him, and so did Sir Gawaine and all the knights of the Round Table except Sir Agravaine and Sir Mordred. Also Queen Guenever was wood wroth with Sir Launcelot, and would by no means speak with him, but estranged herself from him; and Sir Launcelot made all the
10 means that he might for to speak with the queen, but it would not be.

Now speak we of the Fair Maiden of Astolat that made such sorrow day and night that she never slept, ate, nor drank, and ever she made her complaint unto Sir Launcelot. So when she had thus endured a ten days, that she feebled so that she must needs pass out of this world, then she shrived her clean, and received her Creator. And ever she complained still upon Sir Launcelot. Then her ghostly father made
20 her leave such thoughts. Then she said, "Why should I leave such thoughts? Am I not an earthly woman? And all the while the breath is in my body I may complain me, for my belief is I do none offence though I love an earthly man; and I take God to my record I loved none but Sir Launcelot du Lake, nor never shall, and a clean maiden I am for him and for all other; and sithen it is the sufferance of God that I shall die for the love of so noble a knight, I beseech the High Father of Heaven to have
30 mercy upon my soul, and upon my innumerable pains that I suffered may be allegeance of part of my sins. For sweet Lord Jesu," said the fair maiden, "I take Thee to record, on Thee I was never great offencer against Thy laws; but that I loved this noble knight, Sir Launcelot, out of measure, and of myself, good Lord, I might not withstand the fervent love wherefore I have my death."

And then she called her father, Sir Bernard, and her brother, Sir Tirre, and heartily she prayed her father that her brother might write a letter like as she did indite it; and so her father granted her. And when the letter was written word for word like as she devised, then she prayed her father that she might be watched until she were dead. "And while my body is hot, let this letter be put in my right hand, and my hand bound fast with the letter until 10 that I be cold; and let me be put in a fair bed with all the richest clothes that I have about me, and so let my bed and all my richest clothes be laid with me in a chariot unto the next place where Thames is; and there let me be put within a barget, and but one man with me, such as ye trust to steer me thither, and that my barget be covered with black samite over and over. Thus, father, I beseech you, let it be done." So her father granted it her faithfully all things should be done like as she had devised. Then her 20 father and her brother made great dole, for when this was done anon, she died. And so when she was dead, the corpse and the bed all was led the next way unto Thames, and there a man and the corpse and all were put into Thames; and so the man steered the barget unto Westminster, and there he rowed a great while to and fro or any espied it.

So by fortune King Arthur and the Queen Guenever were speaking together at a window, and so as they looked into Thames they espied this black 30 barget, and had marvel what it meant. Then the king called Sir Kay, and showed it him. "Sir," said Sir Kay, "wit you well there is some new tidings." "Go thither," said the king to Sir Kay, "and take with you Sir Brandiles and Agravaine, and bring me ready word what is there." Then these four knights departed and came to the barget and went in; and there they found the fairest corpse lying in a rich bed, and a poor man sitting in the barget's end, and no word would he speak. So these four knights returned unto the king again, and told him what they found. "That fair corpse will I see," said the king. And so then the king took the queen by the hand, and went thither.

Then the king made the barget to be holden fast, and then the king and the queen entered with certain knights with them; and there he saw the fairest woman lie in a rich bed, covered unto her middle with many rich clothes, and all was of cloth of gold, and she lay as though she had smiled. Then the queen espied a letter in her right hand, and told it to the king. Then the king took it and said, "Now am I sure this letter will tell what she was, and why she is come hither." So then the king and the queen went out of the barget, and so commanded a certain man to wait upon the barget.

And so when the king was come within his chamber, he called many knights about him, and said that he would wit openly what was written within that letter. Then the king brake it, and made a clerk to read it, and this was the intent of the letter. "Most noble knight, Sir Launcelot, now hath death made us two at debate for your love. I was your lover that men called the Fair Maiden of Astolat; therefore unto all ladies I make my moan, yet pray for my soul and bury me at least, and offer ye my mass-penny; this is my last request; and a clean maiden I died, I take God to witness; pray for my soul, Sir Launcelot, as thou art peerless." This was all the substance in the letter. And when it was read, the king, the queen, and all the knights wept for pity of the doleful complaints. Then was Sir Launcelot sent for. And when he was come, King Arthur made the letter to be read to him.

And when Sir Launcelot heard it word by word, he said, "My lord Arthur, wit ye well I am right heavy of the death of this fair damosel; God knoweth I was never causer of her death by my willing, and that will I report me to her own brother; here he is, Sir Lavaine. I will not say nay," said Sir Launcelot, "but that she was both fair and good, and much I was beholden unto her, but she loved me out of measure." "Ye might have shewed her," 10 said the queen, "some bounty and gentleness that might have preserved her life." "Madam," said Sir Launcelot, "she would none other ways be answered but that she would be my wife outher else my paramour; and of these two I would not grant her, but I proferred her, for her good love that she shewed me, a thousand pound yearly to her and to her heirs, and to wed any manner knight that she could find best to love in her heart. For, madam," said Sir Launcelot, "I love not to be constrained to love. For 20 love must arise of the heart, and not by no constraint." "That is truth," said the king, "and many knight's love is free in himself and never will be bounden, for where he is bounden, he loseth himself. Then," said the king unto Sir Launcelot, "it will be your worship that ye oversee that she be interred worshipfully." "Sir," said Sir Launcelot, "that shall be done as I can best devise." And so many knights yede thither to behold that fair maiden; and so upon the morn she was interred richly, and Sir Launcelot 30 offered her mass-penny; and all the knights of the Table Round that were there at that time offered with Sir Launcelot. And then the poor man went again with the barget. Then the queen sent for Sir Launcelot, and prayed him of mercy, for why that she had been wroth with him causeless. "This is not the first time," said Sir Launcelot, "that ye had been displeased with me causeless, but, madam, ever I must suffer you, but what sorrow I endure I take no force." So this passed on all that winter, with all manner of hunting and hawking, and jousts and tourneys were many betwixt many great lords, and ever in all places Sir Lavaine gat great worship, so that he was nobly renowned among many knights of the Table Round.

Enmity arising between them, King Arthur wars with Launcelot in the latter's territory beyond the seas.

As Sir Mordred was ruler of all England, he did do make letters as though that they came from be-
10 yond the sea, and the letters specified that King Arthur was slain in battle with Sir Launcelot. Wherefore Sir Mordred made a parliament and called the lords together, and there he made them to choose him king; and so was he crowned at Canterbury and held a feast there fifteen days; and afterward he drew him unto Winchester, and there he took the Queen Guenever and said plainly that he would wed her which was his uncle's wife and his father's wife. And so he made ready for the feast,
20 and a day prefixed that they should be wedded; wherefore Queen Guenever was passing heavy. But she durst not discover her heart but spake fair and agreed to Sir Mordred's will. Then she desired of Sir Mordred for to go to London to buy all manner of things that longed unto the wedding. And because of her fair speech Sir Mordred trusted her well enough and gave her leave to go. And so when she came to London, she took the Tower of London, and suddenly in all haste possible she stuffed it with

all manner of victual and well garnished it with men and so kept it.

Then when Sir Mordred wist and understood how he was beguiled, he was passing wroth out of measure. And a short tale for to make, he went and laid a mighty siege about the Tower of London, and made many great assaults thereat, and threw many great engines unto them, and shot great guns. But all might not prevail Sir Mordred, for Queen Guene-
10 ver would never for fair speech nor for foul, would never trust to come in his hands again.

Then came the Bishop of Canterbury, the which was a noble clerk and an holy man, and thus he said to Sir Mordred, "Sir, what will ye do? Will ye first displease God and sithen shame yourself, and all knighthood? Is not King Arthur your uncle, no farther but your mother's brother, and on her himself King Arthur begat you upon his own sister, therefore how may you wed your father's wife?
20 Sir," said the noble clerk, "leave this opinion or I shall curse you with book and bell and candle." "Do thou thy worst," said Sir Mordred. "Wit thou well I shall defy thee." "Sir," said the Bishop, "and wit you well I shall not fear me to do that me ought to do. Also where ye noise where my lord Arthur is slain, and that is not so, and therefore ye will make a foul work in this land." "Peace, thou false priest," said Sir Mordred, "for an thou chafe me any more I shall make strike off thy head." So the Bishop
30 departed and did the cursing in the most orgulist wise that might be done. And then Sir Mordred sought the Bishop of Canterbury, for to have slain him. Then the Bishop fled, and took part of his goods with him, and went nigh unto Glastonbury; and there he was as priest hermit in a chapel and lived in poverty and in holy prayers, for well he understood that mischievous war was at hand.

Then Sir Mordred sought on Queen Guenever by letters and sonds, and by fair means and foul means, for to have her to come out of the Tower of London; but all this availed not, for she answered him shortly, openly and privily, that she had liefer slay herself than to be married with him. Then came word to Sir Mordred that King Arthur had araised the siege for Sir Launcelot, and he was coming homeward with a great host, to be avenged upon Sir Mordred;
10 wherefore Sir Mordred made write writs to all the barony of this land, and much people drew to him. For then was the common voice among them that with Arthur was none other life but war and strife. And with Sir Mordred was great joy and bliss. Thus was Sir Arthur depraved, and evil said of. And many there were that King Arthur had made up of nought and given them lands, might not then say him a good word. Lo ye all Englishmen, see ye not what a mischief here was, for he that was the
20 most king and knight of the world and most loved the fellowship of noble knights, and by him they were all upholden, now might not these Englishmen hold them content with him. Lo thus was the old custom and usage of this land. And also men say that we of this land have not yet lost or forgotten that custom and usage. Alas this is a great default of us Englishmen. For there may no thing please us no term. And so fared the people at that time; they were better pleased with Sir Mordred than they
30 were with King Arthur; and much people drew unto Sir Mordred and said they would abide with him for better and for worse; and so Sir Mordred drew with a great host to Dover, for there he heard say that Sir Arthur would arrive, and so he thought to beat his own father from his lands; and the most part of all England held with Sir Mordred, the people were so newfangle.

And so as Sir Mordred was at Dover with his host, there came King Arthur with a great navy of ships, and galleys, and carracks. And there was Sir Mordred ready awaiting upon his londage to let his own father to land up the land that he was king over. Then there was launching of great boats and small, and full of noble men of arms; and there was much slaughter of gentle knights, and many a full bold baron was laid full low, on both parties. But King Arthur was so courageous that there might no manner of knights let him to land, and his knights fiercely followed him; and so they landed maugre Sir Mordred's and all his power, and put Sir Mordred aback, that he fled and all his people.

So when this battle was done, King Arthur let bury his people that were dead. And then was noble Sir Gawaine found in a great boat, lying more than half dead. When Sir Arthur wist that Sir Gawaine was laid so low, he went unto him; and there the king made sorrow out of measure, and took Sir Gawaine in his arms, and thrice he there swooned. And then when he awaked, he said, "Alas, Sir Gawaine, my sister's son, here now thou liest, the man in the world that I loved most; and now is my joy gone, for now, my nephew Sir Gawaine, I will discover me unto your person: in Sir Launcelot and you I most had my joy, and mine affiance, and now have I lost my joy of you both; wherefore all mine earthly joy is gone from me." "Mine uncle King Arthur," said Sir Gawaine, "wit you well my death-day is come, and all is through mine own hastiness and wilfulness; for I am smitten upon the old wound the which Sir Launcelot gave me, on the which I feel well I must die; and had Sir Launcelot been with you as he was, this unhappy war had never begun; and of all this am I causer, for Sir Launcelot and his blood, through their prowess, held all your cankered enemies in subjection and daunger. And now," said Sir Gawaine, "ye shall miss Sir Launcelot. But alas, I would not accord with him, and therefore," said Sir Gawaine, "I pray you, fair uncle, that I may have paper, pen, and ink, that I may write to Sir Launcelot a cedle with mine own hands."

And then when paper and ink was brought, then Gawaine was set up weakly by King Arthur, for he
10 was shriven a little to-fore; and then he wrote thus, as the French book maketh mention, "Unto Sir Launcelot, flower of all noble knights that ever I heard of or saw by my days, I, Sir Gawaine, King Lot's son of Orkney, sister's son unto the noble King Arthur, send thee greeting and let thee have knowledge that the tenth day of May I was smitten upon the old wound that thou gavest me afore the city of Benwick, and through the same wound that thou gavest me I am come to my death-day. And
20 I will that all the world wit that I, Sir Gawaine, knight of the Table Round, sought my death and not through thy deserving, but it was mine own seeking; wherefore I beseech thee, Sir Launcelot, to return again unto this realm, and see my tomb, and pray some prayer more or less for my soul. And this same day that I wrote this cedle, I was hurt to the death in the same wound, the which I had of thy hand, Sir Launcelot. For of a more nobler man might I not be slain. Also Sir Launce-
30 lot, for all the love that ever was betwixt us, make no tarrying, but come over the sea in all haste that thou mayst with thy noble knights rescue that noble king that made thee knight, that is my lord Arthur; for he is full straitly bestead with a false traitor, that is my half-brother, Sir Mordred; and he hath let crown him king and would have wedded my lady Guenever, and so had he done had she not put her-

self in the Tower of London. And so the tenth day of May last past, my lord Arthur and we all landed upon them at Dover; and there we put that false traitor, Sir Mordred to flight and there it misfortuned me to be stricken upon thy stroke. And at the date of this letter was written but two hours and a half before my death, written with mine own hand, and so subscribed with part of my heart's blood. And I require of thee, most famous knight of the world, that thou wilt see my tomb." And then Sir Gawaine wept, and King Arthur wept. And then they swooned both. And when they awaked both, the king made Sir Gawaine to receive his Saviour. And then Sir Gawaine prayed the king for to send for Sir Launcelot and to cherish him above all other knights.

And so at the hour of noon Sir Gawaine yielded up the spirit; and the king let inter him in a chapel within Dover Castle; and there yet all men may see the skull of him, and the same wound is seen that Sir Launcelot gave him in battle. Then was it told the king that Sir Mordred had pight a new field upon Barham Down. And upon the morn the king rode thither to him, and there was a great battle betwixt them, and much people was slain on both parties; but at the last Sir Arthur's party stood best, and Sir Mordred and his party fled unto Canterbury.

And then the king let search all the towns for his knights that were slain, and interred them; and salved them with soft salves that so sore were wounded. Then much people drew unto King Arthur. And then they said that Sir Mordred warred upon King Arthur with wrong. And then King Arthur drew him with his host down by the seaside, westward toward Salisbury; and there was a day assigned betwixt King Arthur and Sir Mordred, that they should meet upon a down beside Salisbury, and not far from the seaside; and this day was assigned on a Monday after Trinity Sunday, whereof King Arthur was passing glad, that he might be avenged upon Sir Mordred. Then Sir Mordred araised much people about London, for they of Kent, Southsex, and Surrey, Estsex, and of Southfolk, and of Northfolk, held the most party with Sir Mordred; and many a full noble knight 10 drew unto Sir Mordred and to the king: but they that loved Sir Launcelot drew unto Sir Mordred.

So upon Trinity Sunday at night, King Arthur dreamed a wonderful dream, and that was this: that him seemed he sat upon a chaflet in a chair, and the chair was fast to a wheel, and thereupon sat King Arthur in the richest cloth of gold that might be made; and the king thought there was under him, far from him, an hideous deep black water, and therein were all manner of serpents and worms and 20 wild beasts, foul and horrible; and suddenly the king thought the wheel turned up-so-down, and he fell among the serpents, and every beast took him by a limb; and then the king cried as he lay in his bed and slept, "Help!" And then knights, squires, and yeomen awaked the king; and then he was so amazed that he wist not where he was; and then he fell a-slumbering again, not sleeping nor thoroughly waking. So the king seemed verily that there came Sir Gawaine unto him with a number of fair ladies 30 with him. And when King Arthur saw him, then he said, "Welcome, my sister's son. I ween thou hadst been dead, and now I see thee alive. Much am I beholding unto Almighty Jesu. O fair nephew and my sister's son, what be these ladies that hither be come with you?" "Sir," said Sir Gawaine, "all these be ladies for whom I have foughten when I was a man living, and all these are those that I did battle for in righteous quarrel; and God hath given them that grace at their great prayer, because I did battle for them, that they should bring me hither unto you; thus much hath God given me leave for to warn you of your death; for an ye fight as to-morn with Sir Mordred, as ye both have assigned, doubt ye not ye must be slain and the most party of your people on both parties; and for the great grace and goodness that Almighty Jesu hath unto you, and for pity of you and many more other good men there shall be slain, God hath sent me to you of his special grace to give you warning that in no wise ye do battle as to-morn, but that ye take a treaty for a month day; and proffer you largely so as to-morn to be put in a delay. For within a month shall come Sir Launcelot with all his noble knights and rescue you worshipfully and slay Sir Mordred and all that ever will hold with him." Then Sir Gawaine and all the ladies vanished.

And anon the king called upon his knights, squires, and yeomen, and charged them wightly to fetch his noble lords and wise bishops unto him. And when they were come, the king told them his avision, what Sir Gawaine had told him, and warned him that if he fought on the morn he should be slain. Then the king commanded Sir Lucan the Butler, and his brother Sir Bedivere, with two bishops with them, and charged them in any wise, an they might, "Take a treaty for a month day with Sir Mordred, and spare not; proffer him lands and goods as much as ye think best." So then they departed, and came to Sir Mordred, where he had a grim host of an hundred thousand men. And there they entreated Sir Mordred long time; and at the last Sir Mordred was agreed for to have Cornwall and Kent, by Arthur's days: after, all England, after the days of King Arthur.

Then were they condescended that King Arthur and Sir Mordred should meet betwixt both their hosts, and everych of them should bring fourteen persons; and they came with this word unto Arthur. Then said he: "I am glad that this is done:" and so he went into the field. And when Arthur should depart, he warned all his host that an they see any 10 sword drawn, "Look ye come on fiercely, and slay that traitor, Sir Mordred, for I in no wise trust him." In like wise Sir Mordred warned his host that, "And ye see any sword drawn, look that ye come on fiercely, and so slay all that ever before you standeth; for in no wise I will not trust for this treaty, for I know well my father will be avenged on me." And so they met as their appointment was, and so they were agreed and accorded thoroughly; and wine was fetched, and they drank. Right soon 20 came an adder out of a little heath bush, and it stung a knight on the foot. And when the knight felt him stung, he looked down and saw the adder, and then he drew his sword to slay the adder, and thought of none other harm. And when the host on both parties saw that sword drawn, then they blew beams, trumpets, and horns, and shouted grimly. And so both hosts dressed them together. And King Arthur took his horse and said, "Alas this unhappy day!" and so rode to his party. And 30 Sir Mordred in like wise. And never was there seen a more dolefuler battle in no Christian land, for there was but rushing and riding, foining and striking, and many a grim word was there spoken either to other, and many a deadly stroke. But ever King Arthur rode throughout the battle of Sir Mordred many times and did full nobly as a noble king should, and at all times he fainted never; and Sir Mordred that day put him in devoir and in great peril. And thus they fought all the long day and never stinted till the noble knights were laid to the cold earth; and ever they fought still till it was near night, and by that time was there an hundred thousand laid dead upon the down. Then was Arthur wood wroth out of measure when he saw his people so slain 10 from him.

Then the king looked about him, and then was he ware of all his host and of all his good knights were left no more alive but two knights; that one was Sir Lucan the Butler, and his brother Sir Bedivere. And they were full sore wounded. "Jesu mercy," said the king, "where are all my noble knights become? Alas that ever I should see this doleful day, for now," said Arthur, "I am come to mine end. But would to God that I wist where were that 20 traitor, Sir Mordred, that hath caused all this mischief." Then was King Arthur ware where Sir Mordred leaned upon his sword among a great heap of dead men. "Now give me my spear," said Arthur unto Sir Lucan. "For yonder I have espied the traitor that all this woe hath wrought." "Sir, let him be," said Sir Lucan, "for he is unhappy. And if ye pass this unhappy day, ye shall be right well revenged upon him. Good lord, remember ye of your night's dream and what the spirit of Sir Ga- 30 waine told you this night; yet God of his great goodness hath preserved you hitherto. Therefore, for God's sake, my lord, leave off by this, for blessed be God, ye have won the field. For here we be three alive, and with Sir Mordred is none alive; and if ye leave off now, this wicked day of destiny is past." "Tide me death, betide me life," saith the king, "now I see him yonder alone he shall never escape mine hands, for at a better avail shall I never have him." "God speed you well," said Sir Bedivere.

Then the king gat his spear in both his hands, and ran toward Sir Mordred, crying, "Traitor, now is thy death-day come." And when Sir Mordred heard Sir Arthur, he ran until him with his sword drawn in his hand. And there King Arthur smote Sir Mordred under the shield, with a foin of his spear, throughout the body, more than a fathom.
10 And when Sir Mordred felt that he had his death's wound he thrust himself with the might that he had up to the bur of King Arthur's spear. And right so he smote his father Arthur, with his sword holden in both his hands, on the side of the head, that the sword pierced the helmet and the brain-pan, and therewithal Sir Mordred fell stark dead to the earth; and the noble Arthur fell in a swoon to the earth, and there he swooned ofttimes. And Sir Lucan the Butler and Sir Bedivere ofttimes heaved him up.
20 And so weakly they led him betwixt them both, to a little chapel not far from the seaside. And when the king was there he thought him well eased.

Then heard they people cry in the field. "Now go thou, Sir Lucan," said the king, "and do me to wit what betokens that noise in the field." So Sir Lucan departed, for he was grievously wounded in many places. And so as he yede, he saw and hearkened by the moonlight, how that pillers and robbers were come into the field, to pill and to rob many a full
30 noble knight of brooches, and beads, of many a good ring, and of many a rich jewel; and who that were not dead all out, there they slew them for their harness and their riches. When Sir Lucan understood this work, he came to the king as soon as he might, and told him all what he had heard and seen. "Therefore by my rede," said Sir Lucan, "it is best

that we bring you to some town." "I would it were so," said the king.

"But I may not stand, my head works so. Ah, Sir Launcelot," said King Arthur, "this day have I sore missed thee. Alas that ever I was against thee, for now I have my death whereof Sir Gawaine me warned in my dream." Then Sir Lucan took up the king the one part, and Sir Bedivere the other part; and in the lifting the king swooned, and Sir 10 Lucan fell in a swoon with the lift that the part of his guts fell out of his body. And therewith the noble knight's heart brast. And when the king awoke, he beheld Sir Lucan, how he lay foaming at the mouth, and part of his guts lay at his feet. "Alas," said the king, "this is to me a full heavy sight, to see this noble duke so die for my sake, for he would have holpen me that had more need of help than I. Alas, he would not complain him, his heart was so set to help me. Now Jesu have mercy 20 upon his soul!" Then Sir Bedivere wept for the death of his brother. "Leave this mourning and weeping," said the king, "for all this will not avail me, for wit thou well, an I might live myself, the death of Sir Lucan would grieve me evermore; but my time hieth fast," said the king. "Therefore," said Arthur unto Sir Bedivere, "take thou Excalibur, my good sword, and go with it to yonder water side, and when thou comest there, I charge thee throw my sword in that water, and come again, and tell 30 me what thou there seest." "My lord," said Bedivere, "your commandment shall be done and lightly bring you word again."

So Sir Bedivere departed, and by the way he beheld that noble sword, that the pommel and the haft was all of precious stones; and then he said to himself, "If I throw this rich sword in the water,

thereof shall never come good, but harm and loss." And then Sir Bedivere hid Excalibur under a tree. And so, as soon as he might, he came again unto the king, and said he had been at the water, and had thrown the sword in the water. "What saw thou there?" said the king. "Sir," he said, "I saw nothing but waves and winds." "That is untruly said of thee," said the king, "therefore go thou lightly again, and do my commandment; as thou art to me
10 lief and dear, spare not, but throw it in." Then Sir Bedivere returned again, and took the sword in his hand; and then him thought sin and shame to throw away that noble sword, and so eft he hid the sword, and returned again, and told to the king that he had been at the water, and done his commandment. "What saw thou there?" said the king. "Sir," he said, "I saw nothing but the waters wap and waves wan." "Ah, traitor untrue," said King Arthur, "now hast thou betrayed me twice. Who would have
20 weened that, thou that hast been to me so lief and dear? And thou art named a noble knight, and would betray me for the richness of the sword. But now go again lightly, for thy long tarrying putteth me in great jeopardy of my life, for I have taken cold. And but if thou do now as I bid thee, if ever I may see thee, I shall slay thee with mine own hands; for thou wouldst for my rich sword see me dead."

Then Sir Bedivere departed, and went to the
30 sword, and lightly took it up, and went to the water side; and there he bound the girdle about the hilts, and then he threw the sword as far into the water as he might; and there came an arm and an hand above the water and met it, and caught it, and so shook it thrice and brandished, and then vanished away the hand with the sword in the water. So Sir Bedivere came again to the king, and told him what

he saw. "Alas," said the king, "help me hence, for I dread me I have tarried over long." Then Sir Bedivere took the king upon his back, and so went with him to that water side. And when they were at the water side, even fast by the bank hoved a little barge with many fair ladies in it, and among them all was a queen, and all they had black hoods, and all they wept and shrieked when they saw King Arthur. "Now put me into the barge," said the king, and so he did softly. And there received him three queens with great mourning; and so they set them down, and in one of their laps King Arthur laid his head; and then that queen said, "Ah, dear brother, why have ye tarried so long from me? Alas this wound on your head hath caught overmuch cold." And so then they rowed from the land, and Sir Bedivere beheld all those ladies go from him. Then Sir Bedivere cried, "Ah, my lord Arthur, what shall become of me, now ye go from me and leave me here alone among mine enemies?" "Comfort thyself," said the king, "and do as well as thou mayst, for in me is no trust for to trust in. For I will into the vale of Avilion to heal me of my grievous wound. And if thou hear never more of me, pray for my soul." But ever the queens and ladies wept and shrieked that it was pity to hear. And as soon as Sir Bedivere had lost the sight of the barge, he wept and wailed and so took the forest; and so he went all that night, and in the morning he was ware betwixt two holts hoar of a chapel and an hermitage.

Then was Sir Bedivere glad, and thither he went; and when he came into the chapel, he saw where lay an hermit grovelling on all four, there fast by a tomb was new graven; when the hermit saw Sir Bedivere, he knew him well, for he was but little to-fore Bishop of Canterbury that Sir Mordred flemed.

"Sir," said Sir Bedivere, "what man is there interred that ye pray so fast for?" "Fair son," said the hermit, "I wot not verily but by my deeming. But this night at midnight here came a number of ladies, and brought hither a dead corpse, and prayed me to bury him; and here they offered an hundred tapers, and they gave me an hundred besants." "Alas," said Sir Bedivere, "that was my lord King Arthur, that here lieth buried in this chapel." Then Sir Bedivere 10 swooned; and when he awoke he prayed the hermit he might abide with him still there, to live with fasting and prayers. "For from hence will I never go," said Sir Bedivere, "by my will, but all the days of my life here to pray for my lord Arthur." "Ye are welcome to me," said the hermit, "for I know ye better than ye ween that I do. Ye are the bold Bedivere, and the full noble duke, Sir Lucan the Butler, was your brother." Then Sir Bedivere told the hermit all as ye have heard to-fore. So there bode 20 Sir Bedivere with the hermit that was to-fore Bishop of Canterbury, and there Sir Bedivere put upon him poor clothes, and served the hermit full lowly in fasting and in prayers.

Thus of Arthur I find never more written in books that be authorised, nor more of the very certainty of his death heard I never read, but thus was he led away in a ship wherein were three queens; that one was King Arthur's sister, Queen Morgan le Fay; the other was the Queen of Northgalis; the third 30 was the Queen of the Waste Lands. Also there was Nimue, the chief lady of the lake, that had wedded Pelleas the good knight; and this lady had done much for King Arthur, for she would never suffer Sir Pelleas to be in no place where he should be in danger of his life; and so he lived to the uttermost of his days with her in great rest. More of the death of King Arthur could I never find, but that ladies brought him to his burials; and such one was buried there, that the hermit bare witness that sometime was Bishop of Canterbury, but yet the hermit knew not in certain that he was verily the body of King Arthur: for this tale Sir Bedivere, knight of the Table Round, made it to be written.

Yet some men say in many parts of England that King Arthur is not dead, but had by the will of our Lord Jesu into another place; and men say that he 10 will come again, and he shall win the holy cross. I will not say it shall be so, but rather I will say here in this world he changed his life; but many men say that there is written upon his tomb this verse, HIC JACET ARTHURUS, REX QUONDAM, REXQUE FUTURUS. Thus leave I here Sir Bedivere with the hermit that dwelled that time in a chapel beside Glastonbury, and there was his hermitage. And they lived in their prayers and fastings and great abstinence. And when Queen Guenever un- 20 derstood that King Arthur was slain, and all the noble knights, Sir Mordred and all the remnant, then the queen stole away and five ladies with her, and so she went to Almesbury; and there she let make herself a nun and ware white clothes and black, and great penance she took as ever did sinful lady in this land, and never creature could make her merry; but lived in fasting, prayers, and alms-deeds, that all manner of people marvelled how virtuously she was changed. Now leave we Queen Guenever at Almes- 30 bury, a nun in white clothes and black, and there she was Abbess and ruler as reason would; and turn we from her, and speak we of Sir Launcelot du Lake.

And when he heard in his country that Sir Mordred was crowned king in England and made war against King Arthur, his own father, and would let him to land in his own land; also it was told Sir Launcelot how that Sir Mordred had laid siege about the Tower of London, because the queen would not wed him; then was Sir Launcelot wroth out of measure, and said to his kinsmen, "Alas, that double traitor Sir Mordred, now me repenteth that ever he escaped my hands, for much shame hath he done unto my lord Arthur; for all I feel by the doleful letter that my lord Sir Gawaine sent me, on whose 10 soul Jesu have mercy, that my lord Arthur is full hard bestead. Alas," said Sir Launcelot, "that ever I should live to hear that most noble king that made me knight thus to be overset with his subject in his own realm. And this doleful letter that my lord, Sir Gawaine, hath sent me afore his death, praying me to see his tomb, wit you well his doleful words shall never go from mine heart, for he was a full noble knight as ever was born; and in an unhappy hour was I born that ever I should have that unhap to slay 20 first Sir Gawaine, Sir Gaheris the good knight, and mine own friend Sir Gareth, that full noble knight. Alas, I may say I am unhappy," said Sir Launcelot, "that ever I should do thus unhappily, and, alas, yet might I never have hap to slay that traitor, Sir Mordred."

"Leave your complaints," said Sir Bors, "and first revenge you of the death of Sir Gawaine; and it will be well done that ye see Sir Gawaine's tomb, and secondly that ye revenge my lord Arthur, and my lady, 30 Queen Guenever." "I thank you," said Sir Launcelot, "for ever ye will my worship."

Then they made them ready in all the haste that might be, with ships and galleys, with Sir Launcelot and his host to pass into England. And so he passed over the sea till he came to Dover, and there he landed with seven kings, and the number was hideous

to behold. Then Sir Launcelot spered of men of Dover where was King Arthur become. Then the people told him how that he was slain, and Sir Mordred and an hundred thousand died on a day; and how Sir Mordred gave King Arthur there the first battle at his landing, and there was good Sir Gawaine slain; and on the morn Sir Mordred fought with the king upon Barham Down, and there the king put Sir Mordred to the worse. "Alas," said
10 Sir Launcelot, "this is the heaviest tidings that ever came to me. Now, fair sirs," said Sir Launcelot, "shew me the tomb of Sir Gawaine." And then certain people of the town brought him into the castle of Dover and shewed him the tomb. Then Sir Launcelot kneeled down and wept and prayed heartily for his soul. And that night he made a dole, and all they that would come had as much flesh, fish, wine, and ale, and every man and woman had twelvepence, come who would. Thus with his own
20 hand dealt he this money in a mourning gown; and ever he wept and prayed them to pray for the soul of Sir Gawaine. And on the morn all the priests and clerks that might be gotten in the country were there and sang mass of Requiem; and there offered first Sir Launcelot, and he offered an hundred pound; and then the seven kings offered forty pound apiece; and also there was a thousand knights, and each of them offered a pound; and the offering dured from morn to night, and Sir Launcelot lay two nights on
30 his tomb in prayers and weeping.

Then on the third day Sir Launcelot called the kings, dukes, earls, barons, and knights, and said thus, "My fair lords, I thank you all of your coming into this country with me, but we came too late, and that shall repent me while I live, but against death may no man rebel. But sithen it is so," said Sir

Launcelot, "I will myself ride and seek my lady, Queen Guenever, for as I hear say she hath had great pain and much disease; and I heard say that she is fled into the west; therefore ye all shall abide me here, and but if I come again within fifteen days, then take your ships and your fellowship and depart into your country, for I will do as I say to you."

Then came Sir Bors de Ganis, and said: "My lord Sir Launcelot, what think ye for to do, now to 10 ride in this realm? Wit ye well ye shall find few friends." "Be as be may," said Sir Launcelot, "keep you still here, for I will forth on my journey, and no man nor child shall go with me." So it was no boot to strive, but he departed and rode westerly, and there he sought a seven or eight days; and at the last he came to a nunnery, and then was Queen Guenever ware of Sir Launcelot as he walked in the cloister. And when she saw him there, she swooned thrice, that all the ladies and gentlewomen had work 20 enough to hold the queen up. So when she might speak, she called ladies and gentlewomen to her, and said, "Ye marvel, fair ladies, why I make this fare. Truly," she said, "it is for the sight of yonder knight that yonder standeth; wherefore I pray you all call him to me."

When Sir Launcelot was brought to her, then she said to all the ladies, "Through this man and me hath all this war been wrought, and the death of the most noblest knights of the world; for through our love 30 that we have loved together is my most noble lord slain. Therefore, Sir Launcelot, wit thou well I am set in such a plight to get my soul-heal; and yet I trust through God's grace that after my death to have a sight of the blessed face of Christ, and at domesday to sit on his right side, for as sinful as ever I was are saints in heaven. Therefore, Sir Launcelot, I require thee and beseech thee heartily, for all the love that ever was betwixt us, that thou never see me more in the visage; and I command thee, on God's behalf, that thou forsake my company, and to thy kingdom thou turn again, and keep well thy realm from war and wrack; for as well as I have loved thee, mine heart will not serve me to see thee, for through thee and me is the flower of kings and knights destroyed; therefore, Sir Launcelot, go to thy realm, and there take thee a wife, and live with her with joy and bliss; and I pray thee heartily, pray for me to our Lord that I may amend my misliving." "Now, sweet madam," said Sir Launcelot, "would ye that I should return again unto my country and there to wed a lady? Nay, madam, wit you well that shall I never do, for I shall never be so false to you of that I have promised; but the same destiny that ye have taken you to, I will take me unto, for to please Jesu, and ever for you I cast me specially to pray." "If thou wilt do so," said the queen, "hold thy promise, but I may never believe but that thou wilt turn to the world again." "Well, madam," said he, "ye say as pleaseth you; yet wist you me never false of my promise, and God defend but I should forsake the world as ye have done; for in the quest of the Sangreal I had forsaken the vanities of the world had not your lord been. And if I had done so at that time, with my heart, will, and thought, I had passed all the knights that were in the Sangreal except Sir Galahad, my son; and, therefore, lady, sithen ye have taken you to perfection, I must needs take me to perfection of right; for I take record of God, in you I have had mine earthly joy; and if I had found you now so disposed, I had cast me to have you into mine own realm."

JOHN BOURCHIER, BARON BERNERS

HUON OF BORDEAUX

LIKE King Arthur, the Emperor Charlemagne with his warriors formed a favorite subject of medieval romances. Treated originally in verse, their exploits in time came to be the subject of prose narrative. *Huon of Bordeaux* is a translation from such a French prose romance and is the best treatment of Charlemagne remaining from medieval England.

The translator, John Bourchier, Baron Berners, was born about 1467, succeeding to his title in 1474. After probably attending Oxford for several years, he was present in the king's retinue at the capture of Terouenne and was marshal of the Earl of Surrey's army in Scotland. He likewise became a member of Parliament and attained the office of chancellor of the exchequer. His wife and he were in the train of Henry VIII at his gorgeous meeting with the French king on the Field of the Cloth of Gold. From 1520, he was deputy of Calais, where, after devoting much of his time to literary work, he fell heavily in debt and died on March 16, 1533. Besides *Huon*, Berners translated the famous chronicles of Froissart.

The story of Huon originally dealt with the quest to the Orient imposed on the hero. Since the narrative was popular, however, there were added, by various authors, at least seven continuations, four of which appear in the French prose account and in Berners' translation. The first concerns the adventures of Huon's wife, Esclaramonde, after their marriage, ending with Huon and her becoming king and queen of fairyland. Thereafter, the enthusiastic reader could prolong his entertainment with three other continuations, recording respectively the adventures of Clariet, daughter of Huon and Esclaramonde; of Clariet's daughter Ide; and, finally, of Ide's son Croissant.

Huon was extremely popular in its English dress. It introduced the figure of Oberon into English literature, and both Spenser and Shakspere may have been acquainted with it.

HUON OF BORDEAUX

Huon of Bordeaux, having killed the Emperor Charlemagne's son Charlot, is ordered by the monarch to go to the court of the Admiral of Babylon, cut off the head of one of his chief nobles, kiss his daughter, and bring back to France a piece of his beard and his four great teeth. Arriving in the Holy Land, Huon meets an old Frenchman named Gerames.

When Huon had heard Gerames, then he demanded further of him if he could go to Babylon.

"Yea, sir," quod Gerames, "I can go thither by two ways; the most surest way is hence a forty journeys, and the other is but fifteen journeys. But I counsel you to take the long way, for if ye take the shorter way, ye must pass throughout a wood a sixteen leagues of length; but the way is so full of the faerie and strange things that such as pass that way 10 are lost, for in that wood abideth a king of the faerie named Oberon. He is of height but of three foot and crooked shouldered, but yet he hath an angelic visage, so that there is no mortal man that seeth him but that taketh great pleasure to behold his face, and ye shall no sooner be entered into that wood, if ye go that way, he will find the manner to speak with you, and, if ye speak to him, ye are lost for ever. And ye shall ever find him before you so that it shall be in manner impossible that ye can scape 20 from him without speaking to him, for his words be so pleasant to hear that there is no mortal man that can well scape without speaking to him. And if he see that ye will not speak a word to him, then he will be sore displeased with you, and or ye can get out of the wood, he will cause rain and wind, hail and snow, and will make marvelous tempests with thunder and lightnings so that it shall seem to you that all the world should perish, and he shall make to seem before you a great running river, black and deep. But ye may pass it at your ease, and it shall not wet the feet of your horse, for all is but fantasy and enchantments that the dwarf shall make to thententent to have you with him, and, if ye can keep yourself without speaking to him, ye may then well scape. But, sir, to eschew all perils, I counsel you take the lenger way, for I think ye can not scape fro him, 10 and then be ye lost for ever."

When Huon had well heard Gerames, he had great marvel, and he had great desire in himself to see that dwarf king of the faerie, and the strange adventures that were in that wood. Then he said to Gerames that for fear of any death he would not leave to pass that way sen he might come to Babylon in fifteen days, for in taking the longer way, he might peradventure find more adventures, and sens he was advertized that with keeping his tongue from 20 speaking he might abridge his journey, he said that surely he would that way whatsoever chance fell.

"Sir," quod Gerames, "ye shall do your pleasure, for whichsoever way ye take, it shall not be without me. I shall bring you to Babylon to the Admiral Gaudys; I know him right well; and when ye be come thither, ye shall see there a damsel, as I have heard say, the most fairest creature in all Inde, and the great and most sweetest and most courteousest that ever was born, and it is she that ye seek, for 30 she is daughter to the Admiral Gaudys."

When Huon had well heard Gerames how he was minded to go with him, he was thereof right joyful and thanked him of his courtesy and service and gave him a goodly horse whereon he mounted and so rode forth together so long that they came into the wood whereas King Oberon haunted most. Then Huon

was weary of travel, and what for famine and heat, the which he and his company had endured two days without bread or meat, so that he was so feeble that he could ride no further and then he began piteously to weep, and complained of the great wrong that King Charlemagne had done to him. And then Garyn [1] and Gerames comforted him and had great pity of him, and they knew well by the reason of his youth hunger oppressed him more than it did to
10 them of greater age. Then they alighted under a great oak, to the entent to search for some fruit to eat; they let their horses go to pasture. When they were thus alighted, the dwarf of the faerie, King Oberon, came riding by and had on a gown so rich that it was marvel to recount the riches and fashion thereof, and it was so garnished with precious stones that the clearness of them shone like the sun. Also he had a goodly bow in his hand so rich that it could not be esteemed and his arrows after the same sort,
20 and they had such property that any beast in the world that he would wish for, the arrow should arrest him. Also he had about his neck a rich horn hanging by two laces of gold. The horn was so rich and fair that there was never seen none such; it was made by four ladies of the faerie in the isle of Chafalone. One of them gave to the horn such a property that whosoever heard the sound thereof, if he were in the greatest sickness in the world, he should incontinent be whole and sound; the lady that
30 gave this gift to this horn was named Gloriande. The second lady was named Translyne. She gave to this horn another property, and that was whosoever heard this horn, if he were in the greatest famine of the world, he should be satisfied as well as though he had eaten all that he would wish for, and in like wise for drink as well as though he had drunken his fill

[1] Huon's uncle who had joined him on this quest.

of the best wine in all the world. The third lady, named Margale, gave to this horn yet a greater gift, and that was, whosoever heard this horn, though he were never so poor or feeble by sickness, he should have such joy in his heart that he should sing and dance. The fourth lady, named Lempatrix, gave to this horn such a gift that whosoever heard it, if he were a hundred journeys off, he should come at the pleasure of him that blew it, far or near. Then 10 King Oberon, who knew well and had seen the fourteen companions, he set his horn to his mouth and blew so melodious a blast that the fourteen companions, being under the tree, had so parfait a joy at their hearts that they all rose up and began to sing and dance.

"Ah, good lord," quod Huon, "what fortune is come to us? Me think we be in paradise. Right now I could not sustain myself for lack of meat and drink, and now I feel myself neither hungry nor 20 thirsty. From whence may this come?"

"Sir," quod Gerames, "know for truth this is done by the dwarf of the faerie, whom ye shall soon see pass by you. But, sir, I require you in jeopardy in losing of your life that ye speak to him no word, without ye purpose to bide ever with him."

"Sir," quod Huon, "have no doubt of me, sen I know the jeopardy."

Therewith the dwarf began to cry aloud and said, "Ye fourteen men that passeth by my wood, God 30 keep you all, and I desire you speak with me, and I conjure you thereto by God Almighty and by the Christendom that ye have received and by all that God hath made, answer me!"

Whan that Huon and his company heard the dwarf speak, they mounted on their horses and rode away as fast as they might, without speaking of any word.

And the dwarf, seeing how that they rode away and would not speak, he was sorrowful and angry. Then he set one of his fingers on his horn, out of the which issued out such a wind and tempest so horrible to hear that it bare down trees and therewith came such a rain and hail that seemed that heaven and the earth had fought together and that the world should have ended. The beasts in the woods brayed and cried, and the fowls of the air fell down dead for fear that they were in; there was not creature but he would have been afrayed of that tempest. Then suddenly appeared before them a great river, that ran swifter than the birds did fly, and the water was so black and so perilous and made such a noise that it might be heard ten leagues off.

"Alas," quod Huon, "I see well now we all be all lost; we shall here be oppressed without God have pity of us. I repent me that ever I entered into this wood; I had been better to have travelled a whole year than to have come hither."

"Sir," quod Gerames, "dismay you not, for all this is done by the dwarf of the faerie."

"Well," quod Huon, "I think it best to alight from our horse, for I think we shall never scape from hence, but that we shall be all oppressed."

Then Garyn and the other companions had great marvel and wherein great fear.

"Ah, Gerames," quod Huon, "ye showed me well that it was great peril to pass this wood; I repent me that I had not believed you."

Then they saw on the other side of the river a fair castle environed with fourteen great towers, and on every tower a clocher[1] of fine gold beseeming; the which they long regarded, and by that time they had gone a little by the river side, they lost

[1] Belfry.

the sight of the castle; it was clean vanished away, whereof Huon and his company were sore abashed.

"Huon," quod Gerames, "of all this that ye see, dismay you not, for all this is done by the crooked dwarf of the faerie, and all to beguile you. But he can not grieve you so ye speak no word; howbeit, or we depart from him, he will make us all abashed, for anon he will come after us like a mad man, because ye will not speak to him. But, sir, I require you as 10 in God's name, be nothing afraid, but ride forth surely, and ever be ware that ye speak to him no word."

"Sir," quod Huon, "have no doubt thereof, for I had rather he were bresten than I should speak one word to him."

Then they rode to pass the river, and then they found there no thing to let them and so rode a five leagues.

"Sir," quod Huon, "we may well thank God that 20 we be thus scaped this dwarf, who thought to have deceived us. I was never in such fear during my life. God confound him."

Thus they rode devising of the little dwarf who had done them so much trouble.

When Gerames understood the company how they thought they were scaped from the dwarf, he began to smile and said: "Sirs, make none avaunt that ye be out of his danger, for I believe ye shall soon see him again."

30 And as soon as Gerames had spoken the same words, they saw before them a bridge, the which they must pass, and they saw the dwarf on the other part. Huon saw him first and said, "I see the devil who hath done us so much trouble."

Oberon heard him and said, "Friend, thou doest me injury without cause, for I was never devil nor ill creature. I am a man as other be, but I conjure thee by the divine puissance to speak to me."

Then Gerames said: "Sir, for God's sake, let him alone, nor speak no word to him, for by his fair language he may deceive us all, as he hath done many other; it is pity that he hath lived so long."

Then they rode forth a good pace and left the dwarf alone sore displeased in that they would not speak to him. Then he took his horn and set it to 10 his mouth and blew it. When Huon and his company heard it, they had no power to ride any further, but they began all to sing.

Then Oberon the dwarf said, "Yonder company are fools and proud that for any salutation that I can give them they disdain to answer me, but, by the God that made me, or they escape me, the refuse of my words shall be dear bought."

Then he took again his horn and strake it three times on his bow and cried out aloud and said, "Ye 20 my men, come and appear before me." Then there came to him a four hundred men of arms and demanded of Oberon what was his pleasure and who had displeased him.

"Sirs," quod Oberon, "I shall show you, howbeit I am grieved to show it. Here in this wood there passed fourteen knights who disdaineth to speak to me, but to the entent that they shall not mock me, they shall dearly buy the refusing of their answer, wherefore I will ye go after them and slay them all; 30 let none escape."

Then one of his knights said, "Sir, for God's sake, have pity of them."

"Certainly," quod Oberon, "mine honor saved, I can not spare them syn they disdain to speak to me."

"Sir," quod Gloriand, "for God's sake do not as ye say, but, sir, work by my counsel, and after do as it please you. Sir, I counsel you yet once again go after them, for, if they do not speak, we shall slay them all; for surely, sir, if they see you return again to them, so shortly they shall be in great fear."

"Friend," quod Oberon, "I shall do as ye have counseled me."

Thus Huon and his company rode forth a great pace, and Huon said, "Sirs, we are now from the dwarf a five leagues; I never saw in my life so fair a creature in the visage. I have great marvel how he 10 can speak of God Almighty, for I think he be a devil of hell. And since he speaketh of God, methink we ought to speak to him, for I think such a creature can have no power to do us any ill; I think he be not past of the age of five years."

"Sir," quod Gerames, "as little as he seemeth and that ye take him for a child, he was born forty year afore the nativity of our Lord Jesus Christ."

"Surely," quod Huon, "I care not what age he be of, but if he come again, ill hap come to me if I keep 20 my words and speech from him. I pray you be not displeased."

And thus as they rode devising fifteen days, suddenly Oberon appeared to them and said, "Sirs, are ye not yet advised to speak to me? Yet again I am come to salute you in the name of the God that made and formed us, and I conjure you, by the puissance that He hath given me, that ye speak to me, for I repute you for fools to think thus to pass thorough my wood and disdain to speak to me. Ah Huon, I 30 know thee well enough, and whither thou wouldst go. I know all thy deeds, and thou slewest Charlot and after discomfited Amaury, and I know the message that Charlemagne hath charged thee to say to the Admiral Gaudys, the which thing is impossible to be done without mine aid, for without me thou shalt never accomplish this enterprise. Speak to me, and I shall do thee that courtesy that I shall cause ye

to achieve thine enterprise, the which is impossible without me. And when thou hast achieved thy message, I shall bring thee again into France in safeguard, and I know the cause that thou wilt not speak to me hath been by reason of old Gerames, who is there with thee. Therefore, Huon, beware of thyself; go no further, for I know well it is three days past since thou didest eat any meat to profit thee. If thou wilt believe me, thou shalt have enough of such
10 sustenance as thou wilt wish for. And as soon as thou hast dined, I will give thee leave to depart, if it be thy pleasure; of this have no doubt."

"Sir," quod Huon, "ye be welcome."

"Ah," quod Oberon, "thy salutation shall be well rewarded. Know for truth thou never didest salutation so profitable for thyself. Thou mayest thank God that He hath sent thee that grace."

Oberon befriends Huon and enables him to succeed in his quest.

JOHN LYLY

EUPHUES, THE ANATOMY OF WIT

Lyly came of the scholarly family founded by William Lyly, the grammarian and the friend of Erasmus and More. Born in 1553 or 1554, he entered Magdalen College, Oxford, in 1569, where he was an irresponsible undergraduate who ran up bills, left once for three years, and finally got his M. A. in 1575. Four years later, Cambridge also gave him an M. A., but there is no trace of his having put in residence there. In 1585 Lyly was "vice master" of St. Paul's Choir School. He wrote excellent plays for the boys' companies, wanted to be Master of the Revels but instead received a minor appointment in that office, read new books for the Bishop of London, and was four times elected to Parliament. He died in 1606.

Euphues was published in 1578; its sequel, *Euphues and His England* followed in 1580. Both were exceedingly popular and, for a time, extensively imitated in substance and even more in style, but they were too soon supplanted and forgotten to leave a permanent effect on English literature. Like the *Morte Darthur*, *Euphues* strives to uphold the ideal of a polished gentleman, but in the process it also warns young men against foreign customs and new vices. It has sometimes been called a novel of manners because it depicts fashionable society.

Lyly was not an original writer. His title, *Euphues*, "The Well-trained Man," he borrowed from the *Schoolmaster* of Ascham, who, in his turn, got the word from Plato. His plot seems to be a combination of the story of the Prodigal Son with Boccaccio's *Tale of Tito and Gisippo* although the theory has been advanced—not altogether convincingly—that it was suggested by actual events which happened near Oxford when the writer was there. His style, the so-called euphuism, may probably be traced to the Renaissance influence of the Greek philosophers, Gorgias and Isocrates, perhaps emphasized by the monastic schools of rhetoric and the ornate medieval technique of writing. It is characterized by antithesis and repetition; the continual use of figures of speech and of proverbs; by alliteration, rime, and other sound devices; and by distorted natural history. These tricks of style were used by both earlier and contemporary English writers, but Lyly employed them with more notable success and greater popularity than had the others, wherefore this tendency is called in general euphuism.

EUPHUES, THE ANATOMY OF WIT

Euphues, a young Athenian gentleman, comes to Naples and there makes the acquaintance of Philautus.

Euphues having sojourned by the space of two months in Naples, whether he were moved by the courtesy of a young gentleman named Philautus or enforced by destiny, whether his pregnant wit or his

pleasant conceits wrought the greater liking in the mind of Eupheus, I know not for certainty; but Euphues shewed such entire love towards him that he seemed to make small account of any others, determining to enter into such an inviolable league of friendship with him, as neither time by piecemeal should impair, neither fancy utterly dissolve, nor any suspicion infringe. "I have read," saith he, "and well I believe it, that a friend is in prosperity a
10 pleasure, a solace in adversity, in grief a comfort, in joy a merry companion, at all times an other I, in all places the express image of mine own person: insomuch that I cannot tell whether the immortal gods have bestowed any gift upon mortal men either more noble or more necessary than friendship. Is there anything in the world to be reputed (I will not say compared) to friendship? Can any treasure in the transitory pilgrimage be of more value than a friend in whose bosom thou mayst sleep secure with-
20 out fear, whom thou mayst make partner of all thy secrets without suspicion of fraud, and partaker of all thy misfortune without mistrust of fleeting, who will account thy bale his bane, thy mishap his misery, the pricking of thy finger the piercing of his heart? But whither am I carried? Have I not also learned that one should eat a bushel of salt with him whom he meaneth to make his friend? that trial maketh trust? that there is falsehood in fellowship? and what then? Doth not the sympathy of manners
30 make the conjunction of minds? Is it not a byword, *like will to like*? Not so common as commendable it is to see young gentlemen choose them such friends with whom they may seem being absent to be present, being asunder to be conversant, being dead to be alive. I will therefore have Philautus for my fere, and by so much the more I made myself sure to

have Philautus, by how much the more I view in him the lively image of Euphues."

Although there be none so ignorant that doth not know, neither any so impudent that will not confess friendship to be the jewel of human joy: yet whosoever shall see this amity grounded upon a little affection will soon conjecture that it shall be dissolved upon a light occasion; as in the sequel of Euphues and Philautus you shall see, whose hot love waxed 10 soon cold. For as the best wine doth make the sharpest vinegar, so the deepest love turneth to the deadliest hate. Who deserved the most blame in mine opinion, it is doubtful and so difficult that I dare not presume to give verdict. For love being the cause for which so many mischiefs have been attempted, I am not yet persuaded whether of them was most to be blamed, but certainly neither of them was blameless. I appeal to your judgment gentlemen, not that I think any of you of the like disposi- 20 tion able to decide the question, but, being of deeper discretion than I am, are more fit to debate the quarrel. Though the discourse of their friendship and falling out be somewhat long, yet, being somewhat strange, I hope the delightfulness of the one will attenuate the tediousness of the other.

Eupheus had continual access to the place of Philautus and no little familiarity with him, and finding him at convenient leisure, in these short terms unfolded his mind unto him.

30 "Gentleman and friend, the trial I have had of thy manners, cutteth off divers terms which to another I would have used in the like matter. And sithens a long discourse argueth folly and delicate words incur the suspicion of flattery, I am determined to use neither of them, knowing either of them to breed offense. Weighing with myself the force of friendship by the effects, I studied ever since my first

coming to Naples to enter league with such a one as might direct my steps, being a stranger, and resemble my manners, being a scholar, the which two qualities as I find in you able to satisfy my desire, so I hope I shall find a heart in you willing to accomplish my request. Which if I may obtain, assure yourself that Damon to his Pythias, Pylades to his Orestes, Titus to his Gysippus, Theseus to his Pirithous, Scipio to his Laelius, was never found
10 more faithful than Euphues will be to his Philautus."

Philautus by how much the less he looked for this discourse, by so much the more he liked it, for he saw all qualities both of body and mind in Euphues, unto whom he replied as followeth.

"Friend Euphues (for so your talk warranteth me to term you), I dare neither use a long process neither loving speech, lest unwittingly I should cause you to convince me of those things which you have already condemned. And verily I am bold to pre-
20 sume upon your courtesy, since you yourself have used so little curiosity, persuading myself, that my short answer will work as great an effect in you, as your few words did in me. And seeing we resemble (as you say) each other in qualities, it cannot be that the one should differ from the other in courtesy; seeing the sincere affection of the mind cannot be expressed by the mouth, and that no art can unfold the entire love of the heart, I am earnestly to beseech you not to measure the firmness of my faith by the
30 fewness of my words, but rather think that the overflowing waves of good will leave no passage for many words. Trial shall prove trust; here is my hand, my heart, my lands and my life at thy commandment. Thou mayst well perceive that I did believe thee, that so soon I did love thee, and I hope thou wilt the rather love me, in that I did believe thee." Either Euphues and Philautus stood in need

of friendship or were ordained to be friends; upon so short warning, to make so soon a conclusion might seem in mine opinion, if it continued, miraculous; if shaken off, ridiculous.

But after many embracings and protestations one to another, they walked to dinner, where they wanted neither meat, neither music, neither any other pastime; and, having banqueted, to digest their sweet confections, they danced all that afternoon; they 10 used not only one board, but one bed, one book (if so be it they thought not one too many). Their friendship augmented every day, insomuch that the one could not refrain the company of the other one minute, all things went in common between them, which all men accounted commendable. Philautus, being a town-born child, both for his own continuance and the great countenance which his father had while he lived, crept into credit with Don Ferardo, one of the chief governors of the city, who, 20 although he had a courtly crew of gentlewomen sojourning in his palace, yet his daughter, heir to his whole revenues, stained the beauty of them all, whose modest bashfulness caused the other to look wan for envy, whose lily cheeks dyed with a vermilion red made the rest to blush at her beauty. For as the finest ruby staineth the color of the rest that be in place, or as the sun dimmeth the moon that she cannot be discerned, so this gallant girl, more fair than fortunate and yet more fortunate than faithful, 30 eclipsed the beauty of them all and changed their colors. Unto her had Philautus access, who won her by right of love and should have worn her by right of law, had not Euphues by strange destiny broken the bonds of marriage and forbidden the banes of matrimony.

It happened that Don Ferardo had occasion to go to Venice about certain his own affairs, leaving his daughter the only steward of his household, who spared not to feast Philautus her friend with all kinds of delights and delicates, reserving only her honesty as the chief stay of her honor. Her father being gone, she sent for her friend to supper, who came not as he was accustomed solitarily alone, but accompanied with his friend Euphues. The gentlewomen, whether it were for niceness or for niggardness of courtesy, gave him such a cold welcome that 10 he repented that he was come.

Euphues, though he knew himself worthy every way to have a good countenance, yet could he not perceive her willing any way to lend him a friendly look. Yet lest he should seem to want gestures or to be dashed out of conceit with her coy countenance, he addressed him to a gentlewoman called Livia, unto whom he uttered this speech. "Fair lady, if it be the guise of Italy to welcome strangers with strangeness, I must needs say the custom is 20 strange and the country barbarous; if the manner of ladies to salute gentlemen with coyness, then I am enforced to think the women without courtesy to use such welcome and the men past shame that will come. But hereafter I will either bring a stool on mine arm for an unbidden guest, or a vizard on my face, for a shameless gossip."

Livia replied, "Sir, our country is civil, and our gentlewomen are courteous, but in Naples it is counted a jest at every word to say, 'In faith you are 30 welcome.'"

As she was yet talking, supper was set on the board; then Philautus spake thus unto Lucilla. "Yet, gentlewoman, I was the bolder to bring my shadow with me, (meaning Euphues) knowing that he should be the better welcome for my sake," unto whom the gentlewoman replied: "Sir, as I never, when I saw you, thought that you came without your shadow, so now I cannot a little marvel to see you so overshot in bringing a new shadow with you."

Euphues though he perceived her coy nip, seemed not to care for it, but taking her by the hand said, "Fair lady, seeing the shade doth often shield your beauty from the parching sun, I hope you will the better esteem of the shadow, and by so much the less it ought to be offensive, by how much the less it is able to offend you, and by so much the more you 10 ought to like it, by how much the more you use to lie in it."

"Well, gentleman," answered Lucilla, "in arguing of the shadow, we forgo the substance; pleaseth it you therefore to sit down to supper." And so they all sat down, but Euphues fed of one dish which ever stood before him, the beauty of Lucilla.

Here Euphues at the first sight was so kindled with desire, that almost he was like to burn to coals. Supper being ended, the order was in Naples that 20 the gentlewomen would desire to hear some discourse, either concerning love or learning. And although Philautus was requested, yet he posted it over to Euphues, whom he knew most fit for that purpose; Euphues, being thus tied to the stake by their importunate entreaty, began as followeth.

"He that worst may is always enforced to hold the candle; the weakest must still to the wall; where none will, the devil himself must bear the cross. But were it not, gentlewomen, that your list stands 30 for law, I would borrow so much leave as to resign mine office to one of you whose experience in love hath made you learned and whose learning hath made you so lovely; for me to entreat of the one, being a novice, or to discourse of the other, being a truant, I may well make you weary but never the wiser and give you occasion rather to laugh at my rashness than to like my reasons. Yet I care the less to excuse my boldness to you, who were the cause of my blindness. And since I am at mine own choice either to talk of love or of learning, I had rather for this time be deemed an unthrift in rejecting profit than a Stoic in renouncing pleasure.

"It hath been a question often disputed, but never determined, whether the qualities of the mind or the composition of the man cause women most to like, or whether beauty or wit move men most to love. Certes by how much the more the mind is to be preferred before the body, by so much the more the graces of the one are to be preferred before the gifts of the other, which if it be so that the contemplation of the inward quality ought to be respected more than the view of the outward beauty, then doubtless women either do or should love those best whose virtue is best, not measuring the deformed man with the reformed mind. The foul toad hath a fair stone in his head; the fine gold is found in the filthy earth; the sweet kernel lieth in the hard shell. Virtue is harbored in the heart of him that most men esteem misshapen. Contrariwise, if we respect more the outward shape than the inward habit, good God into how many mischiefs do we fall; into what blindness are we led? Do we not commonly see that in painted pots is hidden the deadliest poison? that in the greenest grass is the greatest serpent? in the clearest water the ugliest toad? Doth not experience teach us that in the most curious sepulchre are enclosed rotten bones? that the cypress tree beareth a fair leaf but no fruit? that the estridge carrieth fair feathers but rank flesh? How frantic are those lovers which are carried away with the gay glistering of the fine face the beauty whereof is parched with the summer's blaze and chipped with the winter's blast, which is of so short continuance that it fadeth before one perceive it flourish, of so small profit that it poisoneth those that possess it, of so little value with the wise that they account it a delicate bait with a deadly hook, a sweet panther with a devouring paunch, a sour poison in a silver pot? Here I could enter into discourse of such fine dames as being in love with their own looks make such course account of their passionate lovers; for commonly, if they be adorned with beauty, they be so straight laced and made so 10 high in the instep that they disdain them most that most desire them. It is a world to see the doting of their lovers and their dealing with them, the revealing of whose subtle trains would cause me to shed tears and you gentlewomen to shut your modest ears. Pardon me, gentlewomen, if I unfold every wile and shew every wrinkle of women's disposition. Two things do they cause their servants to bow unto them,—secrecy and sovereignty, the one to conceal their enticing sleights, by the other to assure them- 20 selves of their only service. Again,—but ho there, if I should have waded any further and sounded the depth of their deceit, I should either have procured your displeasure or incurred the suspicion of fraud,—either armed you to practise the like subtlety or accused myself of perjury. But I mean not to offend your chaste minds with the rehearsal of their unchaste manners, whose ears I perceive to glow and hearts to be grieved at that which I have already uttered,—not that amongst you there be 30 any such, but that in your sex there should be any such. Let not gentlewomen, therefore, make too much of their painted sheath; let them not be so curious in their own conceit or so currish to their loyal lovers. When the black crow's foot shall appear in their eye or the black ox tread on their foot, when their beauty shall be like the blasted rose, their wealth wasted, their bodies worn, their faces

wrinkled, their fingers crooked, who will like of them in their age, who loved none in their youth? If you will be cherished when you be old, be courteous while you be young; if you look for comfort in your hoary hairs, be not coy when you have your golden locks; if you would be embraced in the waning of your bravery, be not squeamish in the waxing of your beauty; if you desire to be kept like the roses when they have lost their color, smell
10 sweet as the rose doth in the bud; if you would be tasted for old wine, be in the mouth a pleasant grape; so shall you be cherished for your courtesy, comforted for your honesty, embraced for your amity; so shall you be preserved with the sweet rose and drunk with the pleasant wine. Thus far I am bold, gentlewomen, to counsel those that be coy that they weave not the web of their own woe nor spin the thread of their own thraldom by their own overthwartness. And seeing we are even in
20 the bowels of love, it shall not be amiss to examine whether man or woman be soonest allured, whether be most constant the male or the female. And in this point I mean not to be mine own carver, lest I should seem either to pick a thank[1] with men or a quarrel with women. If therefore it might stand with your pleasure, Mistress Lucilla, to give your censure, I would take the contrary, for sure I am, though your judgment be sound, yet affection will shadow it."

30 Lucilla, seeing his pretense, thought to take advantage of his large proffer, unto whom she said. "Gentleman, in mine opinion, women are to be won with every wind, in whose sex there is neither force to withstand the assaults of love neither constancy to remain faithful. And because your discourse hath

[1] To pick a thank—to be a flatterer.

hitherto bred delight, I am loth to hinder you in the sequel of your devices."

Euphues, perceiving himself to be taken napping, answered as followeth. "Mistress Lucilla, if you speak as you think, these gentlewomen present have little cause to thank you; if you cause me to commend women, my tale will be accounted a mere trifle, and your words the plain truth. Yet knowing promise to be debt, I well pay it with performance. And I would the gentlemen here present were as ready to credit my proof, as the gentlewomen are willing to hear their own praises, or I as able to overcome, as Mistress Lucilla would be content to be overthrown. Howsoever the matter shall fall out, I am of the surer side, for if my reasons be weak, then is our sex strong; if forcible, then your judgment feeble; if I find truth on my side, I hope I shall for my wages win the good will of women; if I want proof, then, gentlewomen, of necessity you must yield to men. But to the matter.

"Touching the yielding to love, albeit their hearts seem tender, yet they harden them like the stone of Sicilia, the which the more it is beaten, the harder it is; for being framed as it were of the perfection of men, they be free from all such cogitations as may any way provoke them to uncleanness, insomuch as they abhor the light love of youth which is grounded upon lust and dissolved upon every light occasion. When they see the folly of men turn to fury, their delight to doting, their affection to frenzy, when they see them as it were pine in pleasure and to wax pale through their own peevishness; their suits, their service, their letters, their labors, their loves, their lives, seem to them so odious that they harden their hearts against such concupiscence, to the end they might convert them from rashness to reason, from such lewd disposition to honest discretion;

hereof it cometh that men accuse women of cruelty; because they themselves want civility, they account them full of wiles in not yielding to their wickedness, faithless for resisting their filthiness. But I had almost forgot myself; you shall pardon me, Mistress Lucilla, for this time, if thus abruptly I finish my discourse; it is neither for want of good will or lack of proof, but that I feel in myself such alteration that I can scarcely utter one word. Ah Euphues, 10 Euphues!"

The gentlewomen were struck into such a quandary with this sudden change that they all changed color. But Euphues taking Philautus by the hand and giving the gentlewomen thanks for their patience and his repast, bade them all farewell and went immediately to his chamber. But Lucilla, who now began to fry in the flames of love, all the company being departed to their lodgings, entered into these terms and contrarieties.

20 "Ah wretched wench Lucilla, how art thou perplexed? What a doubtful fight dost thou feel betwixt faith and fancy, hope and fear, conscience and concupiscence? O my Euphues, little dost thou know the sudden sorrow that I sustain for thy sweet sake. Whose wit hath bewitched me, whose rare qualities have deprived me of mine old quality, whose courteous behavior without curiosity, whose comely feature without fault, whose filed speech without fraud, hath wrapped me in this misfortune. 30 And canst thou, Lucilla, be so light of love in forsaking Philautus to fly to Euphues? Canst thou prefer a stranger before thy countryman, a starter before thy companion? Why, Euphues doth perhaps desire my love, but Philautus hath deserved it. Why, Euphues' feature is worthy as good as I, but Philautus his faith is worthy a better. Ay, but the latter love is most fervent! Ay, but the first ought

to be most faithful! Ay, but Euphues hath greater perfection! Ay, but Philautus hath deeper affection!

"Ah fond wench, dost thou think Euphues will deem thee constant to him, when thou hast been unconstant to his friend? Weenest thou that he will have no mistrust of thy faithfulness, when he hath had trial of thy fickleness? Will he have no doubt of thine honor, when thou thyself callest thine honesty in question? Yes, yes, Lucilla, well doth he
10 know that the glass once crazed will with the least clap be cracked, that the cloth which staineth with milk will soon loose his color with vinegar, that the eagle's wing will waste [1] the feather as well of the phoenix as of the pheasant, that she that hath been faithless to one will never be faithful to any. But can Euphues convince me of fleeting, seeing for his sake I break my fidelity? Can he condemn me of disloyalty, when he is the only cause of my disliking? May he justly condemn me of treachery,
20 who hath this testimony as trial of my good will? Doth not he remember that the broken bone, once set together, is stronger than ever it was? that the greatest blot is taken off with the pumice? that though the spider poison the fly, she cannot infect the bee? that although I have been light to Philautus, yet I may be lovely to Euphues? It is not my desire but his deserts that moveth my mind to this choice, neither the want of the like good will in Philautus, but the lack of the like good qualities
30 that removeth my fancy from the one to the other.

"For as the bee that gathereth honey out of the weed, when she espieth the fair flower flieth to the sweetest; or as the kind spaniel, though he hunt after birds, yet forsakes them to retrieve the partridge; or as we commonly feed on beef hungerly at

[1] Exhaust.

first, yet seeing the quail more dainty, change our diet; so I, although I loved Philautus for his good properties, yet seeing Euphues to excel him, I ought by nature to like him better. By so much the more, therefore, my change is to be excused by how much the more my choice is excellent; and by so much the less I am to be condemned by how much the more Euphues is to be commended. Is not the diamond of more value than the ruby because he is of more
10 virtue? Is not the emerald preferred before the sapphire for his wonderful property? Is not Euphues more praiseworthy than Philautus being more witty? But fie Lucilla, why dost thou flatter thyself in thine own folly? Canst thou feign Euphues thy friend, whom by thine own words thou hast made thy foe? Didest not thou accuse women of inconstancy? Didest not thou account them easy to be won? Didest not thou condemn them of weakness? What sounder argument can he have against thee
20 than thine own answer? what better proof than thine own speech? what greater trial than thine own talk? If thou hast belied women, he will judge thee unkind; if thou have revealed the truth, he must needs think thee unconstant; if he perceive thee to be won with a nut, he will imagine that thou wilt be lost with an apple. If he find thee wanton before thou be wooed, he will guess thou wilt be wavering when thou art wedded.

"But suppose that Euphues love thee, that Philau-
30 tus leave thee, will thy father, thinkest thou, give thee liberty to live after thine own lust? Will he esteem him worthy to inherit his possessions, whom he accounteth unworthy to enjoy thy person? Is it like that he will match thee in marriage with a stranger, with a Grecian, with a mean man? Ay, but what knoweth my father whether he be wealthy,

whether his revenues be able to countervail my father's lands, whether his birth be noble, yea or no? Can anyone make doubt of his gentle blood, that seeth his gentle conditions? Can his honor be called into question, whose honesty is so great? Is he to be thought thriftless, who in all qualities of the mind is peerless? No, no, the tree is knowen by his fruit, the gold by his touch, the son by the sire. And as the soft wax receiveth whatsoever print be in
10 the seal and sheweth no other impression, so the tender babe being sealed with his father's gifts representeth his image most lively. But were I once certain of Euphues' good will, I would not so superstitiously account of my father's ill will. Time hath weaned me from my mother's teat, and age rid me from my father's correction; when children are in their swathe clouts, then are they subject to the whip and ought to be careful of the rigor of their parents. As for me, seeing I am not fed with their pap, I am
20 not to be led by their persuasions. Let my father use what speeches he list, I will follow mine own lust. Lust, Lucilla, what sayst thou? No, no, mine own love I should have said, for I am as far from lust, as I am from reason and as near to love as I am to folly. Then stick to thy determination, and shew thyself what love can do, what love dares do, what love hath done. Albeit I can no way quench the coals of desire with forgetfulness; yet will I rake them up in the ashes of modesty, seeing I dare not
30 discover my love for maidenly shamefastness, I will dissemble it till time I have opportunity. And I hope so to behave myself as Euphues shall think me his own, and Philautus persuade himself I am none but his. But I would to God Euphues would repair hither, that the sight of him might mitigate some part of my martyrdom."

SIR PHILIP SIDNEY

ARCADIA

Sir Philip Sidney, the ideal gentleman of the Elizabethan age, was born on November 30, 1554. A student at Christ Church College, Oxford, by 1568, he left without a degree and made a three year tour of the continent, during which he witnessed in Paris the Massacre of St. Bartholomew, an experience which strongly influenced his later views. On his return, Sidney pursued his brilliant career as courtier, soldier, diplomat, and author. He accompanied Queen Elizabeth when she was gorgeously entertained at Kenilworth Castle. In Ireland, he saw military service, and he went on embassies to the Imperial Court and later to France. The first version of the *Arcadia* he wrote about 1578 to entertain his sister, the Countess of Pembroke. His death was typical of the man's chivalrous and idealistic temperament. During a military campaign on the continent, Sidney, with some five hundred English attacked at Zutphen a convoy protected by three thousand Spaniards. At the beginning of the battle, seeing a friend unprovided with cuisses or thigh armor, he had foolishly thrown away his own, with the result that he was mortally wounded in this part of the leg. Water was brought to satisfy his tormenting thirst, but, seeing a poor soldier glance at it with longing, he gave it to the man, with the words, "Thy necessity is yet greater than mine." After lingering nearly a month, he died on October 17, 1586, mourned by all England.

When Sidney first wrote the *Arcadia* for his sister's amusement, he composed it in comparatively simple form. No printed edition of this version appeared at the time, and it was only in 1907 that several manuscripts of this so-called "old *Arcadia*" unexpectedly turned up. At some later time, however, Sidney began to rewrite his novel, enormously complicating it, especially by the addition of many subplots which he carries on for a while, drops, and then later takes up once more. The result is one of the most highly organized and confusing bits of fiction in English. Sidney did not live to complete this revision, but what he did finish was published in 1590.

The *Arcadia,* as the result of this reworking, is a romance of chivalry with a background of shepherd life, the chivalric element being the more important. The action is supposed to take place in the Grecian Arcadia, which nevertheless is really only a vague no man's land. The main plot concerns the Greek princes, Musidorus and Pyrocles, who arrive in Arcadia where the king, Basilius, is living in retirement. The two young men fall in love respectively with Pamela and Philoclea, the king's two daughters. After endless battles and innumerable adventures, during many of which Pyrocles is disguised as an Amazon, the heroes win the hands of their ladies. Of the two selections in this volume, the first, which is the opening passage of the *Arcadia,* is drawn from the main plot; the second is from a subplot.

In writing his novel, Sidney was influenced by the literature of various epochs and countries. In the first place, certain Greek romances, penned in the fourth or fifth century after Christ, set the *Arcadia* a model for its grandiose plot and provided stock incidents, such as shipwrecks, adventures with pirates, and people scoffing at love only to become enslaved later. Various romances written in southern Europe afforded further material. An Italian novel of shepherd's life, Sannazaro's *Arcadia,* gave Sidney's work its name and certain details. A Spanish pastoral and chivalric romance, the *Diana,* provided certain others; and still more were borrowed from another famous book written in the Spanish peninsula, *Amadis of Gaul,* one of the volumes that crazed Don Quixote.

Sidney, earnest idealist that he was, put into the *Arcadia* many of his moral and political views, especially those derived from the Greek philosopher, Aristotle. The work might indeed be called a prose *Faerie Queene.*

The style of the *Arcadia* is highly artificial, using numerous metaphors, rejoicing in personifications and circumlocutions, not averse to plays on words and some alliteration, but it is not of the school of Lyly. Various critics have seen in it the influence of the Greek romances, or of Cicero combined with medieval romances and the Bible.

The *Arcadia* was extremely popular with its contemporaries and for some time afterward, so that by 1674 it reached its fifteenth edition. King Charles I is said to have been especially fond of a prayer uttered by the heroine Pamela,—a fondness which caused Milton to censure his "having stolen a prayer word for word from the mouth of a heathen woman praying to a heathen god," and to dub the *Arcadia* "a vain amatorious poem." Finally Sidney's novel furnished the main plots to plays by Beaumont and Fletcher and by Shirley, and the Gloucester subplot to Shakespeare's *King Lear.*

ARCADIA

It was in the time that the earth begins to put on her new apparel against the approach of her lover, and that the sun, running a most even course, becomes an indifferent arbiter between the night and the day, when the hopeless shepherd Strephon was come to the sands which lie against the island of Cythera; where viewing the place with a heavy kind of delight and sometimes casting his eyes to the isleward, he called his friendly rival the pastor Claius
10 unto him, and setting first down in his darkened countenance a doleful copy of what he would speak, "O my Claius," said he, "hither we are now come to pay the rent for which we are so called unto by over-busy remembrance, remembrance, restless remembrance which claims not only this duty of us, but for it will have us forget ourselves. I pray you when we were amid our flock, and that of other shepherds some were running after their sheep, strayed beyond their bounds; some delighting their
20 eyes with seeing them nibble upon the short and sweet grass; some medicining their sick ewes; some setting a bell for an ensign of a sheepish squadron; some with more leisure inventing new games of exercising their bodies and sporting their wits; did remembrance grant us any holiday either for pastime or devotion, nay either for necessary food or natural rest, but that still it forced our thoughts to work upon this place where we last (alas that the word *last* should so long last) did graze our eyes
30 upon her ever-flourishing beauty, did it not still cry

within us: 'Ah, you base-minded wretches!—are your thoughts so deeply bemired in the trade of ordinary worldlings as for respect of gain some paltry wool may yield you, to let so much time pass without knowing perfectly her estate, especially in so troublesome a season; to leave that shore unsaluted from whence you may see to the island where she dwelleth, to leave those steps unkissed wherein Urania printed the farewell of all beauty?'

10 "Well then, remembrance commanded, we obeyed, and here we find that as our remembrance came everclothed unto us in the form of this place, so this place gives new heat to the fever of our languishing remembrance. Yonder, my Claius, Urania lighted; the very horse, methought, bewailed to be so disburdened; and as for thee, poor Claius, when thou wentest to help her down, I saw reverence and desire so divide thee that thou didst at one instant both blush and quake and, instead of bearing her, wert ready to 20 fall down thyself. There she sat, vouchsafing my cloak (then most gorgeous) under her; at yonder rising of the ground she turned herself, looking back towards her wonted abode, and, because of her parting, bearing much sorrow in her eyes, the lightsomeness whereof had yet so natural a cheerfulness that it made even sorrow seem to smile; at that turning she spake to us all, opening the cherry of her lips, and Lord, how greedily mine ears did feed upon the sweet words she uttered! And here she 30 laid her hand over thine eyes when she saw the tears springing in them, as if she would conceal them from other and yet herself feel some of thy sorrow. But woe is me,—yonder, yonder, did she put her foot into the boat at that instant, as it were, dividing her heavenly beauty between the earth and the sea. But when she was embarked, did you not mark how the winds whistled and the seas danced

for joy, how the sails did swell with pride, and all because they had Urania? O Urania, blessed be thou, Urania, the sweetest fairness and the fairest sweetness!"

With that word his voice brake so with sobbing that he could say no farther, and Claius thus answered:

"Alas, my Strephon," said he, "what needs this score to reckon up only our losses? What doubt
10 is there but that the sight of this place doth call our thoughts to appear at the court of affection, held by that racking steward remembrance? As well may sheep forget to fear when they spy wolves, as we can miss such fancies when we see any place made happy by her treading. Who can choose that saw her but think where she stayed, where she walked, where she turned, where she spoke? But what is all this? Truly no more but as this place served us to think of those things, so those things
20 serve as places to call to memory more excellent matters. No, no, let us think with consideration, and consider with acknowledging, and acknowledge with admiration, and admire with love, and love with joy in the midst of all woes. Let us in such sort think, I say, that our poor eyes were so enriched as to behold and our low hearts so exalted as to love a maid who is such that, as the greatest thing the world can show is her beauty, so the least thing that may be praised in her is her beauty. Certainly
30 as her eye-lids are more pleasant to behold than two white kids climbing up a fair tree and browsing on its tenderest branches, and yet are nothing compared to the day-shining stars contained in them; and as her breath is more sweet than a gentle south-west wind which comes creeping over flowery fields and shadowed waters in the extreme heat of summer; and yet is nothing compared to the honey-flowing

speech that breath doth carry; no more all that our eyes can see of her (though when they have seen her, what else they shall ever see is but dry stubble after clover-grass) is to be matched with the flock of unspeakable virtues laid up delightfully in that best builded fold. But indeed, as we can better consider the sun's beauty by marking how he gilds these waters and mountains than by looking upon his own face too glorious for our weak eyes, so it may 10 be our conceits (not able to bear her sun-staining excellency) will better weigh it by her works upon some meaner subject employed. And alas, who can better witness that than we whose experience is grounded upon feeling? Hath not the only love of her made us (being silly ignorant shepherds) raise up our thoughts above the ordinary level of the world so that great clerks do not disdain our conference? Hath not the desire to seem worthy in her eyes made us, when others were sleeping, to sit 20 viewing the course of the heavens; when others were running at base, to run over learned writings; when others mark their sheep, we to mark ourselves? Hath not she thrown reason upon our desires and, as it were, given eyes unto Cupid? Hath in any, but in her, love-fellowship maintained friendship between rivals and beauty taught the beholders chastity?"

He was going on with his praises, but Strephon bade him stay and look, and so they both perceived a thing which floated, drawing nearer and nearer to the 30 bank but rather by the favorable working of the sea than by any self-industry. They doubted a while what it should be till it was cast up even hard before them, at which time they fully saw it was a man. Whereupon, running for pity's sake unto him, they found his hands (as it should appear constanter friends to his life than his memory) fast gripping upon the edge of a square small coffer which lay all under his breast, else in himself no show of life so that the board seemed to be but a bier to carry him a land to his sepulchre. So drew they up a young man of goodly shape and well-pleasing favor that one would think death had in him a lovely countenance; and that, though he were naked, nakedness was to him an apparel. That sight increased their compassion, and their compassion called up their care, so that lifting his feet above his head, making a great deal of salt water come out of his mouth, they laid him upon some of their garments and fell to rub and chafe him till they brought him to recover both breath, the servant, and warmth, the companion, of living. At length, opening his eyes, he gave a great groan (a doleful note but a pleasant ditty, for by that they found not only life but strength of life in him). They therefore continued on their charitable office until, his spirits being well returned, he—without so much as thanking them for their pains—gat up and, looking round about to the uttermost limits of sight, and crying upon the name of Pyrocles, nor seeing nor hearing cause of comfort, "What," said he, "and shall Musidorus live after Pyrocles's destruction?"

Therewithal he offered wilfully to cast himself again into the sea, a strange sight to the shepherds to whom it seemed that before being in appearance dead, had yet saved his life, and now coming to his life, should be a cause to procure his death; but they ran unto him and pulling him back, (then too feeble for them) by force stickled that unnatural fray.

"I pray you," said he, "honest men, what such right have you in me as not to suffer me to do with myself what I list, and what policy have you to bestow a benefit where it is accounted an injury?"

They hearing him speak in Greek (which was their natural language) became the more tender-hearted towards him, and considering by his calling and looking that the loss of some dear friend was great cause of his sorrow, told him they were poor men that were bound by course of humanity to prevent so great a mischief, and that they wished him, if opinion of some body's perishing bred such desperate anguish in him, that he should be comforted by his own proof who had lately escaped as apparent danger as any might be.

10 "No, no," said he, "it is not for me to attend so high a blissfulness; but since you take care of me, I pray you find means that some barque may be provided that will go out of the haven that if it be possible we may find the body, far, far too precious food for fishes; and for that hire," said he, "I have within this casket of value sufficient to content them."

Claius presently went to a fisherman, and having agreed with him and provided some apparel for the 20 naked stranger, he embarked and the shepherds with him; and were no sooner gone beyond the mouth of the haven but that some way into the sea they might discern, as it were, a stain of the water's color and by times some sparks and smoke mounting thereout. But the young man no sooner saw it but that beating his breast he cried that there was the beginning of his ruin, entreating them to bend their course as near unto it as they could; telling how that smoke was but the small relic of a great fire which had 30 driven both him and his friend rather to commit themselves to the cold mercy of the sea than to abide the hot cruelty of the fire; and that therefore, though they both had abandoned the ship, that he was (if any were) in that course to be met withal. They steered therefore as nearly thither-ward as they could; but when they came so near that their eyes were full masters of the object, they saw a sight

full of piteous strangeness: a ship, or rather the carcase of the ship, or rather some few bones of the
carcase hulling there, part broken, part burned, part
drowned, death having used more than one dart to
that destruction. About it floated great store of very
rich things and many chests which might promise no
less. And amidst the precious things were a number
of dead bodies, which likewise did not only testify
both elements' violence, but that the chief violence
10 was grown of human inhumanity, for their bodies
were full of grisly wounds, and their blood had, as
it were, filled the wrinkles of the sea's visage, which
it seemed the sea would not wash away that it might
witness it is not always its fault when we do condemn its cruelty. In sum, a defeat where the conquered kept both field and spoil, a shipwreck
without storm or ill-footing, and a waste of fire in
the midst of the water.

But a little way off they saw the mast whose proud
20 height now lay along, like a widow having lost her
mate of whom she held her honor, but upon the mast
they saw a young man (at least if he were a man)
bearing show of about eighteen years of age, who
sat (as on horse back) having nothing upon him but
his shirt, which being wrought with blue silk and
gold had a kind of resemblance to the sea, on which
the sun (then near his western home) did shoot some
of his beams. His hair (which the young men of
Greece used to wear very long) was stirred up and
30 down with the wind which seemed to have a sport
to play with it as the sea had to kiss his feet, himself full of admirable beauty set forth by the
strangeness both of his seat and gesture. For, holding his head up full of unmoved majesty, he held a
sword aloft with his fair arm, which often he waved
about his crown as though he would threaten the
world in that extremity. But the fishermen, when

they came so near him that it was time to throw out a rope by which hold they might draw him, their simplicity bred such amazement and their amazement such superstition that (assuredly thinking it was some God begotten between Neptune and Venus that had made all this terrible slaughter), as they went under sail by him, held up their hands and made their prayers. Which when Musidorus saw, though he were almost as much ravished with joy as they
10 with astonishment, he leaped to the mariner and took the cord out of his hand and (saying, "Dost thou live and art thou well?" who answered, "Thou canst tell best since most of my well-being stands in thee") threw it out, but already the ship was passed beyond Pyrocles, and therefore Musidorus could do no more but persuade the mariners to cast about again, assuring them that he was but a man, although of most divine excellencies, and promising great rewards for their pain.

20 And now they were already come upon the stays; when one of the sailors described a galley which came with sails and oars directly in the chase of them; and straight perceived it was a well-known pirate who hunted not only for goods but for bodies of men, which he employed either to be his galley slaves or to sell at the best market. Which when the master understood, he commanded forthwith to set on all the canvas they could and fly homeward, leaving in that sort poor Pyrocles so near to be
30 rescued. But what did not Musidorus say, what did he not offer to persuade them to venture to fight, but fear standing at the gates of their ears put back all persuasions, so that he had nothing whatever to accompany Pyrocles but his eyes nor to succour him but his wishes. Therefore praying for him, and casting a long look that way, he saw the galley leave the pursuit of them and turn to take up the spoils of

the other wreck and lastly he might well see them lift up the young man; and "Alas," said he to himself, "dear Pyrocles, shall that body of thine be enchained; shall those victorious hands of thine be commanded to base offices; shall virtue become a slave to those that be slaves to viciousness? Alas, better had it been thou hadst ended nobly thy noble days; what death is so evil as unworthy servitude?"

But that opinion soon ceased when he saw the 10 galley setting upon another ship which held long and strong fight with her; for then he began afresh to fear the life of his friend and to wish well to the pirates whom before he hated, lest in their ruin he might perish. But the fishermen made such speed into the haven that they absented his eyes from beholding the issue; where being entered, he could procure neither them or any other as then, to put themselves into the sea; so that being as full of sorrow for being unable to do anything as void of 20 counsel how to do anything, besides that sickness grew something upon him, the honest shepherds Strephon and Claius, who being themselves true friends did the more perfectly judge the justness of his sorrow, advise him that he should mitigate somewhat of his woe since he had gotten an amendment in fortune, being come from assured persuasion of his death to have no cause to despair of his life; as one that had lamented the death of his sheep should after know they were but strayed would receive 30 pleasure, though readily he knew not where to find them.

"Now, sir," said they, "thus for ourselves it is; we are in profession but shepherds and in this country of Laconia little better than strangers and therefore neither in skill nor ability of power greatly to stead you. But what we can present unto you is this: Arcadia, of which country we are, is but a

little way hence; and even upon the next confines there dwelleth a gentleman by name Kalander, who vouchsafeth much favor unto us; a man who for his hospitality is so much haunted that no news stir but comes to his ears, for his upright dealings so beloved of his neighbors that he hath many ever ready to do him their uttermost service; and by the great good will our prince bears him may soon obtain the use of his name and credit which hath a principal
10 sway not only in his own Arcadia but in all these countries of Peloponnesus; and, which is worth all, all these things give him not so much power as his nature gives him will to benefit, so that it seems no music is so sweet to his ears as deserved thanks. To him we will bring you, and there you may recover again your health, without which you cannot be able to make any diligent search for your friend, and therefore you must labor for it. Besides we are sure the comfort of courtesy and ease of wise counsel
20 shall not be wanting."

Musidorus (who, besides he was merely unacquainted in the country, had his wits astonished with sorrow) gave easy consent to that from which he saw no reason to disagree; and therefore, defraying the mariners with a ring bestowed upon them, they took their journey together through Laconia, Claius and Strephon by course carrying his chest for him, Musidorus only bearing in his countenance evident marks of a sorrowful mind supported with a weak
30 body; which they perceiving, and knowing that the violence of sorrow is not at the first to be striven withal (being like a mighty beast sooner tamed with following than overthrown by withstanding) they gave way unto it for that day and the next, never troubling him either with asking questions or finding fault with his melancholy, but rather fitting to his

dolor dolorous discourses of their own and other folks' misfortunes. Which speeches, though they had not a lively entrance to his senses shut up in sorrow, yet like one half asleep he took hold of much of the matter spoken unto him, so as a man may say e'er sorrow was aware, they made his thoughts bear away something else beside his own sorrow, which wrought so in him that at length he grew content to mark their speeches, then to marvel at such wit in
10 shepherds, after to like their company, and lastly to vouchsafe conference; so that the third day after, in the time that the morning did strew roses and violets in the heavenly floor against the coming of the sun, the nightingales (striving one with the other which could in most dainty variety recount their wrong-caused sorrow) made them put off their sleep, and rising from under a tree, which that night had been their pavilion, they went on their journey, which by and by welcomed Musidorus' eyes, wearied
20 with the wasteful soil of Laconia, with delightful prospects.

There were hills which garnished their proud heights with stately trees; humble valleys whose base estate seemed comforted with refreshing of silver rivers; meadows enameled with all sorts of eye-pleasing flowers; thickets which, being lined with most pleasant shade, were witnessed so too by the cheerful disposition of many well-tuned birds; each pasture stored with sheep feeding with sober security
30 while the pretty lambs with bleating oratory craved the dams' comfort; here a shepherd's boy piping as though he should never be old; there a young shepherdess knitting and withal singing, and it seemed that her voice comforted her hands to work and her hands kept time to her voice's music. As for the houses of the country (for many houses came under

their eye) they were all scattered, no two being one by the other, and yet not so far off as that it barred mutual succor, a show, as it were, of an accompanable solitariness and of a civil wildness. "I pray you," said Musidorus, then first unsealing his long silent lips, "what countries be these we pass through which are so divers in show, the one wanting no store, the other having no store but of want?"

"The country," answered Claius, "where you were 10 cast ashore and now are passed through is Laconia, not so poor by the barrenness of the soil, though in itself not passing fertile, as by a civil war which being these two years within the bowels of that estate between the gentlemen and the peasants (by them named Helots) hath in this sort, as it were, disfigured the face of nature and made it so unhospitable as now you have found it; the towns neither of the one side nor the other willingly opening their gates to strangers, nor strangers willingly entering 20 for fear of being mistaken.

"But this country where now you set your foot is Arcadia, and even hard by is the house of Kalander whither we lead you. This country being thus decked with peace and (the child of peace) good husbandry, these houses you see so scattered are of men, as we two are, that live upon the commodity of their sheep; and therefore in the division of the Arcadian estate are termed shepherds, a happy people wanting little because they desire not much."

THE TALE OF ERONA

30 Of late there reigned a king in Lydia who had for the blessing of his marriage this only daughter of his, Erona, a princess worthy for her beauty as much

praise, as beauty may be praiseworthy. This princess Erona, being nineteen years of age, seeing the country of Lydia so much devoted to Cupid as that in every place his naked pictures and images were superstitiously adored (either moved there unto by the esteeming that it could be no god-head which could breed wickedness or the shamefaced consideration of such nakedness) procured so much of her father as utterly to pull down and deface all those
10 statues and pictures; which how terribly he punished (for to that the Lydians impute it) quickly after appeared.

For she had not lived a year longer when she was stricken with most obstinate love to a young man but of mean parentage, in her father's court, named Antiphilus, so mean as that he was but the son of her nurse, and by that means without other desert became known of her. Now so evil could she conceal her fire and so wilfully persevered she in it that
20 her father offering her the marriage of the great Tiridates, king of Armenia, who desired her more than the joys of heaven, she for Antiphilus's sake refused it. Many ways her father sought to withdraw her from it, sometimes persuasions, sometimes threatenings; once hiding Antiphilus and giving her to understand that he was fled the country, lastly making a solemn execution to be done of another under the name of Antiphilus, whom he kept in prison. But neither she liked persuasion nor feared
30 threatenings nor changed for absence; and when she thought him dead, she sought all means as well by poison as knife to send her soul at least to be married in the eternal church with him. This so broke the tender father's heart that, leaving things as he found them, he shortly after died. Then forthwith Erona, being seized of the crown and arming her

will with authority, sought to advance her affection to the holy title of matrimony.

But before she could accomplish all the solemnities, she was overtaken with a war the King Tiridates made upon her only for her person, towards whom for her ruin love had kindled his cruel heart, indeed cruel and tyrannous; for being far too strong in the field, he spared not man, woman, nor child, but as though there could be found no foil to set forth
10 the extremity of his love but extremity of hatred, wrote, as it were, the sonnets of his love in the blood and tuned them in the cries of her subjects; although his fair sister Artaxia, who would accompany him in the army, sought all means to appease his fury; till lastly he besieged Erona in her best city, vowing to win her or lose his life. And now had he brought her to the point either of a woeful consent or a ruinous denial, when there came thither, following the course which virtue and fortune led them, two
20 excellent young princes, Pyrocles and Musidorus, the one prince of Macedon, the other of Thessalia; two princes as Plangus said (and he witnessed his saying with sighs and tears) the most accomplished both in body and mind that the sun ever looked upon. (While Philoclea spoke those words, O sweet words, thought Zelmane to herself, which are not only a praise to me but a praise to praise herself which out of that mouth issueth.) [1]

These two princes, (said Philoclea), as well to
30 help the weaker—especially being a lady—as to save a Greek people from being ruined by such whom we call and count barbarous, gathering together such of the honestest Lycians as would venture their lives to succor their princess, giving order by a secret

[1] Philoclea is relating this story to the Amazon, Zelmane, who is really Pyrocles in disguise.

message they sent into the city that they should issue with all force at an appointed time, they set upon Tiridates' camp with so well guided a fierceness that being of both sides assaulted, he was like to be overthrown, but that this Plangus, being general of Tiridates' horsemen, especially aided by the two mighty men, Euardes and Barzanes, rescued the footmen, even almost defeated, but yet could not bar the princes with their succors both of men and victual 10 to enter the city.

Which when Tiridates found would make the war long, which length seemed to him worse than a languishing consumption, he made a challenge of three princes in his retinue against those two princes and Antiphilus; and that thereupon the quarrel should be decided with compact that neither side should help his fellow, but of whose side the more overcame, with him the victory should remain. Antiphilus (though Erona chose rather to bide the brunt of 20 war than venture him) yet could not for shame refuse the offer, especially since the two strangers, that had no interest in it, did willingly accept it; besides that, he saw it like enough that the people, weary of the miseries of war, would rather give him up, if they saw him shrink, than for his sake venture their ruin, considering that the challengers were of far greater worthiness than himself. So it was agreed upon; and against Pyrocles was Euardes, king of Bithynia; Barzanes of Hircania against 30 Musidorus, two men that thought the world scarce able to resist them; and against Antiphilus he placed this same Plangus, being his own cousin german and son to the king of Iberia. Now so it fell out that Musidorus slew Barzanes, and Pyrocles Euardes, which victory those princes esteemed above all that ever they had; but of the other side Plangus took

Antiphilus prisoner; under which color, as if the matter had been equal, though indeed it was not, the greater part being overcome of his side, Tiridates continued his war; and to bring Erona to a compelled yielding, sent her word that he would, the third morrow after, before the walls of the town, strike off Antiphilus's head without his suit in that space were granted, adding withal because he had heard of her desperate affection, that if in the mean 10 time she did herself any hurt, what tortures could be devised should be lain upon Antiphilus.

Then lo, if Cupid be a god or that the tyranny of our own thoughts seem as a god unto us—but whatsoever it was—then it did set forth the miserableness of his effects, she being drawn to two contraries by one cause, for the love of him commanded her to yield to no other, the love of him commanded her to preserve his life, which knot might well be cut but untied it could not be. So that love in her 20 passions like a right make-bate whispered to both sides arguments of quarrel. "What," said he, "of the one side dost thou love Antiphilus, O Erona, and shall Tiridates enjoy thy body? With what eyes wilt thou look upon Antiphilus when he shall know that another possesseth thee? But if thou wilt do it, canst thou do it? Canst thou force thy heart? Think with thyself, if this man have thee, thou shalt never have more part of Antiphilus than if he were dead. But thus much more, that the affectation shall 30 be still gnawing and the remorse still present. Death perhaps will cool the rage of thy affection; where thus thou shalt ever love and ever lack. Think this beside: if thou mary Tiridates, Antiphilus is so excellent a man that long he cannot be from being in some high place married; canst thou suffer that too? If another kill him, he doth him the wrong; if thou abuse thy body, thou dost him the wrong. His death is a work of nature and either now or at another time he shall die. But it shall be thy work, thy shameful work, which is in thy power to shun, to make him live to see thy faith falsified, and his bed defiled." But when love had well kindled that party of her thoughts, then went he to the other side. "What," said he, "O Erona, and is thy love of Antiphilus come to that point as thou dost now make it a question whether he shall die or no? O excellent 10 affection, which for too much love will see his head off! Mark well the reasons of the other side, and thou shall see it is but love of thyself which so disputeth. Thou canst not abide Tiridates; this is but love of thyself; thou shalt be ashamed to look upon him afterwards; this is but fear of shame and love of thyself; thou shalt want him as much then; this is but love of thyself; he shall be married; if he be well, why should that grieve thee but for love of thyself? No, no, pronounce these words if thou canst, 20 *Let Antiphilus die.*" Then the images of each side stood before her understanding; one time she thought she saw Antiphilus dying, another time she thought Antiphilus saw her by Tiridates enjoyed; twenty times calling for a servant to carry message of yielding, but, before he came, the mind was altered. She blushed when she considered the effect of granting; she was pale when she remembered the fruits of denying. For weeping, sighing, wringing her hands, and tearing her hair, were indifferent of 30 both sides. Easily she would have agreed to have broken all disputations with her own death, but that the fear of Antiphilus's further torments stayed her. At length, even the evening before the day appointed for his death, the determination of yielding prevailed, especially growing upon a message from Antiphilus, who with all the conjuring terms he could devise, besought her to save his life upon any conditions. But she had no sooner sent her messenger to Tiridates but her mind changed, and she went to the two young princes, Pyrocles and Musidorus, and falling down at their feet, desired them to try some way for her deliverance, showing herself resolved not to overlive Antiphilus, nor yet to yield to Tiridates.

They, that knew not what she had done in private, prepared that night accordingly; and as sometimes 10 it falls out that what is inconstancy seems cunning, so did this change indeed stand in as good stead as a witty dissimulation. For it made the king as reckless as them diligent, so that in the dead time of the night the princes issued out of the town, with whom she would needs go, either to die herself or rescue Antiphilus, having no armor or weapon but affection. And I cannot tell you how or by what device, though Plangus at large described it, the conclusion was the wonderful valor of the two princes 20 so prevailed that Antiphilus was succored and the king slain. Plangus was then the chief man left in the camp; and therefore seeing no other remedy, conveyed in safety into her country Artaxia, now Queen of Armenia, who with true lamentations made known to the world that her new greatness did no way comfort her in respect of her brother's loss, whom she studied by all means possible to revenge upon every one of the occasioners, having, as she thought, overthrown her brother by a most abom- 30 inable treason. Insomuch that being at home she proclaimed great rewards to any private man, and herself in marriage to any prince, that would destroy Pyrocles and Musidorus. But thus was Antiphilus redeemed, and though against the consent of all her nobility, married to Erona; in which case the two Greek princes, being called away by another adventure, left them.

THOMAS LODGE

ROSALYNDE

THOMAS LODGE was born about 1558, the second son of a Lord Mayor of London. He attended Oxford, from which he probably received a degree about 1577. He then for a time turned to legal studies, his mother having left him by will part of her property and the rest of it later unless he should "discontinue his studies" and cease to be what "a good student ought to be." Literature, however, proved more attractive than the law, and he wrote numerous plays, verses, and prose romances. With Elizabethan versatility he also went on voyages, at one time even visiting the Straits of Magellan. In middle life he became a doctor, and, having joined the Roman Catholic Church, practiced medicine especially among members of his own religion. He died in 1625.

Of Lodge's works, the best are his lyrics and his prose romances, and of both these his masterpiece *Rosalynde*, printed in 1590, is a good example. This narrative, according to his own declaration, was written on a voyage to the Canaries, and is "rough as hatched in the storms of the ocean and feathered in the surges of many perilous seas." "If you like it, so," he continues, "and yet I will be yours in duty if you be mine in favor." But if any critic fails to approve of the book, he threatens truculently, "I'll down into the hold and fetch out a rusty poleaxe that saw no sun this seven year, and either will baste him or heave the coxcomb overboard to feed cods."

The basis of the plot of *Rosalynde* is the Middle English verse *Tale of Gamelyn*, formerly ascribed to Chaucer. In this vigorous, though rude, story, full of the spirit of outdoor life, Gamelyn has many of the same adventures as the hero of Lodge's romance,—suffering at the hands of an unscrupulous brother, wrestling at court, and at length becoming an outlaw in the forest. In one respect, however, the two plots are markedly different: in *Gamelyn* there is no love story. The shepherd element of *Rosalynde*, furthermore, like that in Sidney's *Arcadia*, is an example of the Renaissance pastoral romance, of which Sannazaro's *Arcadia* is the real beginning. As regards style, finally, *Rosalynde* is clearly of the school of Lyly. Indeed this relationship is stressed by a subtitle intended to appeal to admirers of that author: "Euphues' Golden Legacy, Found after his Death in his Cell at Silexedra." Euphues, we learn in a preface, bequeathed the manuscript to his friend Philautus to help in the education of the latter's children.

Rosalynde derives much interest from being the source of the plot and much of the sylvan atmosphere of Shakespeare's *As You Like It.* The great dramatist, however, besides changing the names of some characters, enriched the theme by the addition of Jaques, Touchestone, Audrey, and William. But quite apart from the greater work it prompted, *Rosalynde* is of decided value for itself. It represents the charm of the Elizabethan romance at its best; its style has a graceful rhythm; and its verses are exquisite in melody and fancy.

ROSALYNDE

There dwelled adjoining to the city of Bordeaux a knight of most honorable parentage, whom fortune had graced with many favors, and nature honored with sundry exquisite qualities, so beautified with the excellence of both, as it was a question whether fortune or nature were more prodigal in deciphering the riches of their bounties. Wise he was, as holding in his head a supreme conceit of policy, reaching with Nestor into the depth of all civil government; and to 10 make his wisdom more gracious, he had that *salem ingenii* and pleasant eloquence that was so highly commended in Ulysses: his valor was no less than his wit, nor the stroke of his lance no less forcible than the sweetness of his tongue was persuasive; for he was for his courage chosen the principal of all the Knights of Malta. This hardy knight, thus enriched with virtue and honor, surnamed Sir John of Bordeaux, having passed the prime of his youth in sundry battles against the Turks, at last (as the date 20 of time hath his course) grew aged. His hairs were

silver-hued, and the map of age was figured on his
forehead: honor sat in the furrows of his face, and
many years were portrayed in his wrinkled lineaments, that all men might perceive his glass was run,
and that nature of necessity challenged her due. Sir
John, that with the Phoenix knew the term of his
life was now expired, and could, with the swan,
discover his end by her songs, having three sons by
his wife Lynida, the very pride of all his fore-passed
10 years, thought now, seeing death by constraint would
compel him to leave them, to bestow upon them such
a legacy as might bewray his love, and increase their
ensuing amity. Calling, therefore, these young gentlemen before him, in the presence of all his fellow
Knights of Malta, he resolved to leave them a memo-
rial of all his fatherly care in setting down a method
of their brotherly duties. Having, therefore, death
in his looks to move them to pity, and tears in his
eyes to paint out the depth of his passions, taking his
20 eldest son by the hand, he began thus:

Sir John of Bordeaux' Legacy he gave to his Sons

"O my sons, you see that fate hath set a period
of my years, and destinies have determined the final
end of my days: the palm tree waxeth away-ward,
for he stoopeth in his height, and my plumes are
full of sick feathers touched with age. I must to
my grave that dischargeth all cares, and leave you
to the world that increaseth many sorrows: my silver
hairs containeth great experience, and in the number
of my years are penned down the subtleties of for-
30 tune. Therefore, as I leave you some fading pelf to
countercheck poverty, so I will bequeath you infallible precepts that shall lead you unto virtue. First,
therefore, unto thee Saladyne, the eldest, and there-

fore the chiefest pillar of my house, wherein should be engraven as well the excellence of thy father's qualities, as the essential form of his proportion, to thee I give fourteen ploughlands, with all my manor houses and richest plate. Next, unto Fernandyne I bequeath twelve ploughlands. But, unto Rosader, the youngest, I give my horse, my armor, and my lance, with sixteen ploughlands; for if the inward thoughts be descovered by outward shadows, Rosa-
10 der will exceed you all in bounty and honor. Thus, my sons, have I parted in your portions the substance of my wealth, wherein if you be as prodigal to spend as I have been careful to get, your friends will grieve to see you more wasteful than I was bountiful, and your foes smile that my fall did begin in your excess. Let mine honor be the glass of your actions, and the fame of my virtues the lodestar to direct the course of your pilgrimage. Aim your deeds by my honorable endeavors, and show yourselves scions worthy
20 of so flourishing a tree, lest, as the birds Halcyones, which exceed in whiteness, I hatch young ones that surpass in blackness. Climb not, my sons: aspiring pride is a vapor that ascendeth high, but soon turneth to a smoke; they which stare at the stars stumble upon stones, and such as gaze at the sun (unless they be eagle-eyed) fall blind. Soar not with the hobby,[1] lest you fall with the lark, nor attempt not with Phaeton, lest you drown with Icarus. Fortune, when she wills you to fly, tempers your plumes with wax;
30 and therefore either sit still and make no wing, or else beware the sun, and hold Daedalus' axiom authentical, *medium tenere tutissimum*. Low shrubs have deep roots, and poor cottages great patience. Fortune looks ever upward, and envy aspireth to nestle with dignity. Take heed, my sons, the mean is sweetest melody; where strings high stretched, either

[1] Falcon.

soon crack, or quickly grow out of tune. Let your country's care be your heart's content, and think that you are not born for yourselves, but to level your thoughts to be loyal to your prince, careful for the common weal, and faithful to your friends; so shall France say, 'These men are as excellent in virtues as they be exquisite in features.' O my sons, a friend is a precious jewel, within whose bosom you may unload your sorrows and unfold your secrets, and he
10 either will relieve with counsel, or persuade with reason: but take heed in the choice: the outward show makes not the inward man, nor are the dimples in the face the calendars of truth. When the liquorice leaf looketh most dry, then it is most wet: when the shores of Lepanthus are most quiet, then they forepoint a storm. The Baaran leaf the more fair it looks, the more infectious it is, and in the sweetest words is oft hid the most treachery. Therefore, my sons, choose a friend as the Hyperborei do
20 the metals, sever them from the ore with fire, and let them not bide the stamp before they be current: so try and then trust, let time be touchstone of friendship, and then friends faithful lay them up for jewels. Be valiant, my sons, for cowardice is the enemy to honor; but not too rash, for that is an extreme. Fortitude is the mean, and that is limited within bonds, and prescribed with circumstance. But above all," and with that he fetched a deep sigh, "beware of love, for it is far more perilous than
30 pleasant, and yet, I tell you, it allureth as ill as the Sirens. O my sons, fancy is a fickle thing, and beauty's paintings are tricked up with time's colors, which, being set to dry in the sun, perish with the same. Venus is a wanton, and though her laws pretend liberty, yet there is nothing but loss and glistering misery. Cupid's wings are plumed with the feathers of vanity, and his arrows, where they pierce,

enforce nothing but deadly desires: a woman's eye, as it is precious to behold, so is it prejudicial to gaze upon; for as it affordeth delight, so it snareth unto death. Trust not their fawning favors, for their loves are like the breath of a man upon steel, which no sooner lighteth on but it leapeth off, and their passions are as momentary as the colors of a polyp, which changeth at the sight of every object. My breath waxeth short, and mine eyes dim: the hour 10 is come, and I must away: therefore let this suffice, women are wantons, and yet men cannot want one: and therefore, if you love, choose her that hath eyes of adamant, that will turn only to one point; her heart of a diamond, that will receive but one form; her tongue of a Sethin leaf, that never wags but with a south-east wind: and yet, my sons, if she have all these qualities, to be chaste, obedient, and silent, yet for that she is a woman, shalt thou find in her sufficient vanities to countervail her virtues. 20 Oh now, my sons, even now take these my last words as my latest legacy, for my thread is spun, and my foot is in the grave. Keep my precepts as memorials of your father's counsels, and let them be lodged in the secret of your hearts; for wisdom is better than wealth, and a golden sentence worth a world of treasure. In my fall see and mark, my sons, the folly of man, that being dust climbeth with Biares to reach at the heavens, and ready every minute to die, yet hopeth for an age of pleasures. Oh, man's 30 life is like lightning that is but a flash, and the longest date of his years but as a bavin's[1] blaze. Seeing then man is so mortal, be careful that thy life be virtuous, that thy death may be full of admirable honors: so shalt thou challenge fame to be thy fautor,[2] and put oblivion to exile with thine

[1] Faggot's.
[2] Patron.

honorable actions. But, my sons, lest you should forget your father's axioms, take this scroll, wherein read what your father dying wills you to execute living." At this he shrunk down in his bed, and gave up the ghost.

John of Bordeaux being thus dead was greatly lamented of his sons, and bewailed of his friends, especially of his fellow Knights of Malta, who attended on his funerals, which were performed with
10 great solemnity. His obsequies done, Saladyne caused, next his epitaph, the contents of the scroll to be portrayed out, which were to this effect:

The Contents of the Schedule which Sir John of Bordeaux gave to his Sons

My sons, behold what portion I do give:
  I leave you goods, but they are quickly lost;
I leave advice, to school you how to live;
  I leave you wit, but won with little cost;
But keep it well, for counsel still is one,
When father, friends, and worldly goods are gone.

In choice of thrift let honor be thy gain,
20 Win it by virtue and by manly might;
In doing good esteem thy toil no pain;
  Protect the fatherless and widow's right:
Fight for thy faith, thy country, and thy king,
For why? this thrift will prove a blessed thing.

In choice of wife, prefer the modest-chaste;
  Lilies are fair in show, but foul in smell:
The sweetest looks by age are soon defaced;
  Then choose thy wife by wit and living well.
Who brings thee wealth and many faults withal,
30 Presents thee honey mixed with better gall.

In choice of friends, beware of light belief;
  A painted tongue may shroud a subtle heart;
The Siren's tears do threaten mickle grief;
  Foresee, my son, for fear of sudden smart:

Choose in thy wants, and he that friends thee then,
When richer grown, befriend him thou again.

Learn with the ant in summer to provide;
Drive with the bee the drone from out thy hive:
Build like the swallows in the summer tide;
Spare not too much, my sons, but sparing thrive:
Be poor in folly, rich in all but sin:
So by thy death thy glory shall begin.

Saladyne having thus set up the schedule, and
10 hanged about his father's hearse many passionate
poems, that France might suppose him to be passing
sorrowful, he clad himself and his brothers all in
black, and in such sable suits discoursed his grief:
but as the hyena when she mourns is then most
guileful, so Saladyne under this show of grief
shadowed a heart full of contented thoughts: the
tiger, though he hide his claws, will at last discover
his rapine: the lion's looks are not the maps of his
meaning, nor a man's physnomy is not the display of
20 his secrets. Fire cannot be hid in the straw, nor the
nature of man so concealed, but at last it will have
his course: nurture and art may do much, but that
natura naturans, which by propagation is ingrafted
in the heart, will be at last perforce predominant
according to the old verse:

Naturam expellas furca licet tamen usque recurret.

So fared it with Saladyne, for after a month's
mourning was passed, he fell to consideration of his
father's testament; how he had bequeathed more to
30 his younger brothers than himself, that Rosader was
his father's darling, but now under his tuition, that
as yet they were not come to years, and he being
their guardian, might, if not defraud them of their
due, yet make such havoc of their legacies and lands,

as they should be a great deal the lighter: whereupon he began thus to meditate with himself:

Saladyne's Meditation with Himself

"Saladyne, how art thou disquieted in thy thoughts, and perplexed with a world of restless passions, having thy mind troubled with the tenor of thy father's testament, and thy heart fired with the hope of present preferment! By the one thou art counselled to content thee with thy fortunes, by the other persuaded to aspire to higher wealth. Riches, Saladyne, is a great royalty, and there is no sweeter physic than store. Avicen, like a fool, forgot in his Aphorisms to say that gold was the most precious restorative, and that treasure was the most excellent medicine of the mind. O Saladyne, what, were thy father's precepts breathed into the wind? hast thou so soon forgotten his principles? did he not warn thee from coveting without honor, and climbing without virtue? did he not forbid thee to aim at any action that should not be honorable? and what will be more prejudicial to thy credit, than the careless ruin of thy brothers' welfare? why, shouldst not thou be the pillar of thy brothers' prosperity? and wilt thou become the subversion of their fortunes? is there any sweeter thing than concord, or a more precious jewel than amity? are you not sons of one father, scions of one tree, birds of one nest, and wilt thou become so unnatural as to rob them, whom thou shouldst relieve? No, Saladyne, entreat them with favors, and entertain them with love, so shalt thou have thy conscience clear and thy renown excellent. Tush, what words are these, base fool, far unfit (if thou be wise) for thy humor? What though thy father at his death talked of many frivolous matters, as one that doated for age and raved in his

sickness; shall his words be axioms, and his talk be so authentical, that thou wilt, to observe them, prejudice thyself? No, no, Saladyne, sick men's wills that are parole and have neither hand nor seal, are like the laws of a city written in dust, which are broken with the blast of every wind. What, man, thy father is dead, and he can neither help thy fortunes, nor measure thy actions; therefore bury his words with his carcase, and be wise for thyself.
10 What, 't is not so old as true,

Non sapit, qui sibi non sapit.

Thy brother is young, keep him now in awe; make him not checkmate with thyself, for

Nimia familiaritas contemptum parit.

Let him know little, so shall he not be able to execute much: suppress his wits with a base estate, and though he be a gentleman by nature, yet form him anew, and make him a peasant by nurture; so shalt thou keep him as a slave, and reign thyself sole lord
20 over all thy father's possessions. As for Fernandyne, thy middle brother, he is a scholar and hath no mind but on Aristotle: let him read on Galen while thou riflest with gold, and pore on his book till thou dost purchase lands: wit is great wealth; if he have learning it is enough: and so let all rest."

In this humor was Saladyne, making his brother Rosader his foot-boy, for the space of two or three years, keeping him in such servile subjection, as if he had been the son of any country vassal. The
30 young gentleman bore all with patience, till on a day, walking in the garden by himself, he began to consider how he was the son of John of Bordeaux, a knight renowned for many victories, and a gentleman famosed for his virtues; how, contrary to the

testament of his father, he was not only kept from his land and entreated as a servant, but smothered in such secret slavery, as he might not attain to any honorable actions.

"Ah," quoth he to himself, nature working these effectual passions, "why should I, that am a gentleman born, pass my time in such unnatural drudgery? Were it not better either in Paris to become a scholar, or in the court a courtier, or in the field a soldier, 10 than to live a foot-boy to my own brother? Nature hath lent me wit to conceive, but my brother denied me art to contemplate: I have strength to perform any honorable exploit, but no liberty to accomplish my virtuous endeavors: those good parts that God hath bestowed upon me, the envy of my brother doth smother in obscurity; the harder is my fortune, and the more his frowardness."

With that casting up his hand he felt hair on his face, and perceiving his beard to bud, for choler he 20 began to blush, and swore to himself he would be no more subject to such slavery. As thus he was ruminating of his melancholy passions, in came Saladyne with his men, and seeing his brother in a brown study, and to forget his wonted reverence, thought to shake him out of his dumps thus:

"Sirrah," quoth he, "what is your heart on your halfpenny, or are you saying a dirge for your father's soul? What, is my dinner ready?"

At this question Rosader, turning his head askance, 30 and bending his brows as if anger there had ploughed the furrows of her wrath, with his eyes full of fire, he made this reply:

"Dost thou ask me, Saladyne, for thy cates? Ask some of thy churls who are fit for such an office: I am thine equal by nature, though not by birth, and though thou hast more cards in the bunch, I have as many trumps in my hands as thyself. Let me question with thee, why thou hast felled my woods, spoiled my manor houses, and made havoc of such utensils as my father bequeathed unto me? I tell thee, Saladyne, either answer me as a brother, or I will trouble thee as an enemy."

At this reply of Rosader's Saladyne smiled as laughing at his presumption, and frowned as checking his folly: he therefore took him up thus shortly:

"What, sirrah! well I see early pricks the tree that 10 will prove a thorn: hath my familiar conversing with you made you coy, or my good looks drawn you to be thus contemptuous? I can quickly remedy such a fault, and I will bend the tree while it is a wand. In faith, sir boy, I have a snaffle for such a headstrong colt. You, sirs, lay hold on him and bind him, and then I will give him a cooling card for his choler."

This made Rosader half mad, that stepping to a great rake that stood in the garden, he laid such load upon his brother's men that he hurt some of them, 20 and made the rest of them run away. Saladyne, seeing Rosader so resolute and with his resolution so valiant, thought his heels his best safety, and took him to a loft adjoining to the garden, whither Rosader pursued him hotly. Saladyne, afraid of his brother's fury, cried out to him thus:

"Rosader, be not so rash: I am thy brother and thine elder, and if I have done thee wrong I'll make thee amends: revenge not anger in blood, for so shalt thou stain the virtue of old Sir John of Bordeaux: 30 say wherein thou art discontent and thou shalt be satisfied. Brothers' frowns ought not to be periods of wrath: what, man, look not so sourly; I know we shall be friends, and better friends than we have been, for, *Amantium ira amoris redintegratio est.*"

These words appeased the choler of Rosader, for he was of a mild and courteous nature, so that he laid down his weapons, and upon the faith of a gen-

tleman assured his brother he would offer him no prejudice: whereupon Saladyne came down, and after a little parley they embraced each other and became friends; and Saladyne promising Rosader the restitution of all his lands, "and what favor else," quoth he, "any ways my ability or the nature of a brother may perform." Upon these sugared reconciliations they went into the house arm in arm together, to the great content of all the old servants of
10 Sir John of Bordeaux.

Thus continued the pad hidden in the straw, till it chanced that Torismond, king of France, had appointed for his pleasure a day of wrastling and of tournament to busy his commons' heads, lest, being idle, their thoughts should run upon more serious matters, and call to remembrance their old banished king. A champion there was to stand against all comers, a Norman, a man of tall stature and of great strength; so valiant, that in many such conflicts he
20 always bare away the victory, not only overthrowing them which he encountered, but often with the weight of his body killing them outright. Saladyne hearing of this, thinking now not to let the ball fall to the ground, but to take opportunity by the forehead, first by secret means convented with the Norman, and procured him with rich rewards to swear that if Rosader came within his claws he should never more return to quarrel with Saladyne for his possessions. The Norman desirous of pelf—as *Quis*
30 *nisi mentis inops oblatum respuit aurum?*—taking great gifts for little gods, took the crowns of Saladyne to perform the stratagem.

Having thus the champion tied to his villainous determination by oath, he prosecuted the intent of his purpose thus. He went to young Rosader, who in all his thoughts reached at honor, and gazed no lower than virtue commanded him, and began to tell him of this tournament and wrastling, how the king should be there, and all the chief peers of France, with all the beautiful damosels of the country.

"Now, brother," quoth he, "for the honor of Sir John of Bordeaux, our renowned father, to famous that house that never hath been found without men approved in chivalry, show thy resolution to be peremptory. For myself thou knowest, though I am eldest by birth, yet never having attempted any deeds of arms, I am youngest to perform any martial exploits, knowing better how to survey my lands than to charge my lance: my brother Fernandyne he is at Paris poring on a few papers, having more insight into sophistry and principles of philosophy, than any warlike endeavors; but thou, Rosader, the youngest in years but the eldest in valor, art a man of strength, and darest do what honor allows thee. Take thou my father's lance, his sword, and his horse, and hie thee to the tournament, and either there valiantly crack a spear, or try with the Norman for the palm of activity."

The words of Saladyne were but spurs to a free horse, for he had scarce uttered them, ere Rosader took him in his arms, taking his proffer so kindly, that he promised in what he might to requite his courtesy. The next morrow was the day of the tournament, and Rosader was so desirous to show his heroical thoughts that he passed the night with little sleep; but as soon as Phoebus had vailed the curtain of the night, and made Aurora blush with giving her the *bezo les labres* in her silver couch, he gat him up, and taking his leave of his brother, mounted himself towards the place appointed, thinking every mile ten leagues till he came there.

But leaving him so desirous of the journey, to Torismond, the king of France, who having by force banished Gerismond, their lawful king, that lived as

an outlaw in the forest of Arden, sought now by all means to keep the French busied with all sports that might breed their content. Amongst the rest he had appointed this solemn tournament, whereunto he in most solemn manner resorted, accompanied with the twelve peers of France, who, rather for fear than love, graced him with the show of their dutiful favors. To feed their eyes, and to make the beholders pleased with the sight of most rare and glis-
10 tering objects, he had appointed his own daughter Alinda to be there, and the fair Rosalynde, daughter unto Gerismond, with all the beautiful damosels that were famous for their features in all France. Thus in that place did love and war triumph in a sympathy; for such as were martial might use their lance to be renowned for the excellence of their chivalry, and such as were amorous might glut themselves with gazing on the beauties of most heavenly creatures. As every man's eye had his several survey, and fancy
20 was partial in their looks, yet all in general applauded the admirable riches that nature bestowed on the face of Rosalynde; for upon her cheeks there seemed a battle between the Graces, who should bestow most favors to make her excellent. The blush that gloried Luna, when she kissed the shepherd on the hills of Latmos, was not tainted with such a pleasant dye as the vermilion flourished on the silver hue of Rosalynde's countenance: her eyes were like those lamps that make the wealthy covert of the heavens more
30 gorgeous, sparkling favor and disdain, courteous and yet coy, as if in them Venus had placed all her amorets, and Diana all her chastity. The trammels of her hair, folded in a caul of gold, so far surpassed the burnished glister of the metal, as the sun doth the meanest star in brightness: the tresses that folds in the brows of Apollo were not half so rich to the sight, for in her hairs it seemed love had laid herself

in ambush, to entrap the proudest eye that durst gaze upon their excellence. What should I need to decipher her particular beauties, when by the censure of all she was the paragon of all earthly perfection? This Rosalynde sat, I say, with Alinda as a beholder of these sports, and made the cavaliers crack their lances with more courage: many deeds of knighthood that day were performed, and many prizes were given according to their several deserts.

10 At last, when the tournament ceased, the wrastling began, and the Norman presented himself as a challenger against all comers, but he looked like Hercules when he advanced himself against Achelous, so that the fury of his countenance amazed all that durst attempt to encounter with him in any deed of activity: till at last a lusty franklin of the country came with two tall men that were his sons, of good lineaments and comely personage. The eldest of these doing his obeisance to the king entered the list, and 20 presented himself to the Norman, who straight coped with him, and as a man that would triumph in the glory of his strength, roused himself with such fury, that not only he gave him the fall, but killed him with the weight of his corpulent personage: which the younger brother seeing, leaped presently into the place, and thirsty after the revenge, assailed the Norman with such valor, that at the first encounter he brought him to his knees; which repulsed so the Norman, that, recovering himself, fear of 30 disgrace doubling his strength, he stepped so sternly to the young franklin, that taking him up in his arms he threw him against the ground so violently, that he broke his neck, and so ended his days with his brother. At this unlooked for massacre the people murmured, and were all in a deep passion of pity; but the franklin, father unto these, never changed his countenance, but as a man of a coura-

geous resolution took up the bodies of his sons without any show of outward discontent.

All this while stood Rosader and saw this tragedy; who, noting the undoubted virtue of the franklin's mind, alighted off from his horse, and presently sate down on the grass, and commanded his boy to pull off his boots, making him ready to try the strength of this champion. Being furnished as he would, he clapped the franklin on the shoulder and said thus:

10 "Bold yeoman, whose sons have ended the term of their years with honor, for that I see thou scornest fortune with patience, and thwartest the injury of fate with content in brooking the death of thy sons, stand awhile, and either see me make a third in their tragedy, or else revenge their fall with an honorable triumph."

The franklin, seeing so goodly a gentleman to give him such courteous comfort, gave him hearty thanks, with promise to pray for his happy success. With 20 that Rosader vailed bonnet to the king, and lightly leaped within the lists, where noting more the company than the combatant, he cast his eyes upon the troop of ladies that glistered there like the stars of heaven; but at last, Love, willing to make him as amorous as he was valiant, presented him with the sight of Rosalynde, whose admirable beauty so inveigled the eye of Rosader, that forgetting himself, he stood and fed his looks on the favor of Rosalynde's face; which she perceiving blushed, which 30 was such a doubling of her beauteous excellence, that the bashful red of Aurora at the sight of unacquainted Phaeton, was not half so glorious.

The Norman seeing this young gentleman fettered in the looks of the ladies drave him out of his *memento* with a shake by the shoulder. Rosader looking back with an angry frown, as if he had been wakened from some pleasant dream, discovered to all by the fury of his countenance that he was a man of some high thoughts: but when they all noted his youth and the sweetness of his visage, with a general applause of favors, they grieved that so goodly a young man should venture in so base an action; but seeing it were to his dishonor to hinder him from his enterprise, they wished him to be graced with the palm of victory. After Rosader was thus called out of his *memento* by the Norman, he roughly clapped 10 to him with so fierce an encounter, that they both fell to the ground, and with the violence of the fall were forced to breathe; in which space the Norman called to mind by all tokens, that this was he whom Saladyne had appointed him to kill; which conjecture made him stretch every limb, and try every sinew, that working his death he might recover the gold which so bountifully was promised him. On the contrary part, Rosader while he breathed was not idle, but still cast his eye upon Rosalynde, who to 20 encourage him with a favor, lent him such an amorous look, as might have made the most coward desperate: which glance of Rosalynde so fired the passionate desires of Rosader, that turning to the Norman he ran upon him and braved him with a strong encounter. The Norman received him as valiantly, that there was a sore combat, hard to judge on whose side fortune would be prodigal. At last Rosader, calling to mind the beauty of his new mistress, the fame of his father's honors, and the dis- 30 grace that should fall to his house by his misfortune, roused himself and threw the Norman against the ground, falling upon his chest with so willing a weight, that the Norman yielded nature her due, and Rosader the victory.

The death of this champion, as it highly contented the franklin, as a man satisfied with revenge, so it drew the king and all the peers into a great admiration, that so young years and so beautiful a personage should contain such martial excellence; but when they knew him to be the youngest son of Sir John of Bordeaux, the king rose from his seat and embraced him, and the peers entreated him with all favorable courtesy, commending both his valor and his virtues, wishing him to go forward in such haughty deeds, that he might attain to the glory of his father's honorable fortunes.

10 As the king and lords graced him with embracing, so the ladies favored him with their looks, especially Rosalynde, whom the beauty and valor of Rosader had already touched: but she accounted love a toy, and fancy a momentary passion, that as it was taken in with a gaze, might be shaken off with a wink, and therefore feared not to dally in the flame; and to make Rosader know she affected him, took from her neck a jewel, and sent it by a page to the young gentleman. The prize that Venus gave to Paris was 20 not half so pleasing to the Troyan as this gem was to Rosader; for if fortune had sworn to make him sole monarch of the world, he would rather have refused such dignity, than have lost the jewel sent him by Rosalynde. To return her with the like he was unfurnished, and yet that he might more than in his looks discover his affection, he stepped into a tent, and taking pen and paper wrote this fancy:

Two suns at once from one fair heaven there shined,
  Ten branches from two boughs, tipped all with roses,
30 Pure locks more golden than is gold refined,
  Two pearled rows that nature's pride encloses;

Two mounts fair marble-white, down-soft and dainty,
  A snow-dyed orb, where love increased by pleasure
Full woeful makes my heart, and body fainty:
  Her fair (my woe) exceeds all thought and measure.

In lines confused my luckless harm appeareth,
Whom sorrow clouds, whom pleasant smiling cleareth.

This sonnet he sent to Rosalynde, which when she read she blushed, but with a sweet content in that she perceived love had allotted her so amorous a servant.

Leaving her to her new entertained fancies, again to Rosader, who triumphing in the glory of this conquest, accompanied with a troop of young gentlemen that were desirous to be his familiars, went home to his brother Saladyne's, who was walking before the gates, to hear what success his brother Rosader 10 should have, assuring himself of his death, and devising how with dissimuled sorrow to celebrate his funerals. As he was in his thought, he cast up his eye, and saw where Rosader returned with the garland on his head, as having won the prize, accompanied with a crew of boon companions. Grieved at this, he stepped in and shut the gate. Rosader seeing this, and not looking for such unkind entertainment, blushed at the disgrace, and yet smothering his grief with a smile, he turned to the gentlemen, and desired 20 them to hold his brother excused, for he did not this upon any malicious intent or niggardize, but being brought up in the country, he absented himself as not finding his nature fit for such youthful company. Thus he sought to shadow abuses proffered him by his brother, but in vain, for he could by no means be suffered to enter: whereupon he ran his foot against the door, and broke it open, drawing his sword, and entering boldly into the hall, where he found none, for all were fled, but one Adam Spencer, 30 an Englishman, who had been an old and trusty servant to Sir John of Bordeaux. He for the love he bare to his deceased master, favored the part of Rosader, and gave him and his such entertainment as he could. Rosader gave him thanks, and looking about, seeing the hall empty, said:

"Gentlemen, you are welcome; frolic and be merry: you shall be sure to have wine enough, whatsoever your fare be. I tell you, cavaliers, my brother hath in his house five tun of wine, and as long as that lasteth, I beshrew him that spares his liquor."

With that he burst open the buttery door, and with the help of Adam Spencer covered the tables, and set down whatsoever he could find in the house; but what they wanted in meat, Rosader supplied with drink, yet had they royal cheer, and withal such a hearty welcome as would have made the coarsest
10 meats seem delicates. After they had feasted and frolicked it twice or thrice with an upsee freeze,[1] they all took their leaves of Rosader and departed. As soon as they were gone, Rosader growing impatient of the abuse, drew his sword, and swore to be revenged on the discourteous Saladyne; yet by the means of Adam Spencer, who sought to continue friendship and amity betwixt the brethren, and through the flattering submission of Saladyne, they were once again reconciled, and put up all fore-
20 passed injuries with a peaceable agreement, living together for a good space in such brotherly love, as did not only rejoice the servants, but made all the gentlemen and bordering neighbors glad of such friendly concord. Saladyne, hiding fire in the straw, and concealing a poisoned hate in a peaceable countenance, yet deferring the intent of his wrath till fitter opportunity, he showed himself a great favorer of his brother's virtuous endeavors: where leaving them in this happy league, let us return to Rosalynde.

30 Rosalynde returning home from the triumph, after she waxed solitary, love presented her with the idea of Rosader's perfection, and taking her at discovert struck her so deep, as she felt herself growing passing passionate. She began to call to mind the comeliness of his person, the honor of his parents, and

[1] A Toast.

the virtues that, excelling both, made him so gracious in the eyes of every one. Sucking in thus the honey of love by imprinting in her thoughts his rare qualities, she began to surfeit with the contemplation of his virtuous conditions; but when she called to remembrance her present estate, and the hardness of her fortunes, desire began to shrink, and fancy to vail bonnet, that between a Chaos of confused thoughts she began to debate with herself in this 10 manner:

Rosalynde's Passion

"Infortunate Rosalynde, whose misfortunes are more than thy years, and whose passions are greater than thy patience! The blossoms of thy youth are mixed with the frosts of envy, and the hope of thy ensuing fruits perish in the bud. Thy father is by Torismond banished from the crown, and thou, the unhappy daughter of a king, detained captive, living as disquieted in thy thoughts as thy father discontented in his exile. Ah Rosalynde, what cares wait 20 upon a crown! what griefs are incident to dignity! what sorrows haunt royal palaces! The greatest seas have the sorest storms, the highest birth subject to the most bale, and of all trees the cedars soonest shake with the wind: small currents are ever calm, low valleys not scorched in any lightnings, nor base men tied to any baleful prejudice. Fortune flies, and if she touch poverty it is with her heel, rather disdaining their want with a frown, than envying their wealth with disparagement. O Rosalynde, hadst 30 thou been born low, thou hadst not fallen so high, and yet being great of blood thine honor is more, if thou brookest misfortune with patience. Suppose I contrary fortune with content, yet fates unwilling to have me anyway happy, have forced love to set my thoughts on fire with fancy. Love, Rosalynde! Becometh it women in distress to think of love? Tush, desire hath no respect of persons: Cupid is blind and shooteth at random, as soon hitting a rag as a robe, and piercing as soon the bosom of a captive as the breast of a libertine. Thou speakest it, poor Rosalynde, by experience; for being every way distressed, surcharged with cares, and 10 overgrown with sorrows, yet amidst the heap of all these mishaps, love hath lodged in thy heart the perfection of young Rosader, a man every way absolute as well for his inward life, as for his outward lineaments, able to content the eye with beauty, and the ear with the report of his virtue. But consider, Rosalynde, his fortunes, and thy present estate: thou art poor and without patrimony, and yet the daughter of a prince; he a younger brother, and void of such possessions as either might maintain thy digni- 20 ties or revenge thy father's injuries. And hast thou not learned this of other ladies, that lovers cannot live by looks, that women's ears are sooner content with a dram of *give me* than a pound of *hear me*, that gold is sweeter than eloquence, that love is a fire and wealth is the fuel, that Venus' coffers should be ever full? Then, Rosalynde, seeing Rosader is poor, think him less beautiful because he is in want, and account his virtues but qualities of course for that he is not endued with wealth. Doth not Horace 30 tell thee what method is to be used in love?

Quaerenda pecunia primum, post nummos virtus.

Tush, Rosalynde, be not over rash: leap not before thou look: either love such a one as may with his lands purchase thy liberty, or else love not at all.

Choose not a fair face with an empty purse, but say as most women use to say:

Si nihil attuleris, ibis Homere foras.

Why, Rosalynde! can such base thoughts harbor in such high beauties? can the degree of a princess, the daughter of Gerismond, harbor such servile conceits, as to prize gold more than honor, or to measure a gentleman by his wealth, not by his virtues? No, Rosalynde, blush at thy base resolution, and say, if 10 thou lovest, 'either Rosader or none!' And why? because Rosader is both beautiful and virtuous." Smiling to herself to think of her new-entertained passions, taking up her lute that lay by her, she warbled out this ditty:

Rosalynde's Madrigal

Love in my bosom like a bee
Doth suck his sweet:
Now with his wings he plays with me,
Now with his feet.
Within mine eyes he makes his nest,
20 His bed amidst my tender breast;
My kisses are his daily feast,
And yet he robs me of my rest.
Ah, wanton, will ye?

And if I sleep, then percheth he
With pretty flight,
And makes his pillow of my knee
The livelong night.
Strike I my lute, he tunes the string,
He music plays if so I sing;
30 He lends me every lovely thing,
Yet cruel he my heart doth sting.
Whist, wanton, still ye!

Else I with roses every day
Will whip you hence,
And bind you, when you long to play,

For your offence;
I'll shut mine eyes to keep you in,
I'll make you fast it for your sin,
I'll count your power not worth a pin.
Alas, what hereby shall I win,
If he gainsay me?

What if I beat the wanton boy
With many a rod?
He will repay me with annoy,
10 Because a God.
Then sit thou safely on my knee,
And let thy bower my bosom be;
Lurk in mine eyes, I like of thee.
O Cupid, so thou pity me,
Spare not but play thee.

Scarce had Rosalynde ended her madrigal, before Torismond came in with his daughter Alinda and many of the peers of France, who were enamored of her beauty; which Torismond perceiving, fearing
20 lest her perfection might be the beginning of his prejudice, and the hope of his fruit end in the beginning of her blossoms, he thought to banish her from the court: "for," quoth he to himself, "her face is so full of favor, that it pleads pity in the eye of every man; her beauty is so heavenly and divine, that she will prove to me as Helen did to Priam; some one of the peers will aim at her love, end the marriage, and then in his wife's right attempt the kingdom. To prevent therefore *had I wist* in all these actions,
30 she tarries not about the court, but shall (as an exile) either wander to her father, or else seek other fortunes." In this humor, with a stern countenance full of wrath, he breathed out this censure unto her before the peers, that charged her that that night she were not seen about the court: "for," quoth he, "I have heard of thy aspiring speeches, and intended treasons." This doom was strange unto Rosalynde, and presently, covered with the shield of her inno-

cence, she boldly brake out in reverent terms to have cleared herself; but Torismond would admit of no reason, nor durst his lords plead for Rosalynde, although her beauty had made some of them passionate, seeing the figure of wrath portrayed in his brow. Standing thus all mute, and Rosalynde amazed, Alinda, who loved her more than herself, with grief in her heart and tears in her eyes, falling down on her knees, began to entreat her father thus:

Alinda's Oration to Her Father in Defence of Fair Rosalynde

10 "If, mighty Torismond, I offend in pleading for my friend, let the law of amity crave pardon for my boldness; for where there is depth of affection, there friendship alloweth a privilege. Rosalynde and I have been fostered up from our infancies, and nursed under the harbor of our conversing together with such private familiarities, that custom had wrought a union of our nature, and the sympathy of our affections such a secret love, that we have two bodies and one soul. Then marvel not, great Toris-20 mond, if, seeing my friend distressed, I find myself perplexed with a thousand sorrows, for her virtuous and honorable thoughts, which are the glories that maketh women excellent, they be such as may challenge love, and rase out suspicion. Her obedience to your majesty I refer to the censure of your own eye, that since her father's exile hath smothered all griefs with patience, and in the absence of nature, hath honored you with all duty, as her own father by nouriture, not in word uttering any discontent, 30 nor in thought, as far as conjecture may reach, hammering on revenge; only in all her actions seeking to please you, and to win my favor. Her wisdom, silence, chastity, and other such rich qualities, I need

not decipher; only it rests for me to conclude in one word, that she is innocent. If then, fortune, who triumphs in variety of miseries, hath presented some envious person (as minister of her intended stratagem) to taint Rosalynde with any surmise of treason, let him be brought to her face, and confirm his accusation by witnesses; which proved, let her die, and Alinda will execute the massacre. If none can avouch any confirmed relation of her intent, use jus-
10 tice, my lord—it is the glory of a king—and let her live in your wonted favor; for if you banish her, myself, as copartner of her hard fortunes, will participate in exile some part of her extremities."

Torismond, at this speech of Alinda, covered his face with such a frown, as tyranny seemed to sit triumphant in his forehead, and checked her up with such taunts, as made the lords, that only were hearers, to tremble.

"Proud girl," quoth he, "hath my looks made thee
20 so light of tongue, or my favors encouraged thee to be so forward, that thou darest presume to preach after thy father? Hath not my years more experience than thy youth, and the winter of mine age deeper insight into civil policy, than the prime of thy flourishing days? The old lion avoids the toils, where the young one leaps into the net: the care of age is provident and foresees much: suspicion is a virtue, where a man holds his enemy in his bosom. Thou, fond girl, measurest all by present affection,
30 and as thy heart loves, thy thoughts censure; but if thou knewest that in liking Rosalynde thou hatchest up a bird to peck out thine own eyes, thou wouldst entreat as much for her absence as now thou delightest in her presence. But why do I allege policy to thee? Sit you down, housewife, and fall to your needle: if idleness make you so wanton, or liberty so malapert, I can quickly tie you to a sharper task.

And you, maid, this night be packing, either into Arden to your father, or whither best it shall content your humor, but in the court you shall not abide."

This rigorous reply of Torismond nothing amazed Alinda, for still she prosecuted her plea in the defence of Rosalynde, wishing her father, if his censure might not be reversed, that he would appoint her partner of her exile; which if he refused to do, either she would by some secret means steal out and 10 follow her, or else end her days with some desperate kind of death. When Torismond heard his daughter so resolute, his heart was so hardened against her, that he set down a definite and peremptory sentence, that they should both be banished, which presently was done, the tyrant rather choosing to hazard the loss of his only child than anyways to put in question the state of his kingdom; so suspicious and fearful is the conscience of an usurper. Well, although his lords persuaded him to retain his own daughter, yet 20 his resolution might not be reversed, but both of them must away from the court without either more company or delay. In he went with great melancholy, and left these two ladies alone. Rosalynde waxed very sad, and sate down and wept. Alinda she smiled, and sitting by her friend began thus to comfort her:

Alinda's Comfort to Perplexed Rosalynde

"Why, how now, Rosalynde, dismayed with a frown of contrary fortune? Have I not oft heard thee say, that high minds were discovered in for- 30 tune's contempt, and heroical scene in the depth of extremities? Thou wert wont to tell others that complained of distress, that the sweetest salve for misery was patience, and the only medicine for want that precious implaister of content. Being such a good physician to others, wilt thou not minister receipts to thyself? But perchance thou wilt say:

Consulenti nunquam caput doluit.

Why then, if the patients that are sick of this disease can find in themselves neither reason to persuade, nor art to cure, yet, Rosalynde, admit of the counsel of a friend, and apply the salves that may appease thy passions. If thou grievest that being the daughter of a prince, and envy thwarteth thee with such
10 hard exigents, think that royalty is a fair mark, that crowns have crosses when mirth is in cottages; that the fairer the rose is, the sooner it is bitten with caterpillars; the more orient the pearl is, the more apt to take a blemish; and the greatest birth, as it hath most honor, so it hath much envy. If then fortune aimeth at the fairest, be patient, Rosalynde, for first by thine exile thou goest to thy father: nature is higher prize than wealth, and the love of one's parents ought to be more precious than all dignities.
20 Why then doth my Rosalynde grieve at the frown of Torismond, who by offering her a prejudice proffers her a greater pleasure? and more, mad lass, to be melancholy, when thou hast with thee Alinda, a friend who will be a faithful copartner of all thy misfortunes, who hath left her father to follow thee, and chooseth rather to brook all extremities than to forsake thy presence. What, Rosalynde,

Solamen miseris socios habuisse doloris.

Cheerly, woman: as we have been bed-fellows in
30 royalty, we will be fellow-mates in poverty: I will ever be thy Alinda, and thou shalt ever rest to me Rosalynde; so shall the world canonize our friendship, and speak of Rosalynde and Alinda, as they did of Pylades and Orestes. And if ever fortune smile, and we return to our former honor, then fold-

ing ourselves in the sweet of our friendship, we shall merrily say, calling to mind our forepassed miseries:

Olim haec meminisse juvabit."

At this Rosalynde began to comfort her, and after she had wept a few kind tears in the bosom of her Alinda, she gave her hearty thanks, and then they sat them down to consult how they should travel. Alinda grieved at nothing but that they might have no man in their company, saying it would be their 10 greatest prejudice in that two women went wandering without either guide or attendant.

"Tush," quoth Rosalynde, "art thou a woman, and hast not a sudden shift to prevent a misfortune? I, thou seest, am of a tall stature, and would very well become the person and apparel of a page; thou shalt be my mistress, and I will play the man so properly, that, trust me, in what company soever I come I will not be discovered. I will buy me a suit, and have my rapier very handsomely at my side, and if 20 any knave offer wrong, your page will show him the point of his weapon."

At this Alinda smiled, and upon this they agreed, and presently gathered up all their jewels, which they trussed up in a casket, and Rosalynde in all haste provided her of robes, and Alinda, from her royal weeds, put herself in more homelike attire. Thus fitted to the purpose, away go these two friends, having now changed their names, Alinda being called Aliena, and Rosalynde Ganymede. They travelled 30 along the vineyards, and by many by-ways at last got to the forest side, where they travelled by the space of two or three days without seeing any creature, being often in danger of wild beasts, and pained with many passionate sorrows. Now the black ox began to tread on their feet, and Alinda thought of her wonted royalty; but when she cast her eyes on her

Rosalynde, she thought every danger a step to honor. Passing thus on along, about midday they came to a fountain, compassed with a grove of cypress trees, so cunningly and curiously planted, as if some goddess had entreated nature in that place to make her an arbor. By this fountain sat Aliena and her Ganymede, and forth they pulled such victuals as they had, and fed as merrily as if they had been in Paris with all the king's delicates, Aliena only grieving that
10 they could not so much as meet with a shepherd to discourse them the way to some place where they might make their abode. At last Ganymede casting up his eye espied where on a tree was engraven certain verses; which as soon as he espied, he cried out:

"Be of good cheer, mistress, I spy the figures of men; for here in these trees be engraven certain verses of shepherds, or some other swains that inhabit hereabout."

20 With that Aliena start up joyful to hear these news, and looked, where they found carved in the bark of a pine tree this passion:

Montanus's Passion

Hadst thou been born whereas perpetual cold
Makes Tanais hard, and mountains silver old;
Had I complained unto a marble stone,
Or to the floods bewrayed my bitter moan,
  I then could bear the burden of my grief.
But even the pride of countries at thy birth,
Whilst heavens did smile, did new array the earth
30 With flowers chief.
Yet thou, the flower of beauty blessèd born,
Hast pretty looks, but all attired in scorn.

Had I the power to weep sweet Mirrha's tears,
Or by my plaints to pierce repining ears;
Hadst thou the heart to smile at my complaint,
To scorn the woes that doth my heart attaint,
  I then could bear the burden of my grief:

But not my tears, but truth with thee prevails,
And seeming sour my sorrows thee assails:
Yet small relief;
For if thou wilt thou art of marble hard,
And if thou please my suit shall soon be heard.

"No doubt," quoth Aliena, "this poesy is the passion of some perplexed shepherd, that being enamored of some fair and beautiful shepherdess, suffered some sharp repulse, and therefore complained of the 10 cruelty of his mistress."

"You may see," quoth Ganymede, "what mad cattle you women be, whose hearts sometimes are made of adamant that will touch with no impression, and sometime of wax that is fit for every form: they delight to be courted, and then they glory to seem coy, and when they are most desired then they freeze with disdain: and this fault is so common to the sex, that you see it painted out in the shepherd's passions, who found his mistress as froward as he 20 was enamored."

"And I pray you," quoth Aliena, "if your robes were off, what mettle are you made of that you are so satirical against women? Is it not a foul bird defiles the own nest? Beware, Ganymede, that Rosader hear you not; if he do, perchance you will make him leap so far from love, that he will anger every vein in your heart."

"Thus," quoth Ganymede, "I keep decorum: I speak now as I am Aliena's page, not as I am Geris- 30 mond's daughter; for put me but into a petticoat, and I will stand in defiance to the uttermost, that women are courteous, constant, virtuous, and what not."

"Stay there," quoth Aliena, "and no more words, for yonder be characters graven upon the bark of the tall beech tree."

"Let us see," quoth Ganymede; and with that they read a fancy written to this effect:

First shall the heavens want starry light,
The seas be robbèd of their waves,
The day want sun, and sun want bright,
The night want shade, the dead men graves,
  The April flowers and leaf and tree,
  Before I false my faith to thee.

First shall the tops of highest hills
10 By humble plains be overpried,
And poets scorn the Muses' quills,
And fish forsake the water glide,
  And Iris loose her colored weed,
  Before I fail thee at thy need.

First direful hate shall turn to peace,
And love relent in deep disdain,
And death his fatal stroke shall cease,
And envy pity every pain,
  And pleasure mourn and sorrow smile,
20 Before I talk of any guile.

First time shall stay his stayless race,
And winter bless his brows with corn,
And snow bemoisten July's face,
And winter spring, and summer mourn,
  Before my pen, by help of fame,
  Cease to recite thy sacred name.

MONTANUS

"No doubt," quoth Ganymede, "this protestation grew from one full of passions."

"I am of that mind too," quoth Aliena, "but see, 30 I pray, when poor women seek to keep themselves chaste, how men woo them with many feigned promises; alluring with sweet words as the Sirens, and after proving as trothless as Aeneas. Thus promised Demophoon to his Phyllis, but who at last grew more false?"

"The reason was," quoth Ganymede, "that they were women's sons, and took that fault of their mother, for if man had grown from man, as Adam did from the earth, men had never been troubled with inconstancy."

"Leave off," quoth Aliena, "to taunt thus bitterly, or else I'll pull off your page's apparel, and whip you, as Venus doth her wantons, with nettles."

"So you will," quoth Ganymede, "persuade me to flattery, and that needs not: but come, seeing we have found here by this fount the tract of shepherds
10 by their madrigals and roundelays, let us forward; for either we shall find some folds, sheepcotes, or else some cottages wherein for a day or two to rest."

"Content," quoth Aliena, and with that they rose up, and marched forward till towards the even, and then coming into a fair valley, compassed with mountains, whereon grew many pleasant shrubs, they might descry where two flocks of sheep did feed. Then, looking about, they might perceive where an old shepherd sat, and with him a young swain,
20 under a covert most pleasantly situated. The ground where they sat was diapered with Flora's riches, as if she meant to wrap Tellus in the glory of her vestments: round about in the form of an amphitheatre were most curiously planted pine trees, interseamed with limons and citrons, which with the thickness of their boughs so shadowed the place, that Phoebus could not pry into the secret of that arbor; so united were the tops with so thick a closure, that Venus might there in her jollity have dallied unseen
30 with her dearest paramour. Fast by, to make the place more gorgeous, was there a fount so crystalline and clear, that it seemed Diana with her Dryades and Hamadryades had that spring, as the secret of all their bathings. In this glorious arbor sat these two shepherds, seeing their sheep feed, playing on their pipes many pleasant tunes, and from music and melody falling into much amorous chat. Drawing

more nigh we might descry the countenance of the one to be full of sorrow, his face to be the very portraiture of discontent, and his eyes full of woes, that living he seemed to die: we, to hear what these were, stole privily behind the thick, where we overheard this discourse:

A Pleasant Eclogue between Montanus and Corydon

CORYDON

Say, shepherd's boy, what makes thee greet so sore?
Why leaves thy pipe his pleasure and delight?
Young are thy years, thy cheeks with roses dight:
10 Then sing for joy, sweet swain, and sigh no more.

This milk-white poppy, and this climbing pine
Both promise shade; then sit thee down and sing,
And make these woods with pleasant notes to ring,
Till Phoebus deign all westward to decline.

MONTANUS

Ah, Corydon, unmeet is melody
To him whom proud contempt hath overborne:
Slain are my joys by Phoebe's bitter scorn;
Far hence my weal, and near my jeopardy.

Love's burning brand is couchèd in my breast,
20 Making a Phoenix of my faintful heart:
And though his fury do enforce my smart,
Aye blithe am I to honor his behest.

Prepared to woes, since so my Phoebe wills,
My looks dismayed, since Phoebe will disdain;
I banish bliss and welcome home my pain:
So stream my tears as showers from Alpine hills.

In error's mask I blindfold judgment's eye,
I fetter reason in the snares of lust,
I seem secure, yet know not how to trust;
30 I live by that which makes me living die.

Devoid of rest, companion of distress,
Plague to myself, consumèd by my thought,

How may my voice or pipe in tune be brought,
Since I am reft of solace and delight?

CORYDON

Ah, lorrel lad, what makes thee hery[1] love?
A sugared harm, a poison full of pleasure,
A painted shrine full filled with rotten treasure;
A heaven in show, a hell to them that prove.

A gain in seeming, shadowed still with want,
A broken staff which folly doth uphold,
A flower that fades with every frosty cold,
10 An orient rose sprung from a withered plant.

A minute's joy to gain a world of grief,
A subtle net to snare the idle mind,
A seeing scorpion, yet in seeming blind,
A poor rejoice, a plague without relief.

Forthy, Montanus, follow mine arede,
(Whom age hath taught the trains that fancy useth)
Leave foolish love, for beauty wit abuseth,
And drowns, by folly, virtue's springing seed.

MONTANUS

So blames the child the flame because it burns,
20 And bird the snare because it doth entrap,
And fools true love because of sorry hap,
And sailor's curse the ship that overturns.

But would the child forbear to play with flame,
And birds beware to trust the fowler's gin,
And fools foresee before they fall and sin,
And masters guide their ships in better frame;

The child would praise the fire because it warms,
And birds rejoice to see the fowler fail,
And fools prevent before their plagues prevail,
30 And sailors bless the barque that saves from harms.

Ah, Corydon, though many be thy years,
And crooked elde hath some experience left,

[1] Praise.

Yet is thy mind of judgment quite bereft,
In view of love, whose power in me appears.

The ploughman little wots to turn the pen,
Or bookman skills to guide the ploughman's cart;
Nor can the cobbler count the terms of art,
Nor base men judge the thoughts of mighty men.

Nor withered age, unmeet for beauty's guide,
Uncapable of love's impression,
Discourse of that whose choice possession
10 May never to so base a man be tied.

But I, whom nature makes of tender mould,
And youth most pliant yields to fancy's fire,
Do build my haven and heaven on sweet desire,
On sweet desire, more dear to me than gold.

Think I of love, oh, how my lines aspire!
How haste the Muses to embrace my brows,
And hem my temples in with laurel boughs,
And fill my brains with chaste and holy fire!

Then leave my lines their homely equipage,
20 Mounted beyond the circle of the sun:
Amazed I read the stile when I have done,
And hery love that sent that heavenly rage.

Of Phoebe then, of Phoebe then I sing,
Drawing the purity of all the spheres,
The pride of earth, or what in heaven appears,
Her honored face and fame to light to bring.

In fluent numbers, and in pleasant veins,
I rob both sea and earth of all their state,
To praise her parts: I charm both time and fate,
30 To bless the nymph that yields me lovesick pains.

My sheep are turned to thoughts, whom froward will
Guides in the restless labyrinth of love;
Fear lends them pasture wheresoe'er they move,
And by their death their life reneweth still.

My sheephook is my pen, mine oaten reed
My paper, where my many woes are written.
Thus silly swain, with love and fancy bitten,
I trace the plains of pain in woeful weed.

Yet are my cares, my broken sleeps, my tears,
My dreams, my doubts, for Phoebe sweet to me:
Who waiteth heaven in sorrow's vale must be,
And glory shines where danger most appears.

Then, Corydon, although I blithe me not,
Blame me not, man, since sorrow is my sweet:
So willeth love, and Phoebe thinks it meet,
And kind Montanus liketh well his lot.

CORYDON

O stayless youth, by error so misguided,
10 Where will proscribeth laws to perfect wits,
Where reason mourns, and blame in triumph sits,
And folly poisoneth all that time provided!

With wilful blindness bleared, prepared to shame,
Prone to neglect Occasion when she smiles:
Alas, that love, by fond and froward guiles,
Should make thee tract the path to endless blame!

Ah, my Montanus, cursèd is the charm,
That hath bewitchèd so thy youthful eyes.
Leave off in time to like these vanities,
20 Be forward to thy good, and fly thy harm.

As many bees as Hybla daily shields,
As many fry as fleet on ocean's face,
As many herds as on the earth do trace,
As many flowers as deck the fragrant fields,

As many stars as glorious heaven contains,
As many storms as wayward winter weeps,
As many plagues as hell enclosèd keeps,
So many griefs in love, so many pains.

Suspicions, thoughts, desires, opinions, prayers,
30 Mislikes, misdeeds, fond joys, and feignèd peace,
Illusions, dreams, great pains, and small increase,
Vows, hopes, acceptance, scorns, and deep despairs,

Truce, war, and woe do wait at beauty's gate;
Time lost, laments, reports, and privy grudge,
And last, fierce love is but a partial judge,
Who yields for service shame, for friendship hate.

MONTANUS

All adder-like I stop mine ears, fond swain,
So charm no more, for I will never change.
Call home thy flocks in time that straggling range,
For lo, the sun declineth hence amain.

TERENTIUS

In amore haec omnia insunt vitia: induciae, inimicitiae, bellum, pax rursum: incerta haec si tu postules ratione certa fieri, nihilo plus agas, quam si des operam, ut cum ratione insanias.

The shepherds having thus ended their eclogue, Aliena stepped with Ganymede from behind the thicket; at whose sudden sight the shepherds arose, and Aliena saluted them thus:

"Shepherds, all hail, for such we deem you by your flocks, and lovers, good luck, for such you seem by your passions, our eyes being witness of the one, and our ears of the other. Although not by love, yet by fortune, I am a distressed gentlewoman, as sorrowful as you are passionate, and as full of woes as you of perplexed thoughts. Wandering this way in a forest unknown, only I and my page, wearied with travel, would fain have some place of rest. May you appoint us any place of quiet harbor, be it never so mean, I shall be thankful to you, contented in myself, and grateful to whosoever shall be mine host."

Corydon, hearing the gentlewoman speak so courteously, returned her mildly and reverently this answer:

"Fair mistress, we return you as hearty a welcome as you gave us a courteous salute. A shepherd I am and this a lover, as watchful to please his wench as to feed his sheep: full of fancies, and therefore, say I, full of follies. Exhort him I may, but persuade him I cannot; for love admits neither of counsel nor reason. But leaving him to his passions, if you be distressed, I am sorrowful such a fair creature is crossed with calamity; pray for you I may, but relieve you I cannot. Marry, if you want lodging, if you vouch to shroud yourselves in a shepherd's cottage, my house for this night shall be your harbor."

Aliena thanked Corydon greatly, and presently sate her down and Ganymede by her. Corydon looking earnestly upon her, and with a curious survey viewing all her perfections, applauded (in his thought) her excellence, and pitying her distress was desirous to hear the cause of her misfortunes, began to question her thus:

"If I should not, fair damosel, occasion offence, or renew your griefs by rubbing the scar, I would fain crave so much favor as to know the cause of your misfortunes, and why, and whither you wander with your page in so dangerous a forest?"

Aliena, that was as courteous as she was fair, made this reply:

"Shepherd, a friendly demand ought never to be offensive, and questions of courtesy carry privileged pardons in their foreheads. Know, therefore, to discover my fortunes were to renew my sorrows, and I should, by discoursing my mishaps, but rake fire out of the cinders. Therefore let this suffice, gentle shepherd: my distress is as great as my travel is dangerous, and I wander in this forest to light on some cottage where I and my page may dwell: for I mean to buy some farm, and a flock of sheep, and so become a shepherdess, meaning to live low, and content me with a country life; for I have heard the swains say, that they drunk without suspicion, and slept without care."

"Marry, mistress," quoth Corydon, "if you mean so, you came in good time, for my landslord intends

to sell both the farm I till, and the flock I keep, and cheap you may have them for ready money: and for a shepherd's life, O mistress, did you but live awhile in their content, you would say the court were rather a place of sorrow than of solace. Here, mistress, shall not fortune thwart you, but in mean misfortunes, as the loss of a few sheep, which, as it breeds no beggary, so it can be no extreme prejudice: the next year may mend all with a fresh increase. Envy
10 stirs not us, we covet not to climb, our desires mount not above our degrees, nor our thoughts above our fortunes. Care cannot harbor in our cottages, nor do our homely couches know broken slumbers: as we exceed not in diet, so we have enough to satisfy: and, mistress, I have so much Latin, *Satis est quod sufficit.*"

"By my troth, shepherd," quoth Aliena, "thou makest me in love with your country life, and therefore send for thy landslord, and I will buy thy farm
20 and thy flocks, and thou shalt still under me be overseer of them both: only for pleasure sake I and my page will serve you, lead the flocks to the field, and fold them. Thus will I live quiet, unknown, and contented."

This news so gladded the heart of Corydon, that he should not be put out of his farm, that putting off his shepherd's bonnet, he did her all the reverence that he might. But all this while sate Montanus in a muse, thinking of the cruelty of his Phoebe, whom
30 he wooed long, but was in no hope to win. Ganymede, who still had the remembrance of Rosader in his thoughts, took delight to see the poor shepherd passionate, laughing at Love, that in all his actions was so imperious. At last, when she had noted his tears that stole down his cheeks, and his sighs that broke from the centre of his heart, pitying his lament,

she demanded of Corydon why the young shepherd looked so sorrowful.

"O sir," quoth he, "the boy is in love."

"Why," quoth Ganymede, "can shepherds love?"

"Ay," quoth Montanus, "and overlove, else shouldst not thou see me so pensive. Love, I tell thee, is as precious in a shepherd's eye, as in the looks of a king, and we country swains entertain fancy with as great delight as the proudest courtier 10 doth affection. Opportunity, that is the sweetest friend to Venus, harboreth in our cottages, and loyalty, the chiefest fealty that Cupid requires, is found more among shepherds than higher degrees. Then, ask not if such silly swains can love."

"What is the cause then," quoth Ganymede, "that love being so sweet to thee, thou lookest so sorrowful?"

"Because," quoth Montanus, "the party beloved is froward, and having courtesy in her looks, holdeth 20 disdain in her tongue's end."

"What hath she, then," quoth Aliena, "in her heart?"

"Desire, I hope madam," quoth he, "or else, my hope lost, despair in love were death."

As thus they chatted, the sun being ready to set, and they not having folded their sheep, Corydon requested she would sit there with her page, till Montanus and he lodged their sheep for that night.

"You shall go," quoth Aliena, "but first I will 30 entreat Montanus to sing some amorous sonnet, that he made when he hath been deeply passionate."

"That I will," quoth Montanus, and with that he began thus:

Montanus's Sonnet

Phoebe sate,
Sweet she sate,
Sweet sate Phoebe when I saw her;

White her brow,
Coy her eye:
  Brow and eye how much you please me!
Words I spent,
Sighs I sent:
  Sighs and words could never draw her.
O my love,
Thou art lost,
  Since no sight could ever ease thee.

10 Phoebe sat
By a fount;
  Sitting by a fount I spied her:
Sweet her touch,
Rare her voice:
  Touch and voice what may distain you?
As she sung
I did sigh,
  And by sighs whilst that I tried her,
O mine eyes!
20 You did lose
  Her first sight whose want did pain you.

Phoebe's flocks,
White as wool:
  Yet were Phoebe's locks more whiter.
Phoebe's eyes
Dovelike mild:
  Dovelike eyes, both mild and cruel.
Montan swears,
In your lamps
30 He will die for to delight her.
Phoebe yield,
Or I die:
  Shall true hearts be fancy's fuel?

Montanus had no sooner ended his sonnet, but Corydon with a low courtesy rose up and went with his fellow, and shut their sheep in the folds; and after returning to Aliena and Ganymede, conducted them home weary to his poor cottage. By the way there was much good chat with Montanus about his 40 loves, he resolving Aliena that Phoebe was the fairest shepherdess in all France, and that in his eye her beauty was equal with the nymphs.

"But," quoth he, "as of all stones the diamond is most clearest, and yet most hard for the lapidary to cut: as of all flowers the rose is the fairest, and yet guarded with the sharpest prickles: so of all our country lasses Phoebe is the brightest, but the most coy of all to stoop unto desire. But let her take heed," quoth he, "I have heard of Narcissus, who for 10 his high disdain against Love, perished in the folly of his own love."

With this they were at Corydon's cottage, where Montanus parted from them, and they went in to rest. Alinda and Ganymede glad of so contented a shelter, made merry with the poor swain; and though they had but country fare and coarse lodging, yet their welcome was so great, and their cares so little, that they counted their diet delicate, and slept as soundly as if they had been in the court of Toris- 20 mond. The next morn they lay long in bed, as wearied with the toil of unaccustomed travel; but as soon as they got up, Aliena resolved there to set up her rest, and by the help of Corydon swept a bargain with his landslord, and so became mistress of the farm and the flock, herself putting on the attire of a shepherdess, and Ganymede of a young swain: every day leading forth her flocks, with such delight, that she held her exile happy, and thought no content to the bliss of a country cottage. Leaving her thus 30 famous amongst the shepherds of Arden, again to Saladyne.

When Saladyne had a long while concealed a secret resolution of revenge, and could no longer hide fire in the flax, nor oil in the flame, for envy is like lightning, that will appear in the darkest fog, it chanced on a morning very early he called up certain of his servants, and went with them to the

chamber of Rosader, which being open, he entered with his crew, and surprised his brother being asleep, and bound him in fetters, and in the midst of his hall chained him to a post. Rosader, amazed at this strange chance, began to reason with his brother about the cause of this sudden extremity, wherein he had wronged, and what fault he had committed worthy so sharp a penance. Saladyne answered him only with a look of disdain, and went his way, leav-
10 ing poor Rosader in a deep perplexity; who, thus abused, fell into sundry passions, but no means of relief could be had: whereupon for anger he grew into a discontented melancholy. In which humor he continued two or three days without meat, insomuch that seeing his brother would give him no food, he fell into despair of his life. Which Adam Spencer, the old servant of Sir John of Bordeaux, seeing, touched with the duty and love he ought to his old master, felt a remorse in his conscience of his son's
20 mishap; and therefore, although Saladyne had given a general charge to his servants that none of them upon pain of death should give either meat or drink to Rosader, yet Adam Spencer in the night rose secretly, and brought him such victuals as he could provide, and unlocked him, and set him at liberty. After Rosader had well feasted himself, and felt he was loose, straight his thoughts aimed at revenge, and now, all being asleep, he would have quit Saladyne with the method of his own mischief. But
30 Adam Spencer did persuade him to the contrary with these reasons:

"Sir," quoth he, "be content, for this night go again into your old fetters, so shall you try the faith of friends, and save the life of an old servant. To-morrow hath your brother invited all your kindred and allies to a solemn breakfast, only to see you, telling them all that you are mad, and fain to be tied to a post. As soon as they come, make complaint to them of the abuse proffered you by Saladyne. If they redress you, why so: but if they pass over your plaints *sicco pede*, and hold with the violence of your brother before your innocence, then thus: I will leave you unlocked that you may break out at your pleasure, and at the end of the hall shall you see stand a couple of good poleaxes, one for you and another for me. When I give you a wink, shake off your 10 chains, and let us play the men, and make havoc amongst them, drive them out of the house and maintain possession by force of arms, till the king hath made a redress of your abuses."

These words of Adam Spencer so persuaded Rosader, that he went to the place of his punishment, and stood there while the next morning. About the time appointed, came all the guests bidden by Saladyne, whom he entreated with courteous and curious entertainment, as they all perceived their 20 welcome to be great. The tables in the hall, where Rosader was tied, were covered, and Saladyne bringing in his guests together, showed them where his brother was bound, and was enchained as a man lunatic. Rosader made reply, and with some invectives made complaints of the wrongs proffered him by Saladyne, desiring they would in pity seek some means for his relief. But in vain, they had stopped their ears with Ulysses, that were his words never so forceable, he breathed only his passions into the 30 wind. They, careless, sat down with Saladyne to dinner, being very frolic and pleasant, washing their heads well with wine. At last, when the fume of the grape had entered pell-mell into their brains, they began in satirical speeches to rail against Rosader: which Adam Spencer no longer brooking, gave the sign, and Rosader shaking off his chains got a poleaxe in his hand, and flew amongst them with such violence and fury, that he hurt many, slew some, and drave his brother and all the rest quite out of the house. Seeing the coast clear, he shut the doors, and being sore anhungered, and seeing such good victuals, he sat him down with Adam Spencer, and such good fellows as he knew were honest men, and there feasted themselves with such provision as Saladyne had prepared for his friends. After they had taken their repast, Rosader rampired up the house, 10 lest upon a sudden his brother should raise some crew of his tenants, and surprise them unawares. But Saladyne took a contrary course, and went to the sheriff of the shire and made complaint of Rosader, who giving credit to Saladyne, in a determined resolution to revenge the gentleman's wrongs, took with him five-and-twenty tall men, and made a vow, either to break into the house and take Rosader, or else to coop him in till he made him yield by famine. In this determination, gathering a crew together, he 20 went forward to set Saladyne in his former estate. News of this was brought unto Rosader, who smiling at the cowardice of his brother, brooked all the injuries of fortune with patience, expecting the coming of the sheriff. As he walked upon the battlements of the house, he descried where Saladyne and he drew near, with a troop of lusty gallants. At this he smiled, and called up Adam Spencer, and showed him the envious treachery of his brother, and the folly of the sheriff to be so credulous.

30 "Now, Adam," quoth he, "what shall I do? It rests for me either to yield up the house to my brother and seek a reconcilement, or else issue out, and break through the company with courage, for cooped in like a coward I will not be. If I submit (ah Adam) I dishonor myself, and that is worse than death, for by such open disgraces, the fame of men grows odious. If I issue out amongst them,

fortune may favor me, and I may escape with life. But suppose the worst; if I be slain, then my death shall be honorable to me, and so inequal a revenge infamous to Saladyne."

"Why then, master, forward and fear not! Out amongst them; they be but faint-hearted losels, and for Adam Spencer, if he die not at your foot, say he is a dastard."

These words cheered up so the heart of young 10 Rosader, that he thought himself sufficient for them all, and therefore prepared weapons for him and Adam Spencer, and were ready to entertain the sheriff; for no sooner came Saladyne and he to the gates, but Rosader, unlooked for, leaped out and assailed them, wounded many of them, and caused the rest to give back, so that Adam and he broke through the prease in despite of them all, and took their way towards the forest of Arden. This repulse so set the sheriff's heart on fire to revenge, that he 20 straight raised all the country, and made hue and cry after them. But Rosader and Adam, knowing full well the secret ways that led through the vineyards, stole away privily through the province of Bordeaux, and escaped safe to the forest of Arden. Being come thither, they were glad they had so good a harbor: but fortune, who is like the chameleon, variable with every object, and constant in nothing but inconstancy, thought to make them mirrors of her mutability, and therefore still crossed 30 them thus contrarily. Thinking still to pass on by the by-ways to get to Lyons, they chanced on a path that led into the thick of the forest, where they wandered five or six days without meat, that they were almost famished finding neither shepherd nor cottage to relieve them; and hunger growing on so extreme, Adam Spencer, being old, began first to faint, and sitting him down on a hill, and looking about him, espied where Rosader lay as feeble and as ill perplexed: which sight made him shed tears, and to fall into these bitter terms:

Adam Spencer's Speech

"Oh, how the life of man may well be compared to the state of the ocean seas, that for every calm hath a thousand storms, resembling the rose tree, that for a few fair flowers hath a multitude of sharp prickles! All our pleasures end in pain, and our highest delights are crossed with deepest dis-
10 contents. The joys of man, as they are few, so are they momentary, scarce ripe before they are rotten, and withering in the blossom, either parched with the heat of envy or fortune. Fortune, O inconstant friend, that in all thy deeds art froward and fickle, delighting, in the poverty of the lowest and the overthrow of the highest, to decipher thy inconstancy. Thou standest upon a globe, and thy wings are plumed with Time's feathers, that thou mayest ever be restless: thou art double-faced like Janus,
20 carrying frowns in the one to threaten, and smiles in the other to betray: thou profferest an eel, and performest a scorpion, and where thy greatest favors be, there is the fear of the extremest misfortunes, so variable are all thy actions. But why, Adam, dost thou exclaim against Fortune? She laughs at the plaints of the distressed, and there is nothing more pleasing unto her, than to hear fools boast in her fading allurements, or sorrowful men to discover the sour of their passions. Glut her not, Adam, then
30 with content, but thwart her with brooking all mishaps with patience. For there is no greater check to the pride of Fortune, than with a resolute courage to pass over her crosses without care. Thou art old, Adam, and thy hairs wax white: the palm tree is

already full of blooms, and in the furrows of thy face appears the calendars of death. Wert thou blessed by Fortune thy years could not be many, nor the date of thy life long; the sith nature must have her due, what is it for thee to resign her debt a little before the day. Ah, it is not this which grieveth me, nor do I care what mishaps Fortune can wage against me, but the sight of Rosader that galleth unto the quick. When I remember the wor-
10 ships of his house, the honor of his fathers, and the virtues of himself, then do I say, that fortune and the fates are most injurious, to censure so hard extremes, against a youth of so great hope. O Rosader, thou art in the flower of thine age, and in the pride of thy years, buxom and full of May. Nature hath prodigally enriched thee with her favors, and virtue made thee the mirror of her excellence; and now, through the decree of the unjust stars, to have all these good parts nipped in the blade,
20 and blemished by the inconstancy of fortune! Ah, Rosader, could I help thee, my grief were the less, and happy should my death be, if it might be the beginning of thy relief: but seeing we perish both in one extreme, it is a double sorrow. What shall I do? prevent the sight of his further misfortune with a present dispatch of mine own life? Ah, despair is a merciless sin!"

As he was ready to go forward in his passion, he looked earnestly on Rosader, and seeing him change
30 color, he rose up and went to him, and holding his temples, said:

"What cheer, master? Though all fail, let not the heart faint: the courage of a man is showed in the resolution of his death."

At these words Rosader lifted up his eye, and looking on Adam Spencer, began to weep.

"Ah, Adam," quoth he, "I sorrow not to die, but I

grieve at the manner of my death. Might I with my lance encounter the enemy, and so die in the field, it were honor and content: might I, Adam, combat with some wild beast and perish as his prey, I were satisfied; but to die with hunger, O Adam, it is the extremest of all extremes!"

"Master," quoth he, "you see we are both in one predicament, and long I cannot live without meat; seeing therefore we can find no food, let the death 10 of the one preserve the life of the other. I am old, and overworn with age; you are young, and are the hope of many honors: let me then die, I will presently cut my veins, and, master, with the warm blood relieve your fainting spirits: suck on that till I end, and you be comforted."

With that Adam Spencer was ready to pull out his knife, when Rosader full of courage (though very faint) rose up, and wished Adam Spencer to sit there till his return; "for my mind gives me," quoth he, 20 "I shall bring thee meat." With that, like a madman, he rose up, and ranged up and down the woods, seeking to encounter some wild beast with his rapier, that either he might carry his friend Adam food, or else pledge his life in pawn for his loyalty.

It chanced that day, that Gerismond, the lawful king of France banished by Torismond, who with a lusty crew of outlaws lived in that forest, that day in honor of his birth made a feast to all his bold yeomen, and frolicked it with store of wine and 30 venison, sitting all at a long table under the shadow of limon trees. To that place by chance fortune conducted Rosader, who seeing such a crew of brave men, having store of that for want of which he and Adam perished, he stepped boldly to the board's end, and saluted the company thus:

"Whatsoever thou be that art master of these lusty squires, I salute thee as graciously as a man in extreme distress may: know that I and a fellow-friend of mine are here famished in the forest for want of food: perish we must, unless relieved by thy favors. Therefore, if thou be a gentleman, give meat to men, and to such men as are every way worthy of life. Let the proudest squire that sits at thy table rise and encounter with me in any honorable point of activity whatsoever, and if he and thou prove me not a man, send me away comfortless. If thou refuse this, as a 10 niggard of thy cates, I will have amongst you with my sword; for rather will I die valiantly, than perish with so cowardly an extreme."

Gerismond, looking him earnestly in the face, and seeing so proper a gentleman in so bitter a passion, was moved with so great pity, that rising from the table, he took him by the hand and bad him welcome, willing him to sit down in his place, and in his room not only to eat his fill, but be lord of the feast.

"Gramercy, sir," quoth Rosader, "but I have a 20 feeble friend that lies hereby famished almost for food, aged and therefore less able to abide the extremity of hunger than myself, and dishonor it were for me to taste one crumb, before I made him partner of my fortunes: therefore I will run and fetch him, and then I will gratefully accept of your proffer."

Away hies Rosader to Adam Spencer, and tells him the news, who was glad of so happy fortune, but so feeble he was that he could not go; whereupon 30 Rosader got him up on his back, and brought him to the place. Which when Gerismond and his men saw, they greatly applauded their league of friendship; and Rosader, having Gerismond's place assigned him, would not sit there himself, but set down Adam Spencer. Well, to be short, those hungry squires fell to their victuals, and feasted themselves with good delicates, and great store of wine. As soon as they had taken their repast, Gerismond, desirous to hear what hard fortune drave them into those bitter extremes, requested Rosader to discourse, if it were not any way prejudicial unto him, the cause of his travel. Rosader, desirous any way to satisfy the courtesy of his favorable host, first beginning his exordium with a volley of sighs, and a few lukewarm tears, prosecuted his discourse, and told him from point to point all his fortunes: how he was the youngest son of Sir John of Bordeaux, his name Rosader, how his brother sundry times had wronged him, and lastly how, for beating the sheriff and hurting his men, he fled.

"And this old man," quoth he, "whom I so much love and honor, is surnamed Adam Spencer, an old servant of my father's, and one, that for his love, never failed me in all my misfortunes."

When Gerismond heard this, he fell on the neck of Rosader, and next discoursing unto him how he was Gerismond, their lawful king, exiled by Torismond, what familiarity had ever been betwixt his father, Sir John of Bordeaux, and him, how faithful a subject he lived, and how honorable he died, promising, for his sake, to give both him and his friend such courteous entertainment as his present estate could minister, and upon this made him one of his foresters. Rosader, seeing it was the king, craved pardon for his boldness, in that he did not do him due reverence, and humbly gave him thanks for his favorable courtesy. Gerismond, not satisfied yet with news, began to inquire if he had been lately in the court of Torismond, and whether he had seen his daughter Rosalynde or no? At this Rosader fetched a deep sigh, and shedding many tears, could not answer: yet at last, gathering his spirits together, he revealed unto the king, how Rosalynde was banished, and how there was such a sympathy of affections between Alinda and her, that she chose rather to be partaker of her exile, than to part fellowship; whereupon the unnatural king banished them both: "and now they are wandered none knows whither, neither could any learn since their departure, the place of their abode." This news drave the king into a great melancholy, that presently he arose from all the company, and went into his privy chamber, so secret as the harbor of the woods would allow him. The company was all dashed at these tidings, and Rosader and Adam Spencer, having such opportunity, went to take their rest. Where we leave them, and return again to Torismond.

The flight of Rosader came to the ears of Torismond, who hearing that Saladyne was sole heir of the lands of Sir John of Bordeaux, desirous to possess such fair revenues, found just occasion to quarrel with Saladyne about the wrongs he proffered to his brother: and therefore, dispatching a herehault, he sent for Saladyne in all post-haste. Who marvelling what the matter should be, began to examine his own conscience, wherein he had offended his highness; but emboldened with his innocence, he boldly went with the herehault unto the court; where, as soon as he came, he was not admitted into the presence of the king, but presently sent to prison. This greatly amazed Saladyne, chiefly in that the jailer had a straight charge over him, to see that he should be close prisoner. Many passionate thoughts came in his head, till at last he began to fall into consideration of his former follies, and to meditate with himself. Leaning his head on his hand, and his elbow on his knee, full of sorrow, grief and disquieted passions, he resolved into these terms:

Saladyne's Complaint

"Unhappy Saladyne! whom folly hath led to these misfortunes, and wanton desires wrapped within the labyrinth of these calamities! Are not the heavens doomers of men's deeds; and holds not God a balance in his fist, to reward with favor, and revenge with justice? O Saladyne, the faults of thy youth, as they were fond, so were they foul, and not only discovering little nurture, but blemishing the excellence of nature. Whelps of one litter are ever most loving, and brothers that are sons of one father should live in friendship without jar. O Saladyne, so it should be; but thou hast with the deer fed against the wind, with the crab strove against the stream, and sought to pervert nature by unkindness. Rosader's wrongs, the wrongs of Rosader, Saladyne, cries for revenge; his youth pleads to God to inflict some penance upon thee; his virtues are pleas that enforce writs of displeasure to cross thee: thou hast highly abused thy kind and natural brother, and the heavens cannot spare to quite thee with punishment. There is no string to the worm of conscience, no hell to a mind touched with guilt. Every wrong I offered him, called now to remembrance, wringeth a drop of blood from my heart; every bad look every frown pincheth me at the quick, and says, 'Saladyne, thou hast sinned against Rosader.' Be penitent, and assign thyself some penance to discover thy sorrow, and pacify his wrath."

In the depth of his passion, he was sent for to the king, who with a look that threatened death entertained him, and demanded of him where his brother was. Saladyne made answer, that upon some riot made against the sheriff of the shire, he was fled from Bordeaux, but he knew not whither.

"Nay, villain," quoth he, "I have heard of the wrongs thou hast proffered thy brother since the death of thy father, and by thy means have I lost a most brave and resolute chevalier. Therefore, in justice to punish thee, I spare thy life for thy father's sake, but banish thee for ever from the court and country of France; and see thy departure be within ten days, else trust me thou shalt lose thy head."

10 And with that the king flew away in a rage, and left poor Saladyne greatly perplexed; who grieving at his exile, yet determined to bear it with patience, and in penance of his former follies to travel abroad in every coast till he had found out his brother Rosader. With whom now I begin.

Rosader, being thus preferred to the place of a forester by Gerismond, rooted out the remembrance of his brother's unkindness by continual exercise, traversing the groves and wild forests, partly to hear 20 the melody of the sweet birds which recorded, and partly to show his diligent endeavor in his master's behalf. Yet whatsoever he did, or howsoever he walked, the lively image of Rosalynde remained in memory: on her sweet perfections he fed his thoughts, proving himself like the eagle a true-born bird, since as the one is known by beholding the sun, so was he by regarding excellent beauty. One day among the rest, finding a fit opportunity and place convenient, desirous to discover his woes to the 30 woods, he engraved with his knife on the bark of a myrtle tree, this pretty estimate of his mistress' perfection:

Sonetto

Of all chaste birds the Phoenix doth excel,
Of all strong beasts the lion bears the bell,
Of all sweet flowers the rose doth sweetest smell,
Of all fair maids my Rosalynde is fairest.

Of all pure metals gold is only purest,
Of all high trees the pine hath highest crest,
Of all soft sweets I like my mistress' breast,
Of all chaste thoughts my mistress' thoughts are rarest.

Of all proud birds the eagle pleaseth Jove,
Of pretty fowls kind Venus likes the dove,
Of trees Minerva doth the olive love,
Of all sweet nymphs I honor Rosalynde.

Of all her gifts her wisdom pleaseth most,
10 Of all her graces virtue she doth boast:
For all these gifts my life and joy is lost,
If Rosalynde prove cruel and unkind.

In these and such like passions Rosader did every day eternize the name of his Rosalynde; and this day especially when Aliena and Ganymede, enforced by the heat of the sun to seek for shelter, by good fortune arrived in that place, where this amorous forester registered his melancholy passions. They saw the sudden change of his looks, his folded arms, his 20 passionate sighs; they heard him often abruptly call on Rosalynde, who, poor soul, was as hotly burned as himself, but that she shrouded her pains in the cinders of honorable modesty. Whereupon, guessing him to be in love, and according to the nature of their sex being pitiful in that behalf, they suddenly brake off his melancholy by their approach, and Ganymede shook him out of his dumps thus:

"What news, forester? Hast thou wounded some deer, and lost him in the fall? Care not man for so 30 small a loss: thy fees was but the skin, the shoulder, and the horns: 't is hunter's luck to aim fair and miss; and a woodman's fortune to strike and yet go without the game."

"Thou art beyond the mark, Ganymede," quoth Aliena: "his passions are greater, and his sighs discovers more loss: perhaps in traversing these thickets, he hath seen some beautiful nymph, and is grown amorous."

"It may be so," quoth Ganymede, "for here he hath newly engraven some sonnet: come, and see the discourse of the forester's poems."

Reading the sonnet over, and hearing him name Rosalynde, Aliena looked on Ganymede and laughed, and Ganymede looking back on the forester, and seeing it was Rosader, blushed; yet thinking to 10 shroud all under her page's apparel, she boldly returned to Rosader, and began thus:

"I pray thee tell me, forester, what is this Rosalynde for whom thou pinest away in such passions? Is she some nymph that waits upon Diana's train, whose chastity thou hast deciphered in such epithets? Or is she some shepherdess that haunts these plains whose beauty hath so bewitched thy fancy, whose name thou shadowest in covert under the figure of Rosalynde, as Ovid did Julia under the name of 20 Corinna? Or say me forsooth, is it that Rosalynde, of whom we shepherds have heard talk, she, forester, that is the daughter of Gerismond, that once was king, and now an outlaw in the forest of Arden?"

At this Rosader fetched a deep sigh, and said:

"It is she, O gentle swain, it is she; that saint it is whom I serve, that goddess at whose shrine I do bend all my devotions; the most fairest of all fairs, the phoenix of all that sex, and the purity of all 30 earthly perfection."

"And why, gentle forester, if she be so beautiful, and thou so amorous, is there such a disagreement in thy thoughts? Happily she resembleth the rose, that is sweet but full of prickles? or the serpent Regius that hath scales as glorious as the sun and a breath as infectious as the Aconitum is deadly? So thy Rosalynde may be most amiable and yet unkind; full of favor and yet froward, coy without wit, and disdainful without reason."

"O Shepherd," quoth Rosader, "knewest thou her personage, graced with the excellence of all perfection, being a harbor wherein the graces shroud their virtues, thou wouldest not breathe out such blasphemy against the beauteous Rosalynde. She is a diamond, bright but not hard, yet of most chaste operation; a pearl so orient, that it can be
10 stained with no blemish; a rose without prickles, and a princess absolute as well in beauty as in virtue. But I, unhappy I, have let mine eye soar with the eagle against so bright a sun that I am quite blind: I have with Apollo enamored myself of a Daphne, not, as she, disdainful, but far more chaste than Daphne: I have with Ixion laid my love on Juno, and shall, I fear, embrace nought but a cloud. Ah, Shepherd, I have reached at a star: my desires have mounted above my degree, and my thoughts above
20 my fortunes. I, being a peasant, have ventured to gaze on a princess, whose honors are too high to vouchsafe such base loves."

"Why, forester," quoth Ganymede, "comfort thyself; be blithe and frolic, man. Love souseth[1] as low as she soareth high: Cupid shoots at a rag as soon as at a robe; and Venus' eye that was so curious, sparkled favor on pole-footed Vulcan. Fear not, man, women's looks are not tied to dignity's feathers, nor make they curious esteem where the stone is found,
30 but what is the virtue. Fear not, forester; faint heart never won fair lady. But where lives Rosalynde now? at the court?"

"Oh no," quoth Rosader, "she lives I know not where, and that is my sorrow; banished by Torismond, and that is my hell: for might I but find her sacred personage, and plead before the bar of her

[1] Swoops.

pity the plaint of my passions, hope tells me she would grace me with some favor, and that would suffice as a recompense of all my former miseries."

"Much have I heard of thy mistress' excellence, and I know, forester, thou canst describe her at the full, as one that hast surveyed all her parts with a curious eye; then do me that favor, to tell me what her perfections be."

"That I will," quoth Rosader, "for I glory to make 10 all ears wonder at my mistress' excellence."

And with that he pulled a paper forth his bosom, wherein he read this:

Rosalynde's Description

Like to the clear in highest sphere
Where all imperial glory shines,
Of selfsame color is her hair,
Whether unfolded or in twines:
Heigh ho, fair Rosalynde!
Her eyes are sapphires set in snow,
Refining heaven by every wink:
20 The gods do fear whenas they glow,
And I do tremble when I think:
Heigh ho, would she were mine.

Her cheeks are like the blushing cloud
That beautifies Aurora's face,
Or like the silver crimson shroud
That Phoebus' smiling looks doth grace:
Heigh ho, fair Rosalynde!
Her lips are like two budded roses,
Whom ranks of lilies neighbor nigh,
30 Within which bounds she balm encloses,
Apt to entice a deity:
Heigh ho, would she were mine.

Her neck, like to a stately tower
Where love himself imprisoned lies,
To watch for glances every hour
From her divine and sacred eyes:
Heigh ho, fair Rosalynde.
Her paps are centres of delight,

Her paps are orbs of heavenly frame,
Where nature moulds the dew of light,
To feed perfection with the same:
Heigh ho, would she were mine.

With orient pearl, with ruby red,
With marble white, with sapphire blue,
Her body every way is fed,
Yet soft in touch, and sweet in view:
Heigh ho, fair Rosalynde.
10 Nature herself her shape admires,
The gods are wounded in her sight,
And Love forsakes his heavenly fires
And at her eyes his brand doth light:
Heigh ho, would she were mine.

Then muse not, nymphs, though I bemoan
The absence of fair Rosalynde,
Since for her fair there is fairer none,
Nor for her virtues so divine:
Heigh ho, fair Rosalynde.
20 Heigh ho, my heart, would God that she were mine!

Periit, quia deperibat.

"Believe me," quoth Ganymede, "either the forester is an exquisite painter, or Rosalynde far above wonder; so it makes me blush to hear how women should be so excellent, and pages so unperfect."

Rosader beholding her earnestly, answered thus: "Truly, gentle page, thou hast cause to complain thee, wert thou the substance, but resembling the shadow content thyself; for it is excellence enough to be like the excellence of nature."

30 "He hath answered you, Ganymede," quoth Aliena, "it is enough for pages to wait on beautiful ladies, and not to be beautiful themselves."

"O mistress," quoth Ganymede, "hold you your peace, for you are partial. Who knows not, but that all women have desire to tie sovereignty to their petticoats, and ascribe beauty to themselves, where, if boys might put on their garments, perhaps they would prove as comely; if not as comely, it may be more courteous. But tell me, forester," and with that she turned to Rosader, "under whom maintainest thou thy walk?"

"Gentle swain, under the king of outlaws," said he, "the unfortunate Gerismond, who having lost his kingdom, crowneth his thoughts with content, accounting it better to govern among poor men in peace, than great men in danger."

10 "But hast thou not," said she, "having so melancholy opportunities as this forest affordeth thee, written more sonnets in commendations of thy mistress?"

"I have, gentle swain," quoth he, "but they be not about me. To-morrow by dawn of day, if your flocks feed in these pastures, I will bring them you, wherein you shall read my passions whilst I feel them, judge my patience when you read it: till when I bid farewell." So giving both Ganymede and
20 Aliena a gentle good-night, he resorted to his lodge, leaving Aliena and Ganymede to their prittle-prattle.

"So Ganymede," said Aliena, the forester being gone, "you are mightily beloved; men make ditties in your praise, spend sighs for your sake, make an idol of your beauty. Believe me, it grieves me not a little to see the poor man so pensive, and you so pitiless."

"Ah, Aliena," quoth she, "be not peremptory in your judgments. I hear Rosalynde praised as I am
30 Ganymede, but were I Rosalynde, I could answer the forester: if he mourn for love, there are medicines for love: Rosalynde cannot be fair and unkind. And so, madam, you see it is time to fold our flocks, or else Corydon will frown and say you will never prove good housewife."

With that they put their sheep into the cotes, and went home to her friend Corydon's cottage, Aliena as merry as might be that she was thus in the company of her Rosalynde; but she, poor soul, that had love her lodestar, and her thoughts set on fire with the flame of fancy, could take no rest, but being alone began to consider what passionate penance poor Rosader was enjoined to by love and fortune, that at last she fell into this humor with herself:

Rosalynde Passionate Alone

"Ah, Rosalynde, how the Fates have set down in their synod to make thee unhappy: for when Fortune hath done her worst, then Love comes in to begin a new tragedy: she seeks to lodge her son in thine eyes, and to kindle her fires in thy bosom. Beware, fond girl, he is an unruly guest to harbor; for cutting in by entreats, he will not be thrust out by force, and her fires are fed with such fuel, as no water is able to quench. Seest thou not how Venus seeks to wrap thee in her labyrinth, wherein is pleasure at the entrance, but within, sorrows, cares, and discontent? She is a Siren, stop thine ears to her melody; she is a basilisk, shut thy eyes and gaze not at her lest thou perish. Thou art now placed in the country content, where are heavenly thoughts and mean desires: in those lawns where thy flocks feed, Diana haunts: be as her nymphs chaste, and enemy to love, for there is no greater honor to a maid, than to account of fancy as a mortal foe to their sex. Daphne, that bonny wench, was not turned into a bay tree, as the poets feign: but for her chastity her fame was immortal, resembling the laurel that is ever green. Follow thou her steps, Rosalynde, and the rather, for that thou art an exile, and banished from the court; whose distress, as it is appeased with patience, so it would be renewed with amorous passions. Have mind on thy forepassed fortunes; fear the worst, and entangle not thyself with present fancies, lest loving in haste, thou repent thee at leisure. Ah, but yet, Rosalynde, it is Rosader that courts thee; one who as he is beautiful, so he is virtuous, and harboreth in his mind as many good qualities as his face is shadowed with gracious favors; and therefore, Rosalynde, stoop to love, lest, being either too coy or too cruel, Venus wax wroth, and plague thee with the reward of disdain."

10 Rosalynde, thus passionate, was wakened from her dumps by Aliena, who said it was time to go to bed. Corydon swore that was true, for Charles' Wain was risen in the north. Whereupon each taking leave of other, went to their rest, all but the poor Rosalynde, who was so full of passions, that she could not possess any content. Well, leaving her to her broken slumbers, expect what was performed by them the next morning.

The sun was no sooner stepped from the bed of 20 Aurora, but Aliena was wakened by Ganymede, who, restless all night, had tossed in her passions, saying it was then time to go to the field to unfold their sheep. Aliena, that spied where the hare was by the hounds, and could see day at a little hole, thought to be pleasant with her Ganymede, and therefore replied thus:

"What, wanton! the sun is but new up, and as yet Iris' riches lie folded in the bosom of Flora: Phoebus hath not dried up the pearled dew, and so long, 30 Corydon hath taught me, it is not fit to lead the sheep abroad, lest, the dew being unwholesome, they get the rot: but now see I the old proverb true, he is in haste whom the devil drives, and where love pricks forward, there is no worse death than delay. Ah, my good page, is there fancy in thine eye, and passions in thy heart? What, hast thou wrapt love in thy looks, and set all thy thoughts on fire by affection? I tell thee, it is a flame as hard to be quenched as that of Aetna. But nature must have her course: women's eyes have faculty attractive like the jet, and retentive like the diamond: they dally in the delight of fair objects, till gazing on the panther's beautiful skin, repenting experience tell them he hath a devouring paunch."

"Come on," quoth Ganymede, "this sermon of yours is but a subtlety to lie still a-bed, because either you think the morning cold, or else I being gone, you would steal a nap: this shift carries no palm, and therefore up and away. And for Love, let me alone; I'll whip him away with nettles, and set disdain as a charm to withstand his forces: and therefore look you to yourself; be not too bold, for Venus can make you bend, nor too coy, for Cupid hath a piercing dart, that will make you cry *Peccavi*."

"And that is it," quoth Aliena, "that hath raised you so early this morning." And with that she slipped on her petticoat, and start up; and as soon as she had made her ready, and taken her breakfast, away go these two with their bag and bottles to the field, in more pleasant content of mind than ever they were in the court of Torismond.

They came no sooner nigh the folds, but they might see where their discontented forester was walking in his melancholy. As soon as Aliena saw him, she smiled and said to Ganymede:

"Wipe your eyes, sweeting, for yonder is your sweetheart this morning in deep prayers, no doubt, to Venus, that she may make you as pitiful as he is passionate. Come on, Ganymede, I pray thee, let's have a little sport with him."

"Content," quoth Ganymede, and with that, to waken him out of his deep *memento*, he began thus:

"Forester, good fortune to thy thoughts, and ease to thy passions. What makes you so early abroad this morn? in contemplation, no doubt, of your Rosalynde. Take heed, forester; step not too far, the ford may be deep, and you slip over the shoes: I tell thee, flies have their spleen, the ants choler, the least hairs shadows, and the smallest loves great desires. 'T is good, forester, to love, but not to overlove, lest in loving her that likes not thee, thou fold thyself in an endless labyrinth."

Rosader, seeing the fair shepherdess and her
10 pretty swain in whose company he felt the greatest ease of his care, he returned them a salute on this manner:

"Gentle shepherds, all hail, and as healthful be your flocks as you happy in content. Love is restless, and my bed is but the cell of my bane, in that there I find busy thoughts and broken slumbers: here (although everywhere passionate) yet I brook love with more patience, in that every object feeds mine eye with variety of fancies. When I look on
20 Flora's beauteous tapestry, checkered with the pride of all her treasure, I call to mind the fair face of Rosalynde, whose heavenly hue exceeds the rose and the lily in their highest excellence: the brightness of Phoebus' shine puts me in mind to think of the sparkling flames that flew from her eyes, and set my heart first on fire: the sweet harmony of the birds puts me in remembrance of the rare melody of her voice, which like the Siren enchanteth the ears of the hearer. Thus in contemplation I salve my
30 sorrows, with applying the perfection of every object to the excellence of her qualities."

"She is much beholding unto you," quoth Aliena, "and so much, that I have oft wished with myself, that if I should ever prove as amorous as Oenone, I might find as faithful a Paris as yourself."

"How say you by this item, forester?" quoth Ganymede, "the fair shepherdess favors you, who is mistress of so many flocks. Leave off, man, the supposition of Rosalynde's love, whenas watching at her you rove beyond the moon, and cast your looks upon my mistress, who no doubt is as fair though not so royal; one bird in the hand is worth two in the wood: better possess the love of Aliena than catch furiously at the shadow of Rosalynde."

"I'll tell thee, boy," quoth Rosader, "so is my fancy fixed on my Rosalynde, that were thy mistress as 10 fair as Leda or Danaë, whom Jove courted in transformed shapes, mine eyes would not vouch to entertain their beauties; and so hath love locked me in her perfections, that I had rather only contemplate in her beauties, than absolutely possess the excellence of any other."

"Venus is to blame, forester, if having so true a servant of you, she reward you not with Rosalynde, if Rosalynde were more fairer than herself. But leaving this prattle, now I'll put you in mind 20 of your promise about those sonnets, which you said were at home in your lodge."

"I have them about me," quoth Rosader, "let us sit down, and then you shall hear what a poetical fury love will infuse into a man." With that they sate down upon a green bank, shadowed with fig trees, and Rosader, fetching a deep sigh, read them this sonnet:

Rosader's Sonnet

In sorrow's cell I laid me down to sleep,
But waking woes were jealous of mine eyes,
30 They made them watch, and bend themselves to weep,
But weeping tears their want could not suffice:
  Yet since for her they wept who guides my heart,
  They weeping smile, and triumph in their smart.

Of these my tears a fountain fiercely springs,
Where Venus bains herself incensed with love,
Where Cupid bowseth[1] his fair feathered wings;

[1] Dips.

But I behold what pains I must approve.
  Care drinks it dry; but when on her I think,
  Love makes me weep it full unto the brink.

Meanwhile my sighs yield truce unto my tears,
By them the winds increased and fiercely blow:
Yet when I sigh the flame more plain appears,
And by their force with greater power doth glow:
  Amid these pains, all phoenix-like I thrive
  Since love, that yields me death, may life revive.

Rosader en esperance.

10 "Now, surely, forester," quoth Aliena, "when thou madest this sonnet, thou wert in some amorous quandary, neither too fearful as despairing of thy mistress' favors, nor too gleesome as hoping in thy fortunes."

"I can smile," quoth Ganymede, "at the sonettos, canzones, madrigals, rounds and roundelays, that these pensive patients pour out when their eyes are more full of wantonness, than their hearts of passions. Then, as the fishers put the sweetest bait to
20 the fairest fish, so these Ovidians, holding *amo* in their tongues, when their thoughts come at haphazard, write that they be rapt in an endless labyrinth of sorrow, when walking in the large lease of liberty, they only have their humors in their inkpot. If they find women so fond, that they will with such painted lures come to their lust, then they triumph till they be full-gorged with pleasures; and then fly they away, like ramage kites, to their own content, leaving the tame fool, their mistress, full
30 of fancy, yet without even a feather. If they miss, as dealing with some wary wanton, that wants not such a one as themselves, but spies their subtlety, they end their amours with a few feigned sighs; and so their excuse is, their mistress is cruel, and they smother passions with patience. Such, gentle forester, we may deem you to be, that rather pass

away the time here in these woods with writing amorets, than to be deeply enamored (as you say) of your Rosalynde. If you be such a one, then I pray God, when you think your fortunes at the highest, and your desires to be most excellent, then that you may with Ixion embrace Juno in a cloud, and have nothing but a marble mistress to release your martyrdom; but if you be true and trusty, eye-pained and heart-sick, then accursed be Rosalynde if 10 she prove cruel: for, forester, (I flatter not) thou art worthy of as fair as she." Aliena, spying the storm by the wind, smiled to see how Ganymede flew to the fist without any call; but Rosader, who took him flat for a shepherd's swain, made him this answer:

"Trust me, swain," quoth Rosader, "but my canzon was written in no such humor; for mine eye and my heart are relatives, the one drawing fancy by sight, the other entertaining her by sorrow. If thou sawest my Rosalynde, with what beauties nature 20 hath favored her, with what perfection the heavens hath graced her, with what qualities the gods have endued her, then wouldst thou say, there is none so fickle that could be fleeting unto her. If she had been Aeneas' Dido, had Venus and Juno both scolded him from Carthage, yet her excellence, despite of them, would have detained him at Tyre. If Phyllis had been as beauteous, or Ariadne as virtuous, or both as honorable and excellent as she, neither had the filbert tree sorrowed in the death of despairing 30 Phyllis, nor the stars have been graced with Ariadne, but Demophoon and Theseus had been trusty to their paragons. I will tell thee, swain, if with a deep insight thou couldst pierce into the secret of my loves, and see what deep impressions of her idea affection hath made in my heart, then wouldst thou confess I were passing passionate, and no less endued with admirable patience."

"Why," quoth Aliena, "needs there patience in love?"

"Or else in nothing," quoth Rosader; "for it is a restless sore that hath no ease, a canker that still frets, a disease that taketh away all hope of sleep. If then so many sorrows, sudden joys, momentary pleasures, continual fears, daily griefs, and nightly woes be found in love, then is not he to be accounted patient that smothers all these passions with silence?"

10 "Thou speakest by experience," quoth Ganymede, "and therefore we hold all thy words for axioms. But is love such a lingering malady?"

"It is," quoth he, "either extreme or mean, according to the mind of the party that entertains it; for, as the weeds grow longer untouched than the pretty flowers, and the flint lies safe in the quarry when the emerald is suffering the lapidary's tool, so mean men are freed from Venus' injuries, when kings are environed with a labyrinth of her cares. The whiter 20 the lawn is, the deeper is the mole [1]; the more purer the chrysolite, the sooner stained; and such as have their hearts full of honor, have their loves full of the greatest sorrows. But in whomsoever," quoth Rosader, "he fixeth his dart, he never leaveth to assault him, till either he hath won him to folly or fancy; for as the moon never goes without the star Lunisequa, so a lover never goeth without the unrest of his thoughts. For proof you shall hear another fancy of my making."

30 "Now do, gentle forester," quoth Ganymede; and with that he read over this sonetto:

Rosader's second Sonetto

Turn I my looks unto the skies,
Love with his arrows wounds mine eyes;
If so I gaze upon the ground,

[1] Stain.

Love then in every flower is found.
Search I the shade to fly my pain,
He meets me in the shade again;
Wend I to walk in secret grove,
Even there I meet with sacred Love.
If so I bain me in the spring,
Even on the brink I hear him sing:
If so I meditate alone,
He will be partner of my moan.
10 If so I mourn, he weeps with me,
And where I am there will he be.
Whenas I talk of Rosalynde
The god from coyness waxeth kind,
And seems in selfsame flames to fry
Because he loves as well as I.
Sweet Rosalynde, for pity rue;
For why, than Love I am more true:
He, if he speed, will quickly fly,
But in thy love I live and die.

20 "How like you this sonnet?" quoth Rosader.

"Marry," quoth Ganymede, "for the pen well, for the passion ill; for as I praise the one, I pity the other, in that thou shouldst hunt after a cloud, and love either without reward or regard."

"'Tis not her frowardness," quoth Rosader, "but my hard fortunes, whose destinies have crossed me with her absence; for did she feel my loves, she would not let me linger in these sorrows. Women, as they are fair, so they respect faith, and estimate 30 more, if they be honorable, the will than the wealth, having loyalty the object whereat they aim their fancies. But leaving off these interparleys, you shall hear my last sonetto, and then you have heard all my poetry." And with that he sighed out this:

Rosader's third Sonnet

Of virtuous love myself may boast alone,
Since no suspect my service may attaint:
For perfect fair she is the only one,
Whom I esteem for my belovèd saint.

Thus, for my faith I only bear the bell,
And for her fair she only doth excel.

Then let fond Petrarch shroud his Laura's praise,
And Tasso cease to publish his affect,
Since mine the faith confirmed at all assays,
And hers the fair, which all men do respect.
My lines her fair, her fair my faith assures;
Thus I by love, and love by me endures.

"Thus," quoth Rosader, "here is an end of my
10 poems, but for all this no release of my passions; so that I resemble him that in the depth of his distress hath none but the echo to answer him."

Ganymede, pitying her Rosader, thinking to drive him out of this amorous melancholy, said that now the sun was in his meridional heat and that it was high noon, "therefore we shepherds say, 'tis time to go to dinner; for the sun and our stomachs are shepherds' dials. Therefore, forester, if thou wilt take such fare as comes out of our homely scrips,
20 welcome shall answer whatsoever thou wantest in delicates."

Aliena took the entertainment by the end, and told Rosader he should be her guest. He thanked them heartily, and sate with them down to dinner, where they had such cates as country state did allow them, sauced with such content, and such sweet prattle, as it seemed far more sweet than all their courtly junkets.

As soon as they had taken their repast, Rosader,
30 giving them thanks for his good cheer, would have been gone; but Ganymede, that was loath to let him pass out of her presence, began thus:

"Nay, forester," quoth she, "if thy business be not the greater, seeing thou sayest thou art so deeply in love, let me see how thou canst woo: I will represent Rosalynde, and thou shalt be as thou art, Rosader. See in some amorous eclogue, how if

Rosalynde were present, how thou couldst court her; and while we sing of love, Aliena shall tune her pipe and play us melody."

"Content," quoth Rosader, and Aliena, she, to show her willingness, drew forth a recorder,[1] and began to wind it. Then the loving forester began thus:

The wooing Eclogue betwixt Rosalynde and Rosader

ROSADER

I pray thee, nymph, by all the working words,
By all the tears and sighs that lovers know,
10 Or what or thoughts or faltering tongue affords,
I crave for mine in ripping up my woe.
Sweet Rosalynde, my love (would God, my love)
My life (would God, my life) ay, pity me!
Thy lips are kind, and humble like the dove,
And but with beauty, pity will not be.
Look on mine eyes, made red with rueful tears,
From whence the rain of true remorse descendeth,
All pale in looks am I though young in years,
And nought but love or death my days befriendeth.
20 Oh let no stormy rigor knit thy brows,
Which love appointed for his mercy seat:
The tallest tree by Boreas' breath it bows;
The iron yields with hammer, and to heat.
O Rosalynde, then be thou pitiful,
For Rosalynde is only beautiful.

ROSALYNDE

Love's wantons arm their trait'rous suits with tears,
With vows, with oaths, with looks, with showers of gold;
But when the fruit of their affects appears,
The simple heart by subtle sleights is sold.
30 Thus sucks the yielding ear the poisoned bait,
Thus feeds the heart upon his endless harms,
Thus glut the thoughts themselves on self-deceit,
Thus blind the eyes their sight by subtle charms.
The lovely looks, the sighs that storm so sore,
The dew of deep-dissembled doubleness,

[1] An old instrument, resembling the flageolet.

These may attempt, but are of power no more
Where beauty leans to wit and soothfastness.
O Rosader, then be thou wittiful,
For Rosalynde scorns foolish pitiful.

ROSADER

I pray thee, Rosalynde, by those sweet eyes
That stain the sun in shine, the morn in clear,
By those sweet cheeks where Love encampèd lies
To kiss the roses of the springing year.
I tempt thee, Rosalynde, by ruthful plaints,
10 Not seasoned with deceit or fraudful guile,
But firm in pain, far more than tongue depaints,
Sweet nymph, be kind, and grace me with a smile.
So may the heavens preserve from hurtful food
Thy harmless flocks; so may the summer yield
The pride of all her riches and her good,
To fat thy sheep, the citizens of field.
Oh, leave to arm thy lovely brows with scorn:
The birds their beak, the lion hath his tail,
And lovers nought but sighs and bitter mourn,
20 The spotless fort of fancy to assail.
O Rosalynde, then be thou pitiful,
For Rosalynde is only beautiful.

ROSALYNDE

The hardened steel by fire is brought in frame:

ROSADER

And Rosalynde, my love, than any wool more softer;
And shall not sighs her tender heart inflame?

ROSALYNDE

Were lovers true, maids would believe them ofter.

ROSADER

Truth, and regard, and honor, guide my love.

ROSALYNDE

Fain would I trust, but yet I dare not try.

ROSADER

O pity me, sweet nymph, and do but prove.

ROSALYNDE

I would resist, but yet I know not why.

ROSADER

O Rosalynde, be kind, for times will change,
Thy looks aye nill be fair as now they be;
Thine age from beauty may thy looks estrange:
Ah, yield in time, sweet nymph, and pity me.

ROSALYNDE

O Rosalynde, thou must be pitiful,
For Rosader is young and beautiful.

ROSADER

Oh, gain more great than kingdoms or a crown!

ROSALYNDE

10 Oh, trust betrayed if Rosader abuse me.

ROSADER

First let the heavens conspire to pull me down
And heaven and earth as abject quite refuse me.
Let sorrows stream about my hateful bower,
And restless horror hatch within my breast:
Let beauty's eye afflict me with a lour,
Let deep despair pursue me without rest,
Ere Rosalynde my loyalty disprove,
Ere Rosalynde accuse me for unkind.

ROSALYNDE

Then Rosalynde will grace thee with her love;
20 Then Rosalynde will have thee still in mind.

ROSADER

Then let me triumph more than Tithon's dear,
Since Rosalynde will Rosader respect:
Then let my face exile his sorry cheer,
And frolic in the comfort of affect;
And say that Rosalynde is only pitiful,
Since Rosalynde is only beautiful.

When thus they had finished their courting eclogue in such a familiar clause, Ganymede, as augur of some good fortunes to light upon their
10 affections, began to be thus pleasant:

"How now, forester, have I not fitted your turn? have I not played the woman handsomely, and showed myself as coy in grants as courteous in desires, and been as full of suspicion as men of flattery? and yet to salve all, jumped I not all up with the sweet union of love? Did not Rosalynde content her Rosader?"

The forester at this smiling, shook his head, and folding his arms made this merry reply:

20 "Truth, gentle swain, Rosader hath his Rosalynde; but as Ixion had Juno, who, thinking to possess a goddess, only embraced a cloud: in these imaginary fruitions of fancy I resemble the birds that fed themselves with Zeuxis' painted grapes; but they grew so lean with pecking at shadows, that they were glad, with Aesop's cock, to scrape for a barley cornel. So fareth it with me, who to feed myself with the hope of my mistress's favors, soothe myself in thy suits, and only in conceit reap a wished-for content;
30 but if my food be no better than such amorous dreams, Venus at the year's end shall find me but a lean lover. Yet do I take these follies for high fortunes, and hope these feigned affections do divine some unfeigned end of ensuing fancies."

"And thereupon," quoth Aliena, "I'll play the

priest: from this day forth Ganymede shall call thee husband, and thou shall call Ganymede wife, and so we'll have a marriage."

"Content," quoth Rosader, and laughed.

"Content," quoth Ganymede, and changed as red as a rose: and so with a smile and a blush, they made up this jesting match, that after proved to a marriage in earnest, Rosader full little thinking he had wooed and won his Rosalynde.

10 But all was well; hope is a sweet string to harp on, and therefore let the forester awhile shape himself to his shadow, and tarry fortune's leisure, till she may make a metamorphosis fit for his purpose. I digress; and therefore to Aliena, who said, the wedding was not worth a pin, unless there were some cheer, nor that bargain well made that was not stricken up with a cup of wine: and therefore she willed Ganymede to set out such cates as they had, and to draw out her bottle, charging the forester, as 20 he had imagined his loves, so to conceit these cates to be a most sumptuous banquet, and to take a mazer of wine and to drink to his Rosalynde; which Rosader did, and so they passed away the day in many pleasant devices. Till at last Aliena perceived time would tarry no man, and that the sun waxed very low, ready to set, which made her shorten their amorous prattle, and end the banquet with a fresh carouse: which done, they all three arose, and Aliena broke off thus:

30 "Now, forester, Phoebus that all this while hath been partaker of our sports, seeing every woodman more fortunate in his loves than he in his fancies, seeing thou hast won Rosalynde when he could not woo Daphne, hides his head for shame and bids us adieu in a cloud. Our sheep, they poor wantons, wander towards their folds, as taught by nature their due times of rest, which tells us, forester, we must

depart. Marry, though there were a marriage, yet I must carry this night the bride with me, and to-morrow morning if you meet us here, I'll promise to deliver you her as good a maid as I find her."

"Content," quoth Rosader, "'tis enough for me in the night to dream on love, that in the day am so fond to doat on love: and so till to-morrow you to your folds, and I will to my lodge." And thus the forester and they parted.

10 He was no sooner gone, but Aliena and Ganymede went and folded their flocks, and taking up their hooks, their bags, and their bottles, hied homeward. By the way Aliena, to make the time seem short, began to prattle with Ganymede thus:

"I have heard them say, that what the fates fore-point, that fortune pricketh down with a period; that the stars are sticklers in Venus' court, and desire hangs at the heel of destiny: if it be so, then by all probable conjectures, this match will be a marriage:
20 for if augurism be authentical, or the divines' dooms principles, it cannot be but such a shadow portends the issue of a substance, for to that end did the gods force the conceit of this eclogue, that they might discover the ensuing consent of your affections: so that ere it be long, I hope, in earnest, to dance at your wedding."

"Tush," quoth Ganymede, "all is not malt that is cast on the kiln: there goes more words to a bargain than one: love feels no footing in the air, and fancy
30 holds it slippery harbor to nestle in the tongue: the match is not yet so surely made, but he may miss of his market; but if fortune be his friend, I will not be his foe: and so I pray you, gentle mistress Aliena, take it."

"I take all things well," quoth she, "that is your content, and am glad Rosader is yours; for now I hope your thoughts will be at quiet; your eye that ever looked at love, will now lend a glance on your lambs, and then they will prove more buxom and you more blithe, for the eyes of the master feeds the cattle."

As thus they were in chat, they spied old Corydon where he came plodding to meet them, who told them supper was ready, which news made them speed them home. Where we leave them to the next morrow, and return to Saladyne.

10 All this while did poor Saladyne, banished from Bordeaux and the court of France by Torismond, wander up and down in the forest of Arden, thinking to get to Lyons, and so travel through Germany into Italy: but the forest being full of by-paths, and he unskilful of the country coast, slipped out of the way, and chanced up into the desert, not far from the place where Gerismond was, and his brother Rosader. Saladyne, weary with wandering up and down and hungry with long fasting, finding a little 20 cave by the side of a thicket, eating such fruit as the forest did afford and contenting himself with such drink as nature had provided and thirst made delicate, after his repast he fell in a dead sleep. As thus he lay, a hungry lion came hunting down the edge of the grove for prey, and espying Saladyne began to seize upon him: but seeing he lay still without any motion, he left to touch him, for that lions hate to prey on dead carcases; and yet desirous to have some food, the lion lay down and watched 30 to see if he would stir. While thus Saladyne slept secure, fortune that was careful over her champion began to smile, and brought it so to pass, that Rosader, having stricken a deer that but lightly hurt fled through the thicket, came pacing down by the grove with a boar-spear in his hand in great haste. He spied where a man lay asleep, and a lion fast by him: amazed at this sight, as he stood gazing, his

nose on the sudden bled, which made him conjecture it was some friend of his. Whereupon drawing more nigh, he might easily discern his visage, and perceive by his physnomy that it was his brother, Saladyne, which drave Rosader into a deep passion, as a man perplexed at the sight of so unexpected a chance, marvelling what should drive his brother to traverse those secret deserts, without any company, in such distress and forlorn sort. But the present time craved no such doubting ambages, for either he must resolve to hazard his life for his relief, or else steal away, and leave him to the cruelty of the lion. In which doubt he thus briefly debated with himself:

Rosader's Meditation

"Now, Rosader, fortune that long hath whipped thee with nettles, means to salve thee with roses, and having crossed thee with many frowns, now she presents thee with the brightness of her favors. Thou that didst count thyself the most distressed of all men, mayest account thyself now the most fortunate amongst men, if Fortune can make men happy, or sweet revenge be wrapped in a pleasing content. Thou seest Saladyne thine enemy, the worker of thy misfortunes, and the efficient cause of thine exile, subject to the cruelty of a merciless lion, brought into this misery by the gods, that they might seem just in revenging his rigor, and thy injuries. Seest thou not how the stars are in a favorable aspect, the planets in some pleasing conjunction, the fates agreeable to thy thoughts, and the destinies performers of thy desires, in that Saladyne shall die, and thou be free of his blood: he receive meed for his amiss, and thou erect his tomb with innocent hands. Now, Rosader, shalt thou return

unto Bordeaux and enjoy thy possessions by birth, and his revenues by inheritance: now mayest thou triumph in love, and hang fortune's altars with garlands. For when Rosalynde hears of thy wealth, it will make her love thee the more willingly: for women's eyes are made of chrysocoll, that is ever unperfect unless tempered with gold, and Jupiter soonest enjoyed Danaë, because he came to her in so rich a shower. Thus shall this lion, Rosader, end
10 the life of a miserable man, and from distress raise thee to be most fortunate." And with that, casting his boar-spear on his neck, away he began to trudge.

But he had not stepped back two or three paces, but a new motion stroke him to the very heart, that resting his boar-spear against his breast, he fell into this passionate humor:

"Ah, Rosader, wert thou the son of Sir John of Bordeaux, whose virtues exceeded his valor, and yet the most hardiest knight in all Europe? Should
20 the honor of the father shine in the actions of the son, and wilt thou dishonor thy parentage, in forgetting the nature of a gentleman? Did not thy father at his last gasp breathe out this golden principle, 'Brothers' amity is like the drops of balsamum, that salveth the most dangerous sores?' Did he make a large exhort unto concord, and wilt thou show thyself careless? O Rosader, what though Saladyne hath wronged thee, and made thee live an exile in the forest, shall thy nature be so cruel, or
30 thy nurture so crooked, or thy thoughts so savage, as to suffer so dismal a revenge? What, to let him be devoured by wild beasts! *Non sapit qui non sibi sapit* is fondly spoken in such bitter extremes. Loose not his life, Rosader, to win a world of treasure; for in having him thou hast a brother, and by hazarding for his life, thou gettest a friend, and reconcilest an enemy: and more honor shalt thou purchase by

pleasuring a foe, than revenging a thousand injuries."

With that his brother began to stir, and the lion to rouse himself, whereupon Rosader suddenly charged him with the boar-spear, and wounded the lion very sore at the first stroke. The beast feeling himself to have a mortal hurt, leapt at Rosader, and with his paws gave him a sore pinch on the breast, that he had almost fallen; yet as a man most valiant, 10 in whom the sparks of Sir John of Bordeaux remained, he recovered himself, and in short combat slew the lion, who at his death roared so loud that Saladyne awaked, and starting up, was amazed at the sudden sight of so monstrous a beast lying slain by him, and so sweet a gentleman wounded. He presently, as he was of a ripe conceit, began to conjecture that the gentleman had slain him in his defence. Whereupon, as a man in a trance, he stood staring on them both a good while, not know- 20 ing his brother, being in that disguise: at last he burst into these terms:

"Sir, whatsoever thou be, as full of honor thou must needs be by the view of thy present valor, I perceive thou hast redressed my fortunes by thy courage, and saved my life with thine own loss, which ties me to be thine in all humble service. Thanks thou shalt have as thy due, and more thou canst not have, for my ability denies me to perform a deeper debt. But if anyways it please thee to 30 command me, use me as far as the power of a poor gentleman may stretch."

Rosader, seeing he was unknown to his brother, wondered to hear such courteous words come from his crabbed nature; but glad of such reformed nurture, he made this answer:

"I am, sir, whatsoever thou art, a forester and ranger of these walks, who, following my deer to

the fall, was conducted hither by some assenting fate, that I might save thee, and disparage myself. For coming into this place, I saw thee asleep, and the lion watching thy awake, that at thy rising he might prey upon thy carcase. At the first sight I conjectured thee a gentleman, for all men's thoughts ought to be favorable in imagination, and I counted it the part of a resolute man to purchase a stranger's relief, though with the loss of his own blood; which
10 I have performed, thou seest, to mine own prejudice. If, therefore, thou be a man of such worth as I value thee by thy exterior lineaments, make discourse unto me what is the cause of thy present fortunes. For by the furrows in thy face thou seemest to be crossed with her frowns: but whatsoever, or howsoever, let me crave that favor, to hear the tragic cause of thy estate."

Saladyne sitting down, and fetching a deep sigh, began thus:

SALADYNE'S DISCOURSE TO ROSADER UNKNOWN

20 "Although the discourse of my fortunes be the renewing of my sorrows, and the rubbing of the scar will open a fresh wound, yet that I may not prove ingrateful to so courteous a gentleman, I will rather sit down and sigh out my estate, than give any offence by smothering my grief with silence. Know therefore, sir, that I am of Bordeaux, and the son and heir of Sir John of Bordeaux, a man for his virtues and valor so famous, that I cannot think but the fame of his honors hath reached farther than
30 the knowledge of his personage. The infortunate son of so fortunate a knight am I; my name, Saladyne; who succeeding my father in possessions, but not in qualities, having two brethren committed by my father at his death to my charge, with such

golden principles of brotherly concord, as might have pierced like the Sirens' melody into any human ear. But I, with Ulysses, became deaf against his philosophical harmony, and made more value of profit than of virtue, esteeming gold sufficient honor, and wealth the fittest title for a gentleman's dignity. I set my middle brother to the university to be a scholar, counting it enough if he might pore on a book while I fed upon his revenues; and for the
10 youngest, which was my father's joy, young Rosader"—And with that, naming of Rosader, Saladyne sate him down and wept.

"Nay, forward man," quoth the forester, "tears are the unfittest salve that any man can apply for to cure sorrows, and therefore cease from such feminine follies, as should drop out of a woman's eye to deceive, not out of a gentleman's look to discover his thoughts, and forward with thy discourse."

"O sir," quoth Saladyne, "this Rosader that
20 wrings tears from mine eyes, and blood from my heart, was like my father in exterior personage and in inward qualities; for in the prime of his years he aimed all his acts at honor, and coveted rather to die than to brook any injury unworthy a gentleman's credit. I, whom envy had made blind, and covetousness masked with the veil of self-love, seeing the palm tree grow straight, thought to suppress it being a twig; but nature will have her course, the cedar will be tall, the diamond bright, the carbuncle glister-
30 ing, and virtue will shine though it be never so much obscured. For I kept Rosader as a slave, and used him as one of my servile hinds, until age grew on, and a secret insight of my abuse entered into his mind; insomuch, that he could not brook it, but coveted to have what his father left him, and to live of himself. To be short, sir, I repined at his fortunes, and he counterchecked me, not with ability but

valor, until at last, by my friends and aid of such as followed gold more than right or virtue, I banished him from Bordeaux, and he, poor gentleman, lives no man knows where, in some distressed discontent. The gods, not able to suffer such impiety unrevenged, so wrought, that the king picked a causeless quarrel against me in hope to have my lands, and so hath exiled me out of France for ever. Thus, thus, sir, am I the most miserable of all men, as having a 10 blemish in my thoughts for the wrongs I proffered Rosader, and a touch in my state to be thrown from my proper possessions by injustice. Passionate thus with many griefs, in penance of my former follies I go thus pilgrim-like to seek out my brother, that I may reconcile myself to him in all submission, and afterward went to the Holy Land, to end my years in as many virtues as I have spent my youth in wicked vanities."

Rosader, hearing the resolution of his brother 20 Saladyne, began to compassionate his sorrows, and not able to smother the sparks of nature with feigned secrecy, he burst into these loving speeches:

"Then know, Saladyne," quoth he, "that thou hast met with Rosader, who grieves as much to see thy distress, as thyself to feel the burden of thy misery." Saladyne, casting up his eye and noting well the physnomy of the forester, knew that it was his brother Rosader, which made him so bash and blush at the first meeting, that Rosader was fain to recom- 30 fort him, which he did in such sort, that he showed how highly he held revenge in scorn. Much ado there was between these two brethren, Saladyne in craving pardon, and Rosader in forgiving and forgetting all former injuries; the one submiss, the other courteous; Saladyne penitent and passionate, Rosader kind and loving, that at length nature working an union of their thoughts, they earnestly em-

braced, and fell from matters of unkindness, to talk of the country life, which Rosader so highly commended, that his brother began to have a desire to taste of that homely content. In this humor Rosader conducted him to Gerismond's lodge, and presented his brother to the king, discoursing the whole matter how all had happened betwixt them. The king looking upon Saladyne, found him a man of a most beautiful personage, and saw in his face sufficient
10 sparks of ensuing honors, gave him great entertainment, and glad of their friendly reconcilement, promised such favor as the poverty of his estate might afford, which Saladyne gratefully accepted. And so Gerismond fell to question of Torismond's life. Saladyne briefly discoursed unto him his injustice and tyrannies, with such modesty, although he had wronged him, that Gerismond greatly praised the sparing speech of the young gentleman.

Many questions passed, but at last Gerismond
20 began with a deep sigh to inquire if there were any news of the welfare of Alinda, or his daughter Rosalynde?

"None, sir," quoth Saladyne, "for since their departure they were never heard of."

"Injurious fortune," quoth the king, "that to double the father's misery, wrongest the daughter with misfortunes!"

And with that, surcharged with sorrows, he went into his cell, and left Saladyne and Rosader, whom
30 Rosader straight conducted to the sight of Adam Spencer, who, seeing Saladyne in that estate, was in a brown study. But when he heard the whole matter, although he grieved for the exile of his master, yet he joyed that banishment had so reformed him, that from a lascivious youth he was proved a virtuous gentleman. Looking a longer while, and seeing what familiarity passed between

them, and what favors were interchanged with brotherly affection, he said thus:

"Ay, marry, thus should it be; this was the concord that old Sir John of Bordeaux wished betwixt you. Now fulfil you those precepts he breathed out at his death, and in observing them, look to live fortunate and die honorable."

"Well said, Adam Spencer," quoth Rosader, "but hast any victuals in store for us?"

10 "A piece of a red deer," quoth he, "and a bottle of wine."

"'Tis foresters' fare, brother," quoth Rosader; and so they sate down and fell to their cates.

As soon as they had taken their repast, and had well dined, Rosader took his brother Saladyne by the hand, and showed him the pleasures of the forest, and what content they enjoyed in that mean estate. Thus for two or three days he walked up and down with his brother to show him all the commodities

20 that belonged to his walk.

In which time he was missed of his Ganymede, who mused greatly, with Aliena, what should become of their forester. Somewhile they thought he had taken some word unkindly, and had taken the pet; then they imagined some new love had withdrawn his fancy, or happily that he was sick, or detained by some great business of Gerismond's, or that he had made a reconcilement with his brother, and so returned to Bordeaux.

30 These conjectures did they cast in their heads, but especially Ganymede, who, having love in her heart, proved restless, and half without patience, that Rosader wronged her with so long absence; for Love measures every minute, and thinks hours to be days, and days to be months, till they feed their eyes with the sight of their desired object. Thus perplexed lived poor Ganymede, while on a day, sitting with

Aliena in a great dump, she cast up her eye, and saw where Rosader came pacing towards them with his forest bill on his neck. At that sight her color changed, and she said to Aliena:

"See, mistress, where our jolly forester comes."

"And you are not a little glad thereof," quoth Aliena; "your nose bewrays what porridge you love: the wind cannot be tied within his quarter, the sun shadowed with a veil, oil hidden in water, nor love kept out of a woman's looks: but no more of that,— *Lupus est in fabula.*"

As soon as Rosader was come within the reach of her tongue's end, Aliena began thus:

"Why, how now, gentle forester, what wind hath kept you from hence that being so newly married, you have no more care of your Rosalynde, but to absent yourself so many days? Are these the passions you painted out so in your sonnets and roundelays? I see well hot love is soon cold, and that the fancy of men is like to a loose feather that wandereth in the air with the blast of every wind."

"You are deceived, mistress," quoth Rosader; "'twas a copy of unkindness that kept me hence, in that, I being married, you carried away the bride; but if I have given any occasion of offence by absenting myself these three days, I humbly sue for pardon, which you must grant of course, in that the fault is so friendly confessed with penance. But to tell you the truth, fair mistress and my good Rosalynde, my eldest brother by the injury of Torismond is banished from Bordeaux, and by chance he and I met in the forest."

And here Rosader discoursed unto them what had happened betwixt them, which reconcilement made them glad, especially Ganymede. But Aliena, hearing of the tyranny of her father, grieved inwardly, and yet smothered all things with such secrecy, that the concealing was more sorrow than the conceit; yet that her estate might be hid still, she made fair weather of it, and so let all pass.

Fortune, that saw how these parties valued not her deity, but held her power in scorn, thought to have a bout with them, and brought the matter to pass thus. Certain rascals that lived by prowling in the forest, who for fear of the provost marshal had caves in the groves and thickets to shroud them-
10 selves from his trains, hearing of the beauty of this fair shepherdess, Aliena, thought to steal her away, and to give her to the king for a present; hoping, because the king was a great lecher, by such a gift to purchase all their pardons, and therefore came to take her and her page away. Thus resolved, while Aliena and Ganymede were in this sad talk, they came rushing in, and laid violent hands upon Aliena and her page, which made them cry out to Rosader; who having the valor of his father stamped in his heart,
20 thought rather to die in defence of his friends, than any way be touched with the least blemish of dishonor, and therefore dealt such blows amongst them with his weapon, as he did witness well upon their carcases that he was no coward. But as *Ne Hercules quidem contra duos*, so Rosader could not resist a multitude, having none to back him; so that he was not only rebated, but sore wounded, and Aliena and Ganymede had been quite carried away by these rascals, had not fortune (that meant to turn her
30 frown into a favor) brought Saladyne that way by chance, who wandering to find out his brother's walk, encountered this crew: and seeing not only a shepherdess and her boy forced, but his brother wounded, he heaved up a forest bill he had on his neck, and the first he stroke had never after more need of the physician, redoubling his blows with such courage that the slaves were amazed at his

valor. Rosader, espying his brother so fortunately arrived, and seeing how valiantly he behaved himself, though sore wounded rushed amongst them, and laid on such load, that some of the crew were slain, and the rest fled, leaving Aliena and Ganymede in the possession of Rosader and Saladyne.

Aliena after she had breathed awhile and was come to herself from this fear, looked about her, and saw where Ganymede was busy dressing up the
10 wounds of the forester: but she cast her eye upon this courteous champion that had made so hot a rescue, and that with such affection, that she began to measure every part of him with favor, and in herself to commend his personage and his virtue, holding him for a resolute man, that durst assail such a troop of unbridled villains. At last, gathering her spirits together, she returned him these thanks:

"Gentle sir, whatsoever you be that have adven-
20 tured your flesh to relieve our fortunes, as we hold you valiant so we esteem you courteous, and to have as many hidden virtues as you have manifest resolutions. We poor shepherds have no wealth but our flocks, and therefore can we not make requital with any great treasures; but our recompense is thanks, and our rewards to her friends without feigning. For ransom, therefore, of this our rescue, you must content yourself to take such a kind gramercy as a poor shepherdess and her page may give, with
30 promise, in what we may, never to prove ingrateful. For this gentleman that is hurt, young Rosader, he is our good neighbor and familiar acquaintance; we'll pay him with smiles, and feed him with love-looks, and though he be never the fatter at the year's end, yet we'll so hamper him that he shall hold himself satisfied."

Saladyne, hearing this shepherdess speak so wisely,

began more narrowly to pry into her perfection, and to survey all her lineaments with a curious insight; so long dallying in the flame of her beauty, that to his cost he found her to be most excellent: for love that lurked in all these broils to have a blow or two, seeing the parties at the gaze, encountered them both with such a veny,[1] that the stroke pierced to the heart so deep as it could never after be rased out. At last, after he had looked so long, till Aliena
10 waxed red, he returned her this answer:

"Fair shepherdess, if Fortune graced me with such good hap as to do you any favor, I hold myself as contented as if I had gotten a great conquest; for the relief of distressed women is the special point that gentlemen are tied unto by honor: seeing then my hazard to rescue your harms was rather duty than courtesy, thanks is more than belongs to the requital of such a favor. But lest I might seem either too coy or too careless of a gentlewoman's
20 proffer, I will take your kind gramercy for a recompense."

All this while that he spake, Ganymede looked earnestly upon him, and said:

"Truly, Rosader, this gentleman favors you much in the feature of your face."

"No marvel," quoth he, "gentle swain, for 'tis my eldest brother Saladyne."

"Your brother?" quoth Aliena, and with that she blushed, "he is the more welcome, and I hold myself
30 the more his debtor; and for that he hath in my behalf done such a piece of service, if it please him to do me that honor, I will call him servant, and he shall call me mistress."

"Content, sweet mistress," quoth Saladyne, "and when I forget to call you so, I will be unmindful of mine own self."

[1] Assault.

"Away with these quirks and quiddities of love," quoth Rosader, "and give me some drink, for I am passing thirsty, and then will I home, for my wounds bleed sore, and I will have them dressed."

Ganymede had tears in her eyes, and passions in her heart to see her Rosader so pained, and therefore stepped hastily to the bottle, and filling out some wine in a mazer, she spiced it with such comfortable drugs as she had about her, and gave it him, which 10 did comfort Rosader, that rising, with the help of his brother, he took his leave of them, and went to his lodge. Ganymede, as soon as they were out of sight, led his flocks down to a vale, and there under the shadow of a beech tree sate down, and began to mourn the misfortunes of her sweetheart.

And Aliena, as a woman passing discontent, severing herself from her Ganymede, sitting under a limon tree, began to sigh out the passions of her new love, and to meditate with herself in this 20 manner:

Aliena's Meditation

"Ay me! now I see, and sorrowing sigh to see, that Diana's laurels are harbors for Venus' doves; that there trace as well through the lawns wantons as chaste ones; that Callisto, be she never so chary, will cast one amorous eye at courting Jove; that Diana herself will change her shape, but she will honor Love in a shadow; that maidens' eyes be they as hard as diamonds, yet Cupid hath drugs to make them more pliable than wax. See, Alinda, how 30 Fortune and Love have interleagued themselves to be thy foes, and to make thee their subject, or else an abject, have inveigled thy sight with a most beautiful object. A-late thou didst hold Venus for a giglot, not a goddess, and now thou shalt be forced to sue suppliant to her deity. Cupid was a boy and blind; but, alas, his eye had aim enough to pierce thee to the heart. While I lived in the court I held love in contempt, and in high seats I had small desires. I knew not affection while I lived in dignity, nor could Venus countercheck me, as long as my fortune was majesty, and my thoughts honor; and shall I now be high in desires, when I am made low by destiny?

10 "I have heard them say, that Love looks not at low cottages, that Venus jets[1] in robes not in rags, that Cupid flies so high, that he scorns to touch poverty with his heel. Tush, Alinda, these are but old wives' tales, and neither authentical precepts, nor infallible principles; for experience tells thee, that peasants have their passions as well as princes, that swains as they have their labors, so they have their amours, and Love lurks as soon about a sheepcote as a palace.

"Ah, Alinda, this day in avoiding a prejudice thou 20 art fallen into a deeper mischief; being rescued from the robbers, thou art become captive to Saladyne: and what then? Women must love, or they must cease to live; and therefore did nature frame them fair, that they might be subjects to fancy. But perhaps Saladyne's eye is levelled upon a more seemlier saint. If it be so, bear thy passions with patience; say Love hath wronged thee, that hath not wrung him; and if he be proud in contempt, be thou rich in content, and rather die than discover 30 any desire: for there is nothing more precious in a woman than to conceal love and to die modest. He is the son and heir of Sir John of Bordeaux, a youth comely enough: O Alinda, too comely, else hadst not thou been thus discontent; valiant, and that fettered thine eyes; wise, else hadst thou not been now won; but for all these virtues banished by thy

[1] Struts.

father, and therefore if he know thy parentage, he will hate the fruit for the tree, and condemn the young scion for the old stock. Well, howsoever, I must love, and whomsoever, I will; and, whatsoever betide, Aliena will think well of Saladyne, suppose he of me as he please."

And with that fetching a deep sigh, she rise up, and went to Ganymede, who all this while sate in a great dump, fearing the imminent danger of her 10 friend Rosader; but now Aliena began to comfort her, herself being overgrown with sorrows, and to recall her from her melancholy with many pleasant persuasions. Ganymede took all in the best part, and so they went home together after they had folded their flocks, supping with old Corydon, who had provided their cates. He, after supper, to pass away the night while bedtime, began a long discourse, how Montanus, the young shepherd that was in love with Phoebe, could by no means obtain any favor at her 20 hands, but, still pained in restless passions, remained a hopeless and perplexed lover.

"I would I might," quoth Aliena, "once see that Phoebe. Is she so fair that she thinks no shepherd worthy of her beauty? or so froward that no love nor loyalty will content her? or so coy that she requires a long time to be wooed? or so foolish that she forgets that like a fop she must have a large harvest for a little corn?"

"I cannot distinguish," quoth Corydon, "of these 30 nice qualities; but one of these days I'll bring Montanus and her down, that you may both see their persons, and note their passions; and then where the blame is, there let it rest. But this I am sure," quoth Corydon, "if all maidens were of her mind, the world would grow to a mad pass; for there would be great store of wooing and little wedding, many words and little worship, much folly and no faith."

At this sad sentence of Corydon, so solemnly brought forth, Aliena smiled, and because it waxed late, she and her page went to bed, both of them having fleas in their ears to keep them awake; Ganymede for the hurt of her Rosader, and Aliena for the affection she bore to Saladyne. In this discontented humor they passed away the time, till falling on sleep, their senses at rest, Love left them to their quiet slumbers, which were not long. For as soon as Phoebus rose from his Aurora, and began to mount him in the sky, summoning the ploughswains to their handy labor, Aliena arose, and going to the couch where Ganymede lay, awakened her page, and said the morning was far spent, the dew small, and time called them away to their folds.

"Ah, ah!" quoth Ganymede, "is the wind in that door? Then in faith I perceive that there is no diamond so hard but will yield to the file, no cedar so strong but the wind will shake, nor any mind so chaste but love will change. Well, Aliena, must Saladyne be the man, and will it be a match? Trust me, he is fair and valiant, the son of a worthy knight, whom if he imitate in perfection, as he represents him in proportion, he is worthy of no less than Aliena. But he is an exile; what then? I hope my mistress respects the virtues not the wealth, and measures the qualities not the substance. Those dames that are like Danaë, that like love in no shape but in a shower of gold, I wish them husbands with much wealth and little wit, that the want of the one may blemish the abundance of the other. It should, my Aliena, stain the honor of a shepherd's life to set the end of passions upon pelf. Love's eyes looks not so low as gold; there is no fees to be paid in Cupid's courts; and in elder time, as Corydon hath told me, the shepherds' love-gifts were apples and chestnuts, and then their desires were loyal, and their thoughts constant. But now

> Quaerenda pecunia primum, post nummos virtus.

And the time is grown to that which Horace in his Satires wrote on:

> omnis enim res,
> Virtus, fama, decus, divina humanaque pulchris
> Divitiis parent; quas qui constrinxerit, ille
> Clarus erit, fortis, justus, sapiens, etiam et rex
> 10 Et quicquid volet—

But, Aliena, let it not be so with thee in thy fancies, but respect his faith and there an end."

Aliena, hearing Ganymede thus forward to further Saladyne in his affections, thought she kissed the child for the nurse's sake, and wooed for him that she might please Rosader, made this reply:

"Why, Ganymede, whereof grows this persuasion? Hast thou seen love in my looks, or are mine eyes grown so amorous, that they discover some new-20 entertained fancies? If thou measurest my thoughts by my countenance, thou mayest prove as ill a physiognomer, as the lapidary that aims at the secret virtues of the topaz by the exterior shadow of the stone. The operation of the agate is not known by the strakes, nor the diamond prized by his brightness, but by his hardness. The carbuncle that shineth most is not ever the most precious; and the apothecaries choose not flowers for their colors, but for their virtues. Women's faces are not always 30 calendars of fancy, nor do their thoughts and their looks ever agree; for when their eyes are fullest of favors, then are they oft most empty of desire; and when they seem to frown at disdain, then are they most forward to affection. If I be melancholy, then, Ganymede, 'tis not a consequence that I am entangled with the perfection of Saladyne. But seeing fire cannot be hid in the straw, nor love kept so covert but it will be spied, what should friends conceal fancies? Know, my Ganymede, the beauty and valor, the wit and prowess of Saladyne hath fettered Aliena so far, as there is no object pleasing to her eyes but the sight of Saladyne; and if Love have done me justice to wrap his thoughts in the folds of my face, and that he be as deeply enamored as I am passionate, I tell thee, Ganymede, there shall 10 not be much wooing, for she is already won, and what needs a longer battery."

"I am glad," quoth Ganymede, "that it shall be thus proportioned, you to match with Saladyne, and I with Rosader: thus have the Destinies favored us with some pleasing aspect, that have made us as private in our loves, as familiar in our fortunes."

With this Ganymede start up, made her ready, and went into the fields with Aliena, where unfolding their flocks, they sate them down under an olive tree, 20 both of them amorous, and yet diversely affected; Aliena joying in the excellence of Saladyne, and Ganymede sorrowing for the wounds of her Rosader, not quiet in thought till she might hear of his health. As thus both of them sate in their dumps, they might espy where Corydon came running towards them, almost out of breath with his haste.

"What news with you," quoth Aliena, "that you come in such post?"

"Oh, mistress," quoth Corydon, "you have a long 30 time desired to see Phoebe, the fair shepherdess whom Montanus loves; so now if you please, you and Ganymede, but to walk with me to yonder thicket, there shall you see Montanus and her sitting by a fountain, he courting with his country ditties, and she as coy as if she held love in disdain."

The news were so welcome to the two lovers, that up they rose, and went with Corydon. As soon as

they drew nigh the thicket, they might espy where Phoebe sate, the fairest shepherdess in all Arden, and he the frolickest swain in the whole forest, she in a petticoat of scarlet, covered with a green mantle, and to shroud her from the sun, a chaplet of roses, from under which appeared a face full of nature's excellence, and two such eyes as might have amated[1] a greater man than Montanus. At gaze upon this gorgeous nymph sat the shepherd, feeding his eyes
10 with her favors, wooing with such piteous looks, and courting with such deep-strained sighs, as would have made Diana herself to have been compassionate. At last, fixing his looks on the riches of her face, his head on his hand, and his elbow on his knee, he sung this mournful ditty:

Montanus' Sonnet

A turtle sate upon a leaveless tree,
Mourning her absent fere
With sad and sorry cheer:
About her wondering stood
20 The citizens of wood,
And whilst her plumes she rents
And for her love laments,
The stately trees complain them,
The birds with sorrow pain them.
Each one that doth her view
Her pain and sorrows rue;
But were the sorrows known
That me hath overthrown,
Oh how would Phoebe sigh if she did look on me?

30 The lovesick Polypheme, that could not see,
Who on the barren shore
His fortunes doth deplore,
And melteth all in moan
For Galatea gone,
And with his piteous cries
Afflicts both earth and skies,
And to his woe betook

[1] Dismayed.

Doth break both pipe and hook,
For whom complains the morn,
For whom the sea-nymphs mourn,
Alas, his pain is nought;
For were my woe but thought,
Oh how would Phoebe sigh if she did look on me!

Beyond compare my pain;
Yet glad am I,
If gentle Phoebe deign
10 To see her Montan die.

After this, Montanus felt his passions so extreme, that he fell into this exclamation against the injustice of Love:

Hélas, tyran plein de rigueur,
Modère un peu ta violence:
Que te sert si grande dépense?
C'est trop de flammes pour un cœur.
Épargnez en une étincelle,
Puis fais ton effort d'émouvoir,
20 La fière qui ne veut point voir,
En quel feu je brûle pour elle.
Exécute, Amour, ce dessein,
Et rabaisse un peu son audace:
Son cœur ne doit être de glace,
Bien qu'elle ait de neige le sein.

Montanus ended his sonnet with such a volley of sighs, and such a stream of tears, as might have moved any but Phoebe to have granted him favor. But she, measuring all his passions with a coy dis-
30 dain, and triumphing in the poor shepherd's pathetical humors, smiling at his martyrdom as though love had been no malady, scornfully warbled out this sonnet:

Phoebe's Sonnet, a Reply to Montanus' Passion

Down a down,
Thus Phyllis sung,
By fancy once distressed;

Whoso by foolish love are stung
Are worthily oppressed.
And so sing I. With a down, down, &c.

When Love was first begot,
And by the mover's will
Did fall to human lot
His solace to fulfil,
Devoid of all deceit,
A chaste and holy fire
10 Did quicken man's conceit,
And women's breast inspire.
The gods that saw the good
That mortals did approve,
With kind and holy mood
Began to talk of Love.

Down a down,
Thus Phyllis sung
By fancy once distressed, &c.

But during this accord,
20 A wonder strange to hear,
Whilst Love in deed and word
Most faithful did appear,
False-semblance came in place,
By Jealousy attended,
And with a double face
Both love and fancy blended;
Which made the gods forsake,
And men from fancy fly,
And maidens scorn a make,[1]
30 Forsooth, and so will I.

Down a down,
Thus Phyllis sung,
By fancy once distressed;
Who so by foolish love are stung
Are worthily oppressed.
And so sing I.
With down a down, a down down, a down a.

Montanus, hearing the cruel resolution of Phoebe, was so overgrown with passions, that from amorous 40 ditties he fell flat into these terms:

[1] Mate.

"Ah, Phoebe," quoth he, "whereof art thou made, that thou regardest not my malady? Am I so hateful an object that thine eyes condemn me for an abject? or so base, that thy desires cannot stoop so low as to lend me a gracious look? My passions are many, my loves more, my thoughts loyalty, and my fancy faith: all devoted in humble devoir to the service of Phoebe; and shall I reap no reward for such fealties? The swain's daily labors is quit with 10 the evening's hire, the ploughman's toil is eased with the hope of corn, what the ox sweats out at the plough he fatteneth at the crib; but infortunate Montanus hath no salve for his sorrows, nor any hope of recompense for the hazard of his perplexed passions. If, Phoebe, time may plead the proof of my truth, twice seven winters have I loved fair Phoebe: if constancy be a cause to farther my suit, Montanus' thoughts have been sealed in the sweet of Phoebe's excellence, as far from change as she 20 from love: if outward passions may discover inward affections, the furrows in my face may decipher the sorrows of my heart, and the map of my looks the griefs of my mind. Thou seest, Phoebe, the tears of despair have made my cheeks full of wrinkles, and my scalding sighs have made the air echo her pity conceived in my plaints: Philomele hearing my passions, hath left her mournful tunes to listen to the discourse of my miseries. I have portrayed in every tree the beauty of my mistress, and the despair 30 of my loves. What is it in the woods cannot witness my woes? and who is it would not pity my plaints? Only Phoebe. And why? Because I am Montanus, and she Phoebe: I a worthless swain, and she the most excellent of all fairs. Beautiful Phoebe! oh, might I say pitiful, then happy were I, though I tasted but one minute of that good hap. Measure Montanus not by his fortunes but by his loves, and balance not his wealth but his desires, and lend but one gracious look to cure a heap of disquieted cares: if not, ah! if Phoebe cannot love, let a storm of frowns end the discontent of my thoughts, and so let me perish in my desires, because they are above my deserts: only at my death this favor cannot be denied me, that all shall say Montanus died for love of hard-hearted Phoebe."

At these words she filled her face full of frowns, 10 and made him this short and sharp reply:

"Importunate shepherd, whose loves are lawless, because restless, are thy passions so extreme that thou canst not conceal them with patience? or art thou so folly-sick, that thou must needs be fancy-sick, and in thy affection tied to such an exigent, as none serves but Phoebe? Well, sir, if your market may be made no where else, home again, for your mart is at the fairest. Phoebe is no lettuce for your lips, and her grapes hangs so high, that gaze at them 20 you may, but touch them you cannot. Yet, Montanus, I speak not this in pride, but in disdain; not that I scorn thee, but that I hate love; for I count it as great honor to triumph over fancy as over fortune. Rest thee content therefore, Montanus: cease from thy loves, and bridle thy looks, quench the sparkles before they grow to a further flame; for in loving me thou shalt live by loss, and what thou utterest in words are all written in the wind. Wert thou, Montanus, as fair as Paris, as hardy as 30 Hector, as constant as Troilus, as loving as Leander, Phoebe could not love, because she cannot love at all: and therefore if thou pursue me with Phoebus, I must fly with Daphne."

Ganymede, overhearing all these passions of Montanus, could not brook the cruelty of Phoebe, but starting from behind the bush said:

"And if, damsel, you fled from me, I would transform you as Daphne to a bay, and then in contempt trample your branches under my feet."

Phoebe at this sudden reply was amazed, especially when she saw so fair a swain as Ganymede; blushing therefore, she would have been gone, but that he held her by the hand, and prosecuted his reply thus:

"What, shepherdess, so fair and so cruel? Disdain beseems not cottages, nor coyness maids; for either they be condemned to be too proud, or too froward. Take heed, fair nymph, that in despising love, you be not overreached with love, and in shaking off all, shape yourself to your own shadow, and so with Narcissus prove passionate and yet unpitied. Oft have I heard, and sometimes have I seen, high disdain turned to hot desires. Because thou art beautiful be not so coy: as there is nothing more fair, so there is nothing more fading; as momentary as the shadows which grows from a cloudy sun. Such, my fair shepherdess, as disdain in youth desire in age, and then are they hated in the winter, that might have been loved in the prime. A wrinkled maid is like to a parched rose, that is cast up in coffers to please the smell, not worn in the hand to content the eye. There is no folly in love to *had I wist*, and therefore be ruled by me. Love while thou art young, least thou be disdained when thou art old. Beauty nor time cannot be recalled, and if thou love, like of Montanus; for if his desires are many, so his deserts are great."

Phoebe all this while gazed on the perfection of Ganymede, as deeply enamored on his perfection as Montanus inveigled with hers; for her eye made survey of his excellent feature, which she found so rare, that she thought the ghost of Adonis had been leaped from Elysium in the shape of a swain. When she blushed at her own folly to look so long on a stranger, she mildly made answer to Ganymede thus:

"I cannot deny, sir, but I have heard of Love, though I never felt love; and have read of such a goddess as Venus, though I never saw any but her picture; and, perhaps"—and with that she waxed red and bashful, and withal silent; which Ganymede perceiving, commended in herself the bashfulness of the maid, and desired her to go forward.

"And perhaps, sir," quoth she, "mine eye hath been more prodigal to-day than ever before"—and 10 with that she stayed again, as one greatly passionate and perplexed.

Aliena seeing the hare through the maze, bade her forward with her prattle, but in vain; for at this abrupt period she broke off, and with her eyes full of tears, and her face covered with a vermilion dye, she sate down and sighed. Whereupon Aliena and Ganymede, seeing the shepherdess in such a strange plight, left Phoebe with her Montanus, wishing her friendly that she would be more pliant to Love, lest 20 in penance Venus joined her to some sharp repentance. Phoebe made no reply, but fetched such a sigh, that Echo made relation of her plaint, giving Ganymede such an adieu with a piercing glance, that the amorous girl-boy perceived Phoebe was pinched by the heel.

But leaving Phoebe to the follies of her new fancy, and Montanus to attend upon her, to Saladyne, who all this last night could not rest for the remembrance of Aliena; insomuch that he framed a sweet conceited 30 sonnet to content his humor, which he put in his bosom, being requested by his brother Rosader to go to Aliena and Ganymede, to signify unto them that his wounds were not dangerous. A more happy message could not happen to Saladyne, that taking his forest bill on his neck, he trudgeth in all haste towards the plains where Aliena's flocks did feed, coming just to the place when they returned from

Montanus and Phoebe. Fortune so conducted this jolly forester, that he encountered them and Corydon, whom he presently saluted in this manner:

"Fair shepherdess, and too fair, unless your beauty be tempered with courtesy, and the lineaments of the face graced with the lowliness of mind, as many good fortunes to you and your page, as yourselves can desire or I imagine. My brother Rosader, in the grief of his green wounds still mindful of his 10 friends, hath sent me to you with a kind salute, to show that he brooks his pains with the more patience, in that he holds the parties precious in whose defence he received the prejudice. The report of your welfare will be a great comfort to his distempered body and distressed thoughts, and therefore he sent me with a strict charge to visit you."

"And you," quoth Aliena, "are the more welcome in that you are messenger from so kind a gentleman, whose pains we compassionate with as great 20 sorrow as he brooks them with grief; and his wounds breeds in us as many passions as in him extremities, so that what disquiet he feels in body we partake in heart, wishing, if we might, that our mishap might salve his malady. But seeing our wills yields him little ease, our orisons are never idle to the gods for his recovery."

"I pray, youth," quoth Ganymede with tears in his eyes, "when the surgeon searched him, held he his wounds dangerous?"

30 "Dangerous," quoth Saladyne, "but not mortal; and the sooner to be cured, in that his patient is not impatient of any pains: whereupon my brother hopes within these ten days to walk abroad to visit you himself."

"In the meantime," quoth Ganymede, "say his Rosalynde commends her to him, and bids him be of good cheer."

"I know not," quoth Saladyne, "who that Rosalynde is, but whatsoever she is, her name is never out of his mouth, but amidst the deepest of his passions he useth Rosalynde as a charm to appease all sorrows with patience. Insomuch that I conjecture my brother is in love, and she some paragon that holds his heart perplexed, whose name he oft records with sighs, sometimes with tears, straight with joy, then with smiles; as if in one person love had lodged
10 a Chaos of confused passions. Wherein I have noted the variable disposition of fancy, that like the polyp in colors, so it changeth into sundry humors, being, as it should seem, a combat mixed with disquiet and a bitter pleasure wrapped in a sweet prejudice, like to the Sinople tree, whose blossoms delight the smell, and whose fruit infects the taste."

"By my faith," quoth Aliena, "sir, you are deep read in love, or grows your insight into affection by experience? Howsoever, you are a great philosopher
20 in Venus' principles, else could you not discover her secret aphorisms. But, sir, our country amours are not like your courtly fancies, nor is our wooing like your suing; for poor shepherds never plain them till love pain them, where the courtier's eyes is full of passions, when his heart is most free from affection; they court to discover their eloquence, we woo to ease our sorrows; every fair face with them must have a new fancy sealed with a forefinger kiss and a far-fetched sigh, we here love one and live to that
30 one so long as life can maintain love, using few ceremonies because we know few subtleties, and little eloquence for that we lightly account of flattery; only faith and troth, that's shepherd's wooing; and, sir, how like you of this?"

"So," quoth Saladyne, "as I could tie myself to such love."

"What, and look so low as a shepherdess, being

the son of Sir John of Bordeaux? Such desires were a disgrace to your honors." And with that surveying exquisitely every part of him, as uttering all these words in a deep passion, she espied the paper in his bosom; whereupon growing jealous that it was some amorous sonnet, she suddenly snatched it out of his bosom and asked if it were any secret. She was bashful, and Saladyne blushed, which she perceiving, said:

10 "Nay then, sir, if you wax red, my life for yours 't is some love-matter. I will see your mistress' name, her praises, and your passions." And with that she looked on it, which was written to this effect:

Saladyne's Sonnet

If it be true that heaven's eternal course
With restless sway and ceaseless turning glides;
If air inconstant be, and swelling source
Turn and returns with many fluent tides;
  If earth in winter summer's pride estrange,
20 And nature seemeth only fair in change;

If it be true that our immortal spright,
Derived from heavenly pure, in wand'ring still,
In novelty and strangeness doth delight,
And by discoverent power discerneth ill;
  And if the body for to work his best
  Doth with the seasons change his place of rest;

Whence comes it that, enforced by furious skies,
I change both place and soil, but not my heart,
Yet salve not in this change my maladies?
30 Whence grows it that each object works my smart?
  Alas, I see my faith procures my miss,
  And change in love against my nature is.

Et florida pungunt.

Aliena having read over his sonnet, began thus pleasantly to descant upon it:

"I see, Saladyne," quoth she, "that as the sun is

no sun without his brightness, nor the diamond accounted for precious unless it be hard, so men are not men unless they be in love; and their honors are measured by their amours, not their labors, counting it more commendable for a gentleman to be full of fancy, than full of virtue. I had thought

> Otia si tollas, periere Cupidinis arcus,
> Contemptaeque jacent et sine luce faces;

but I see Ovid's axiom is not authentical, for even
10 labor hath her loves, and extremity is no pumice-stone to rase out fancy. Yourself exiled from your wealth, friends, and country by Torismond, sorrows enough to suppress affections, yet amidst the depth of these extremities, love will be lord, and show his power to be more predominant than fortune. But I pray you, sir, if without offence I may crave it, are they some new thoughts, or some old desires?"

Saladyne, that now saw opportunity pleasant, thought to strike while the iron was hot, and there-
20 fore taking Aliena by the hand, sate down by her; and Ganymede, to give them leave to their loves, found herself busy about the folds, whilst Saladyne fell into this prattle with Aliena:

"Fair mistress, if I be blunt in discovering my affections, and use little eloquence in levelling out my loves, I appeal for pardon to your own principles, that say, shepherds use few ceremonies, for that they acquaint themselves with few subtleties: to frame myself, therefore, to your country fashion
30 with much faith and little flattery, know, beautiful shepherdess, that whilst I lived in the court I knew not love's cumber, but I held affection as a toy, not as a malady; using fancy as the Hyperborei do their flowers, which they wear in their bosom all day, and cast them in the fire for fuel at night. I liked all, because I loved none, and who was most fair, on her

I fed mine eye, but as charily as the bee, that as soon as she hath sucked honey from the rose, flies straight to the next marigold. Living thus at mine own list, I wondered at such as were in love, and when I read their passions, I took them only for poems that flowed from the quickness of the wit, not the sorrows of the heart. But now, fair nymph, since I became a forester, Love hath taught me such a lesson that I must confess his deity and dignity, 10 and say as there is nothing so precious as beauty, so there is nothing more piercing than fancy. For since first I arrived at this place, and mine eye took a curious survey of your excellence, I have been so fettered with your beauty and virtue, as, sweet Aliena, Saladyne without further circumstance loves Aliena. I could paint out my desires with long ambages; but seeing in many words lies mistrust, and that truth is ever naked, let this suffice for a country wooing: Saladyne loves Aliena, and none 20 but Aliena."

Although these words were most heavenly harmony in the ears of the shepherdess, yet to seem coy at the first courting, and to disdain love howsoever she desired love, she made this reply:

"Ah, Saladyne, though I seem simple, yet I am more subtle than to swallow the hook because it hath a painted bait: as men are wily so women are wary, especially if they have that wit by others' harms to beware. Do we not know, Saladyne, men's tongues 30 are like Mercury's pipe, that can enchant Argus with an hundred eyes, and their words as prejudicial as the charms of Circes, that transform men into monsters. If such Sirens sing, we poor women had need stop our ears, lest in hearing we prove so foolish hardy as to believe them, and so perish in trusting much and suspecting little. Saladyne, *piscator ictus sapit*, he that hath been once poisoned and after-

wards fears not to bowse of every potion, is worthy to suffer double penance. Give me leave then to mistrust, though I do not condemn. Saladyne is now in love with Aliena, he a gentleman of great parentage, she a shepherdess of mean parents; he honorable and she poor. Can love consist of contrarieties? Will the falcon perch with the kestrel, the lion harbor with the wolf? Will Venus join robes and rags together, or can there be a sympathy
10 between a king and a beggar? Then, Saladyne, how can I believe thee that love should unite our thoughts, when fortune hath set such a difference between our degrees? But suppose thou likest Aliena's beauty: men in their fancy resemble the wasp, which scorns that flower from which she hath fetched her wax; playing like the inhabitants of the island Tenerifa, who, when they have gathered the sweet spices, use the trees for fuel; so men, when they have glutted themselves with the fair of women's faces, hold
20 them for necessary evils, and wearied with that which they seemed so much to love, cast away fancy as children do their rattles, and loathing that which so deeply before they liked; especially such as take love in a minute and have their eyes attractive, like jet, apt to entertain any object, are as ready to let it slip again."

Saladyne, hearing how Aliena harped still upon one string, which was the doubt of men's constancy, he broke off her sharp invective thus:

30 "I grant, Aliena," quoth he, "many men have done amiss in proving soon ripe and soon rotten; but particular instances infer no general conclusions, and therefore I hope what others have faulted in shall not prejudice my favors. I will not use sophistry to confirm my love, for that is subtlety; nor long discourses lest my words might be thought more than my faith: but if this will suffice, that by the honor

of a gentleman I love Aliena, and woo Aliena, not to crop the blossoms and reject the tree, but to consummate my faithful desires in the honorable end of marriage."

At the word marriage Aliena stood in a maze what to answer, fearing that if she were too coy, to drive him away with her disdain, and if she were too courteous, to discover the heat of her desires. In a dilemma thus what to do, at last this she said:

10 "Saladyne, ever since I saw thee, I favored thee; I cannot dissemble my desires, because I see thou dost faithfully manifest thy thoughts, and in liking thee I love thee so far as mine honor holds fancy still in suspense; but if I knew thee as virtuous as thy father, or as well qualified as thy brother Rosader, the doubt should be quickly decided: but for this time to give thee an answer, assure thyself this, I will either marry with Saladyne, or still live a virgin."

20 And with this they strained one another's hand; which Ganymede espying, thinking he had had his mistress long enough at shrift, said:

"What, a match or no?"

"A match," quoth Aliena, "or else it were an ill market."

"I am glad," quoth Ganymede. "I would Rosader were well here to make up a mess."

"Well remembered," quoth Saladyne; "I forgot I left my brother Rosader alone, and therefore lest 30 being solitary he should increase his sorrows, I will haste me to him. May it please you, then, to command me any service to him, I am ready to be a dutiful messenger."

"Only at this time commend me to him," quoth Aliena, "and tell him, though we cannot pleasure him we pray for him."

"And forget not," quoth Ganymede, "my commendations; but say to him that Rosalynde sheds as many tears from her heart as he drops of blood from his wounds, for the sorrow of his misfortunes, feathering all her thoughts with disquiet, till his welfare procure her content. Say thus, good Saladyne, and so farewell."

He having his message, gave a courteous adieu to them both, especially to Aliena, and so playing loath to depart, went to his brother. But Aliena, she
10 perplexed and yet joyful, passed away the day pleasantly, still praising the perfection of Saladyne, not ceasing to chat of her new love till evening drew on; and then they, folding their sheep, went home to bed. Where we leave them and return to Phoebe.

Phoebe, fired with the uncouth flame of love, returned to her father's house, so galled with restless passions, as now she began to acknowledge, that as there was no flower so fresh but might be parched with the sun, no tree so strong but might be shaken
20 with a storm, so there was no thought so chaste, but time armed with love could make amorous; for she that held Diana for the goddess of her devotion, was now fain to fly to the altar of Venus, as suppliant now with prayers, as she was froward before with disdain. As she lay in her bed, she called to mind the several beauties of young Ganymede; first his locks, which being amber-hued, passeth the wreath that Phoebus puts on to make his front glorious; his brow of ivory was like the seat where love and
30 majesty sits enthroned to enchain fancy; his eyes as bright as the burnishing of the heaven, darting forth frowns with disdain and smiles with favor, lightening such looks as would inflame desire, were she wrapped in the circle of the frozen zone; in his cheeks the vermilion teinture of the rose flourished upon natural alabaster, the blush of the morn and Luna's silver show were so lively portrayed, that

the Troyan that fills out wine to Jupiter was not half so beautiful; his face was full of pleasance, and all the rest of his lineaments proportioned with such excellence, as Phoebe was fettered in the sweetness of his feature. The idea of these perfections tumbling in her mind made the poor shepherdess so perplexed, as feeling a pleasure tempered with intolerable pains, and yet a disquiet mixed with a content, she rather wished to die than to live in this
10 amorous anguish. But wishing is little worth in such extremes, and therefore was she forced to pine in her malady, without any salve for her sorrows. Reveal it she durst not, as daring in such matters to make none her secretary; and to conceal it, why, it doubled her grief; for as fire suppressed grows to the greater flame, and the current stopped to the more violent stream, so love smothered wrings the heart with the deeper passions.

Perplexed thus with sundry agonies, her food
20 began to fail, and the disquiet of her mind began to work a distemperature of her body, that, to be short, Phoebe fell extreme sick, and so sick as there was almost left no recovery of health. Her father, seeing his fair Phoebe thus distressed, sent for his friends, who sought by medicine to cure, and by counsel to pacify, but all in vain; for although her body was feeble through long fasting, yet she did *magis aegrotare animo quam corpore*. Which her friends perceived and sorrowed at, but salve it they
30 could not.

The news of her sickness was bruited abroad through all the forest, which no sooner came to Montanus' ear, but he, like a madman, came to visit Phoebe. Where sitting by her bedside he began his exordium with so many tears and sighs, that she, perceiving the extremity of his sorrows, began now as a lover to pity them, although Ganymede held her

from redressing them. Montanus craved to know the cause of her sickness, tempered with secret plaints, but she answered him, as the rest, with silence, having still the form of Ganymede in her mind, and conjecturing how she might reveal her loves. To utter it in words she found herself too bashful; to discourse by any friend she would not trust any in her amours; to remain thus perplexed still and conceal all, it was a double death. Where-
10 upon, for her last refuge, she resolved to write unto Ganymede, and therefore desired Montanus to absent himself a while, but not to depart, for she would see if she could steal a nap. He was no sooner gone out of the chamber, but reaching to her standish, she took pen and paper, and wrote a letter to this effect:

"Phoebe to Ganymede wisheth what she wants herself.

"Fair shepherd—and therefore is Phoebe infortunate, because thou art so fair—although hitherto
20 mine eyes were adamants to resist love, yet I no sooner saw thy face, but they became amorous to entertain love; more devoted to fancy than before they were repugnant to affection, addicted to the one by nature and drawn to the other by beauty: which, being rare and made the more excellent by many virtues, hath so snared the freedom of Phoebe, as she rests at thy mercy, either to be made the most fortunate of all maidens, or the most miserable of all women. Measure not, Ganymede, my loves by my
30 wealth, nor my desires by my degrees; but think my thoughts are as full of faith, as thy face of amiable favors. Then, as thou knowest thyself most beautiful, suppose me most constant. If thou deemest me hard-hearted because I hated Montanus, think I was forced to it by fate; if thou sayest I am kind-hearted

because so lightly I love thee at the first look, think I was driven to it by destiny, whose influence, as it is mighty, so is it not to be resisted. If my fortunes were anything but infortunate love, I would strive with fortune: but he that wrests against the will of Venus, seeks to quench fire with oil, and to thrust out one thorn by putting in another. If then, Ganymede, love enters at the eye, harbors in the heart, and will neither be driven out with physic nor
10 reason, pity me, as one whose malady hath no salve but from thy sweet self, whose grief hath no ease but through thy grant; and think I am a virgin who is deeply wronged when I am forced to woo, and conjecture love to be strong, that is more forcible than nature. Thus distressed unless by thee eased, I expect either to live fortunate by thy favor, or die miserable by thy denial. Living in hope. Farewell.

She that must be thine,
20 or not be at all,
Phoebe."

To this letter she annexed this sonnet:

Sonetto

My boat doth pass the straits
of seas incensed with fire,
Filled with forgetfulness;
amidst the winter's night,
A blind and careless boy,
brought up by fond desire,
Doth guide me in the sea
30 of sorrow and despite.

For every oar he sets
a rank of foolish thoughts,
And cuts, instead of wave,
a hope without distress;
The winds of my deep sighs,
that thunder still for noughts,

Have split my sails with fear,
with care, with heaviness.

A mighty storm of tears,
a black and hideous cloud,
A thousand fierce disdains
do slack the halyards oft;
Till ignorance do pull,
and error hale the shrouds,
No star for safety shines,
10 no Phoebe from aloft.

Time hath subdued art,
and joy is slave to woe:
Alas, Love's guide, be kind!
what, shall I perish so?

This letter and the sonnet being ended, she could find no fit messenger to send it by, and therefore she called in Montanus, and entreated him to carry it to Ganymede. Although poor Montanus saw day at a little hole, and did perceive what passion pinched 20 her, yet, that he might seem dutiful to his mistress in all service, he dissembled the matter, and became a willing messenger of his own martyrdom. And so, taking the letter, went the next morn very early to the plains where Aliena fed her flocks, and there he found Ganymede, sitting under a pomegranate tree, sorrowing for the hard fortunes of her Rosader. Montanus saluted him, and according to his charge delivered Ganymede the letters, which, he said, came from Phoebe. At this the wanton blushed, as being 30 abashed to think what news should come from an unknown shepherdess; but taking the letters, unripped the seals, and read over the discourse of Phoebe's fancies. When she had read and over-read them, Ganymede began to smile, and looking on Montanus, fell into a great laughter, and with that called Aliena, to whom she showed the writings. Who, having perused them, conceited them very pleasantly, and smiled to see how love had yoked her, who before would not stoop to the lure; Aliena whispering Ganymede in the ear, and saying, "Knew Phoebe what want there were in thee to perform her will, and how unfit thy kind is to be kind to her, she would be more wise, and less enamored; but leaving that, I pray thee let us sport with this swain." At that word Ganymede, turning to Montanus, began to glance at him thus:

10 "I pray thee, tell me, shepherd, by those sweet thoughts and pleasing sighs that grow from my mistress' favors, art thou in love with Phoebe?"

"Oh, my youth," quoth Montanus, "were Phoebe so far in love with me, my flocks would be more fat and their master more quiet; for through the sorrows of my discontent grows the leanness of my sheep."

"Alas, poor swain," quoth Ganymede, "are thy passions so extreme or thy fancy so resolute, that no 20 reason will blemish the pride of thy affection, and rase out that which thou strivest for without hope?"

"Nothing can make me forget Phoebe, while Montanus forget himself; for those characters which true love hath stamped, neither the envy of time nor fortune can wipe away."

"Why but, Montanus," quoth Ganymede, "enter with a deep insight into the despair of thy fancies, and thou shalt see the depth of thine own follies; for, poor man, thy progress in love is a regress to 30 loss, swimming against the stream with the crab, and flying with Apis Indica against wind and weather. Thou seekest with Phoebus to win Daphne, and she flies faster than thou canst follow: thy desires soar with the hobby, but her disdain reacheth higher than thou canst make wing. I tell thee, Montanus, in courting Phoebe, thou barkest with the wolves of Syria against the moon, and rovest at such a mark, with thy thoughts, as is beyond the pitch of thy bow, praying to Love, when Love is pitiless, and thy malady remediless. For proof, Montanus, read these letters, wherein thou shalt see thy great follies and little hope."

With that Montanus took them and perused them, but with such sorrow in his looks, as they bewrayed a source of confused passions in his heart; at every line his color changed, and every sentence was ended 10 with a period of sighs.

At last, noting Phoebe's extreme desire toward Ganymede and her disdain towards him, giving Ganymede the letter, the shepherd stood as though he had neither won nor lost. Which Ganymede perceiving wakened him out of his dream thus:

"Now, Montanus, dost thou see thou vowest great service and obtainest but little reward; but in lieu of thy loyalty, she maketh thee, as Bellerophon, carry thine own bane. Then drink not willingly of that 20 potion wherein thou knowest is poison; creep not to her that cares not for thee. What, Montanus, there are many as fair as Phoebe, but most of all more courteous than Phoebe. I tell thee, shepherd, favor is love's fuel; then since thou canst not get that, let the flame vanish into smoke, and rather sorrow for a while than repent thee for ever."

"I tell thee, Ganymede," quoth Montanus, "as they which are stung with the scorpion, cannot be recovered but by the scorpion, nor he that was 30 wounded with Achilles' lance be cured but with the same truncheon, so Apollo was fain to cry out that love was only eased with love, and fancy healed by no medicine but favor. Phoebus had herbs to heal all hurts but this passion; Circes had charms for all chances but for affection, and Mercury subtle reasons to refel all griefs but love. Persuasions are bootless, reason lends no remedy, counsel no comfort, to such whom fancy hath made resolute; and therefore though Phoebe loves Ganymede, yet Montanus must honor none but Phoebe."

"Then," quoth Ganymede, "may I rightly term thee a despairing lover, that livest without joy, and lovest without hope. But what shall I do, Montanus, to pleasure thee? Shall I despise Phoebe, as she disdains thee?"

"Oh," quoth Montanus, "that were to renew my 10 griefs, and double my sorrows; for the sight of her discontent were the censure of my death. Alas, Ganymede! though I perish in my thoughts, let not her die in her desires. Of all passions, love is most impatient: then let not so fair a creature as Phoebe sink under the burden of so deep a distress. Being lovesick, she is proved heartsick, and all for the beauty of Ganymede. Thy proportion hath entangled her affection, and she is snared in the beauty of thy excellence. Then, sith she loves thee so dear, 20 mislike not her deadly. Be thou paramour to such a paragon: she hath beauty to content thine eye, and flocks to enrich thy store. Thou canst not wish for more than thou shalt win by her; for she is beautiful, virtuous and wealthy, three deep persuasions to make love frolic."

Aliena seeing Montanus cut it against the hair, and plead that Ganymede ought to love Phoebe, when his only life was the love of Phoebe, answered him thus:

"Why, Montanus, dost thou further this motion, 30 seeing if Ganymede marry Phoebe thy market is clean marred?"

"Ah, mistress," quoth he, "so hath love taught me to honor Phoebe, that I would prejudice my life to pleasure her, and die in despair rather than she should perish for want. It shall suffice me to see her contented, and to feed mine eye on her favor. If she marry, though it be my martyrdom, yet if she be pleased, I will brook it with patience, and triumph in mine own stars to see her desires satisfied. Therefore, if Ganymede be as courteous as he is beautiful, let him show his virtues in redressing Phoebe's miseries." And this Montanus pronounced with such an assured countenance, that it amazed both Aliena and Ganymede to see the resolution of his loves; so that they pitied his passions and commended his patience, devising how they might by 10 any subtlety get Montanus the favor of Phoebe. Straight (as women's heads are full of wiles) Ganymede had a fetch to force Phoebe to fancy the shepherd, malgrado the resolution of her mind: he prosecuted his policy thus:

"Montanus," quoth he, "seeing Phoebe is so forlorn, lest I might be counted unkind in not salving so fair a creature, I will go with thee to Phoebe, and there hear herself in word utter that which she hath discoursed with her pen; and then, as love wills me, 20 I will set down my censure. I will home by our house, and send Corydon to accompany Aliena."

Montanus seemed glad of this determination and away they go towards the house of Phoebe.

When they drew nigh to the cottage, Montanus ran before, and went in and told Phoebe that Ganymede was at the door. This word "Ganymede," sounding in the ears of Phoebe, drave her into such an ecstasy for joy, that rising up in her bed, she was half revived, and her wan color began to wax 30 red; and with that came Ganymede in, who saluted Phoebe with such a courteous look, that it was half a salve to her sorrows. Sitting him down by her bedside, he questioned about her disease, and where the pain chiefly held her? Phoebe looking as lovely as Venus in her night-gear, tainting her face with as ruddy a blush as Clytia did when she bewrayed her loves to Phoebus, taking Ganymede by tne hand began thus:

"Fair shepherd, if love were not more strong than nature, or fancy the sharpest extreme, my immodesty were the more, and my virtues the less; for nature hath framed women's eyes bashful, their hearts full of fear, and their tongues full of silence; but love, that imperious love, where his power is predominant, then he perverts all, and wresteth the wealth of nature to his own will: an instance in myself, fair Ganymede, for such a fire hath he kindled in my thoughts, that to find ease for the flame, I was forced to pass the bounds of modesty, and seek a salve at thy hands for my secret harms. Blame me not if I be overbold for it is thy beauty, and if I be too forward it is fancy, and the deep insight into thy virtues that makes me thus fond. For let me say in a word what may be contained in a volume,—Phoebe loves Ganymede."

At this she held down her head and wept, and Ganymede rose as one that would suffer no fish to hang on his fingers, made this reply:

"Water not thy plants, Phoebe, for I do pity thy plaints, nor seek not to discover thy loves in tears, for I conjecture thy truth by thy passions: sorrow is no salve for loves, nor sighs no remedy for affection. Therefore frolic, Phoebe; for if Ganymede can cure thee, doubt not of recovery. Yet this let me say without offence, that it grieves me to thwart Montanus in his fancies, seeing his desires have been so resolute, and his thoughts so loyal. But thou allegest that thou art forced from him by fate: so I tell thee, Phoebe, either some star or else some destiny fits my mind, rather with Adonis to die in chase than be counted a wanton on Venus' knee. Although I pity thy martyrdom, yet I can grant no marriage; for though I held thee fair, yet mine eye is not fettered:

love grows not, like the herb Spattana, to his perfection in one night, but creeps with the snail, and yet at last attains to the top. *Festina lente,* especially in love, for momentary fancies are oft-times the fruits of follies. If, Phoebe, I should like thee as the Hyperborei do their dates, which banquet with them in the morning and throw them away at night, my folly should be great, and thy repentance more. Therefore I will have time to turn my thoughts, and
10 my loves shall grow up as the watercresses, slowly, but with a deep root. Thus, Phoebe, thou mayest see I disdain not, though I desire not; remaining indifferent till time and love makes me resolute. Therefore, Phoebe, seek not to suppress affection, and with the love of Montanus quench the remembrance of Ganymede; strive thou to hate me as I seek to like of thee, and ever have the duties of Montanus in thy mind, for I promise thee thou mayest have one more wealthy, but not more loyal."
20 These words were corrosives to the perplexed Phoebe, but sobbing out sighs, and straining out tears, she blubbered out these words:

"And shall I then have no salve of Ganymede but suspense, no hope but a doubtful hazard, no comfort, but be posted off to the will of time? Justly have the goods balanced my fortunes, who, being cruel to Montanus, found Ganymede as unkind to myself; so in forcing him perish for love, I shall die myself with overmuch love."

30 "I am glad," quoth Ganymede, "you look into your own faults, and see where your shoe wrings you, measuring now the pains of Montanus by your own passions."

"Truth," quoth Phoebe, "and so deeply I repent me of my frowardness toward the shepherd, that could I cease to love Ganymede, I would resolve to like Montanus."

"What, if I can with reason persuade Phoebe to mislike of Ganymede, will she then favor Montanus?"

"When reason," quoth she, "doth quench that love that I owe to thee, then will I fancy him; conditionally, that if my love can be suppressed with no reason, as being without reason Ganymede will only wed himself to Phoebe."

"I grant it, fair shepherdess," quoth he; "and to 10 feed thee with the sweetness of hope, this resolve on: I will never marry myself to woman but unto thyself."

And with that Ganymede gave Phoebe a fruitless kiss, and such words of comfort, that before Ganymede departed she arose out of her bed, and made him and Montanus such cheer, as could be found in such a country cottage; Ganymede in the midst of their banquet rehearsing the promises of either in Montanus' favor, which highly pleased the shepherd. 20 Thus, all three content, and soothed up in hope, Ganymede took his leave of his Phoebe and departed, leaving her a contented woman, and Montanus highly pleased. But poor Ganymede, who had her thoughts on her Rosader, when she called to remembrance his wounds, filled her eyes full of tears, and her heart full of sorrows, plodded to find Aliena at the folds, thinking with her presence to drive away her passions. As she came on the plains, she might espy where Rosader and Saladyne sate with Aliena under 30 the shade; which sight was a salve to her grief, and such a cordial unto her heart, that she tripped alongst the lawns full of joy.

At last Corydon, who was with them, spied Ganymede, and with that the clown rose, and, running to meet him, cried:

"O sirrah, a match, a match! our mistress shall be married on Sunday."

Thus the poor peasant frolicked it before Ganymede, who coming to the crew saluted them all, and especially Rosader, saying that he was glad to see him so well recovered of his wounds.

"I had not gone abroad so soon," quoth Rosader, "but that I am bidden to a marriage, which, on Sunday next, must be solemnized between my brother and Aliena. I see well where love leads, delay is loathsome, and that small wooing serves where both the parties are willing."

"Truth," quoth Ganymede; "but a happy day should it be, if Rosader that day might be married to Rosalynde."

"Ah, good Ganymede," quoth he, "by naming Rosalynde, renew not my sorrows; for the thought of her perfections is the thrall of my miseries."

"Tush, be of good cheer, man," quoth Ganymede: "I have a friend that is deeply experienced in negromancy and magic; what art can do shall be acted for thine advantage: I will cause him to bring in Rosalynde, if either France or any bordering nation harbor her; and upon that take the faith of a young shepherd."

Aliena smiled to see how Rosader frowned, thinking that Ganymede had jested with him. But, breaking off from those matters, the page, somewhat pleasant, began to discourse unto them what had passed between him and Phoebe; which, as they laughed, so they wondered at, all confessing that there is none so chaste but love will change. Thus they passed away the day in chat, and when the sun began to set they took their leaves and departed; Aliena providing for their marriage day such solemn cheer and handsome robes as fitted their country estate, and yet somewhat the better, in that Rosader had promised to bring Gerismond thither as a guest. Ganymede, who then meant to discover herself before her father, had made her a gown of green, and a kirtle of the finest sendal, in such sort that she seemed some heavenly nymph harbored in country attire.

Saladyne was not behind in care to set out the nuptials, nor Rosader unmindful to bid guests, who invited Gerismond and all his followers to the feast, who willingly granted, so that there was nothing but the day wanting to this marriage.

10 In the meanwhile, Phoebe being a bidden guest made herself as gorgeous as might be to please the eye of Ganymede; and Montanus suited himself with the cost of many of his flocks to be gallant against that day, for then was Ganymede to give Phoebe an answer of her loves, and Montanus either to hear the doom of his misery, or the censure of his happiness. But while this gear was a-brewing, Phoebe passed not one day without visiting her Ganymede, so far was she wrapped in the beauties of this lovely swain.

20 Much prattle they had, and the discourse of many passions, Phoebe wishing for the day, as she thought, of her welfare, and Ganymede smiling to think what unexpected events would fall out at the wedding. In these humors the week went away, that at last Sunday came. No sooner did Phoebus' henchman appear in the sky, to give warning that his master's horses should be trapped in his glorious coach, but Corydon, in his holiday suit, marvellous seemly, in a russet jacket, welted with the same and faced with

30 red worsted, having a pair of blue chamlet sleeves, bound at the wrists with four yellow laces, closed before very richly with a dozen of pewter buttons; his hose was of grey kersey, with a large slop[1] barred overthwart the pocket-holes with three fair guards, stitched of either side with red thread; his

[1] Breeches.

stock was of the own, sewed close to his breech, and for to beautify his hose, he had trussed himself round with a dozen of new-threaden points [1] of medley color; his bonnet was green, whereon stood a copper brooch with the picture of Saint Denis; and to want nothing that might make him amorous in his old days, he had a fair shirt-band of fine lockram, whipped over with Coventry blue of no small cost. Thus attired, Corydon bestirred himself as chief stickler in these actions, and had strowed all the house with flowers, that it seemed rather some of Flora's choice bowers than any country cottage.

Thither repaired Phoebe with all the maids of the forest, to set out the bride in the most seemliest sort that might be; but howsoever she helped to prank out Aliena, yet her eye was still on Ganymede, who was so neat in a suit of grey, that he seemed Endymion when he won Luna with his looks, or Paris when he played the swain to get the beauty of the nymph Oenone. Ganymede, like a pretty page, waited on his mistress Aliena, and overlooked that all was in a readiness against the bridegroom should come; who, attired in a forester's suit, came accompanied with Gerismond and his brother Rosader early in the morning; where arrived, they were solemnly entertained by Aliena and the rest of the country swains; Gerismond very highly commending the fortunate choice of Saladyne, in that he had chosen a shepherdess, whose virtues appeared in her outward beauties, being no less fair than seeming modest. Ganymede coming in, and seeing her father, began to blush, nature working affects by her secret effects. Scarce could she abstain from tears to see her father in so low fortunes, he that was wont to sit in his royal palace, attended on by twelve noble peers,

[1] Laces.

now to be contented with a simple cottage, and a troop of revelling woodmen for his train. The consideration of his fall made Ganymede full of sorrows; yet, that she might triumph over fortune with patience, and not any way dash that merry day with her dumps, she smothered her melancholy with a shadow of mirth, and very reverently welcomed the king, not according to his former degree, but to his present estate, with such diligence as Gerismond began to commend the page for his exquisite person and excellent qualities.

As thus the king with his foresters frolicked it among the shepherds, Corydon came in with a fair mazer full of cider, and presented it to Gerismond with such a clownish salute that he began to smile, and took it of the old shepherd very kindly, drinking to Aliena and the rest of her fair maids, amongst whom Phoebe was the foremost. Aliena pledged the king, and drunk to Rosader; so the carouse went round from him to Phoebe, &c. As they were thus drinking and ready to go to church, came in Montanus, apparelled all in tawny, to signify that he was forsaken; on his head he wore a garland of willow, his bottle hanged by his side, whereon was painted despair, and on his sheep-hook hung two sonnets, as labels of his loves and fortunes.

Thus attired came Montanus in, with his face as full of grief as his heart was of sorrows, showing in his countenance the map of extremities. As soon as the shepherds saw him, they did him all the honor they could, as being the flower of all the swains in Arden; for a bonnier boy was there not seen since that wanton wag of Troy that kept sheep in Ida. He, seeing the king, and guessing it to be Gerismond, did him all the reverence his country courtesy could afford; insomuch that the king, wondering at his attire, began to question what he was. Montanus overhearing him, made this reply:

"I am, sir," quoth he, "Love's swain, as full of inward discontents as I seem fraught with outward follies. Mine eyes like bees delight in sweet flowers, but sucking their full on the fair of beauty, they carry home to the hive of my heart far more gall than honey, and for one drop of pure dew, a ton full of deadly Aconiton. I hunt with the fly to pursue 10 the eagle, that flying too nigh the sun, I perish with the sun; my thoughts are above my reach, and my desires more than my fortunes, yet neither greater than my loves. But daring with Phaëthon, I fall with Icarus, and seeking to pass the mean, I die for being so mean; my night-sleeps are waking slumbers, as full of sorrows as they be far from rest; and my days' labors are fruitless amours, staring at a star and stumbling at a straw, leaving reason to follow after repentance; yet every passion is a pleasure 20 though it pinch, because love hides his wormseed in figs, his poisons in sweet potions, and shadows prejudice with the mask of pleasure. The wisest counsellors are my deep discontents, and I hate that which should salve my harm, like the patient which stung with the Tarantula loathes music, and yet the disease incurable but by melody. Thus, sir, restless I hold myself remediless, as loving without either reward or regard, and yet loving because there is none worthy to be loved but the mistress of my thoughts. 30 And that I am as full of passions as I have discoursed in my plaints, sir, if you please, see my sonnets, and by them censure of my sorrows."

These words of Montanus brought the king into a great wonder, amazed as much at his wit as his attire, insomuch that he took the papers off his hook, and read them to this effect:

Montanus' first Sonnet

Alas! how wander I amidst these woods
  Whereas no day-bright shine doth find access;
But where the melancholy fleeting floods,
  Dark as the night, my night of woes express.
Disarmed of reason, spoiled of nature's goods,
  Without redress to salve my heaviness
    I walk, whilst thought, too cruel to my harms,
    With endless grief my heedless judgment charms.

My silent tongue assailed by secret fear,
10 My traitorous eyes imprisoned in their joy,
My fatal peace devoured in feignèd cheer,
  My heart enforced to harbor in annoy,
My reason robbed of power by yielding ear,
  My fond opinions slave to every toy.
    O Love! thou guide in my uncertain way,
    Woe to thy bow, thy fire, the cause of my decay.

Et florida pungunt.

When the king had read this sonnet, he highly commended the device of the shepherd, that could so wittily wrap his passions in a shadow, and so 20 covertly conceal that which bred his chiefest discontent; affirming, that as the least shrubs have their tops, the smallest hairs their shadows, so the meanest swains had their fancies, and in their kind were as chary of love as a king. Whetted on with this device, he took the second and read it: the effects were these:

Montanus' second Sonnet

When the Dog
Full of rage,
  With his ireful eyes
30 Frowns amidst the skies,
The shepherd, to assuage
  The fury of the heat,
  Himself doth safely seat

By a fount
Full of fair,
    Where a gentle breath,
    Mounting from beneath,
Tempereth the air.
There his flocks
Drink their fill,
    And with ease repose,
    Whilst sweet sleep doth close
10 Eyes from toilsome ill.
But I burn
Without rest,
    No defensive power
    Shields from Phoebe's lour;
Sorrow is my best.
Gentle Love,
Lour no more;
    If thou wilt invade
    In the secret shade,
20 Labor not so sore.
I myself
And my flocks,
    They their love to please,
    I myself to ease,
Both leave the shady oaks;
    Content to burn in fire,
    Sith Love doth so desire.

Et florida pungunt.

Gerismond, seeing the pithy vein of those sonnets, began to make further inquiry what he was. Whereupon Rosader discoursed unto him the love of Montanus to Phoebe, his great loyalty and her deep cruelty, and how in revenge the gods had made the curious nymph amorous of young Ganymede. Upon this discourse the king was desirous to see Phoebe, who being brought before Gerismond by Rosader, shadowed the beauty of her face with such a vermilion teinture, that the king's eyes began to dazzle at the purity of her excellence. After Gerismond had fed his looks awhile upon her fair, he questioned with her why she rewarded Montanus' love with so little regard, seeing his deserts were many, and his passions extreme. Phoebe, to make reply to the king's demand, answered thus:

"Love, sir, is charity in his laws, and whatsoever he sets down for justice, be it never so unjust, the sentence cannot be reversed; women's fancies lend favors not ever by desert, but as they are enforced by their desires; for fancy is tied to the wings of fate, and what the stars decree, stands for an infal-
10 lible doom. I know Montanus is wise, and women's ears are greatly delighted with wit, as hardly escaping the charm of a pleasant tongue, as Ulysses the melody of the Sirens. Montanus is beautiful, and women's eyes are snared in the excellence of objects, as desirous to feed their looks with a fair face, as the bee to suck on a sweet flower. Montanus is wealthy, and an ounce of *give me* persuades a woman more than a pound of *hear me*. Danaë was won with a golden shower, when she could not be gotten with all
20 the entreaties of Jupiter: I tell you, sir, the string of a woman's heart reacheth to the pulse of her hand; and let a man rub that with gold, and 't is hard but she will prove his heart's gold. Montanus is young, a great clause in fancy's court; Montanus is virtuous, the richest argument that love yields; and yet knowing all these perfections, I praise them and wonder at them, loving the qualities, but not affecting the person, because the destinies have set down a contrary censure. Yet Venus, to add revenge, hath
30 given me wine of the same grape, a sip of the same sauce, and firing me with the like passion, hath crossed me with as ill a penance; for I am in love with a shepherd's swain, as coy to me as I am cruel to Montanus, as peremptory in disdain as I was perverse in desire; and that is," quoth she, "Aliena's page, young Ganymede."

Gerismond, desirous to prosecute the end of these

passions, called in Ganymede, who, knowing the case, came in graced with such a blush, as beautified the crystal of his face with a ruddy brightness. The king noting well the physnomy of Ganymede, began by his favors to call to mind the face of his Rosalynde, and with that fetched a deep sigh. Rosader, that was passing familiar with Gerismond, demanded of him why he sighed so sore.

"Because Rosader," quoth he, "the favor of Ganymede puts me in mind of Rosalynde."

At this word Rosader sighed so deeply, as though his heart would have burst.

"And what's the matter," quoth Gerismond, "that you quite me with such a sigh?"

"Pardon me, sir," quoth Rosader, "because I love none but Rosalynde."

"And upon that condition," quoth Gerismond, "that Rosalynde were here, I would this day make up a marriage betwixt her and thee."

At this Aliena turned her head and smiled upon Ganymede, and she could scarce keep countenance. Yet she salved all with secrecy; and Gerismond, to drive away his dumps, questioned with Ganymede, what the reason was he regarded not Phoebe's love, seeing she was as fair as the wanton that brought Troy to ruin. Ganymede mildly answered:

"If I should affect the fair Phoebe, I should offer poor Montanus great wrong to win that from him in a moment, that he hath labored for so many months. Yet have I promised to the beautiful shepherdess to wed myself never to woman except unto her; but with this promise, that if I can by reason suppress Phoebe's love towards me, she shall like of none but of Montanus."

"To that," quoth Phoebe, "I stand; for my love is so far beyond reason, as will admit no persuasion of reason."

"For justice," quoth he, "I appeal to Gerismond."

"And to his censure will I stand," quoth Phoebe.

"And in your victory," quoth Montanus, "stands the hazard of my fortunes; for if Ganymede go away with conquest, Montanus is in conceit love's monarch; if Phoebe win then am I in effect most miserable."

"We will see this controversy," quoth Gerismond, "and then we will to church. Therefore, Ganymede, let us hear your argument."

"Nay, pardon my absence a while," quoth she, "and you shall see one in store."

In went Ganymede and dressed herself in woman's attire, having on a gown of green, with kirtle of rich sendal, so quaint, that she seemed Diana triumphing in the forest; upon her head she wore a chaplet of roses, which gave her such a grace that she looked like Flora perked in the pride of all her flowers. Thus attired came Rosalynde in, and presented herself at her father's feet, with her eyes full of tears, craving his blessing, and discoursing unto him all her fortunes, how she was banished by Torismond, and how ever since she lived in that country disguised.

Gerismond, seeing his daughter, rose from his seat and fell upon her neck, uttering the passions of his joy in watery plaints, driven into such an ecstasy of content, that he could not utter one word. At this sight, if Rosader was both amazed and joyful, I refer myself to the judgment of such as have experience in love, seeing his Rosalynde before his face whom so long and deeply he had affected. At last Gerismond recovered his spirits, and in most fatherly terms entertained his daughter Rosalynde, after many questions demanding of her what had passed between her and Rosader?

"So much, sir," quoth she, "as there wants nothing but your grace to make up the marriage."

"Why, then," quoth Gerismond, "Rosader take her: she is thine, and let this day solemnize both thy brother's and thy nuptials." Rosader beyond measure content, humbly thanked the king, and embraced his Rosalynde, who turning to Phoebe, demanded if she had shown sufficient reason to suppress the force of her loves.

10 "Yea," quoth Phoebe, "and so great a persuasive, that if it please you, madam, and Aliena to give us leave, Montanus and I will make this day the third couple in marriage."

She had no sooner spake this word, but Montanus threw away his garland of willow, his bottle, where was painted despair, and cast his sonnets in the fire, showing himself as frolic as Paris when he handselled his love with Helena. At this Gerismond and the rest smiled, and concluded that Montanus and 20 Phoebe should keep their wedding with the two brethren. Aliena seeing Saladyne stand in a dump, to wake him from his dream began thus:

"Why how now, my Saladyne, all amort? what melancholy, man, at the day of marriage? Perchance thou art sorrowful to think on thy brother's high fortunes, and thine own base desires to choose so mean a shepherdess. Cheer up thy heart, man; for this day thou shalt be married to the daughter of a king; for know, Saladyne, I am not Aliena, but Alinda, 30 the daughter of thy mortal enemy Torismond."

At this all the company was amazed, especially Gerismond, who rising up, took Alinda in his arms, and said to Rosalynde:

"Is this that fair Alinda famous for so many virtues, that forsook her father's court to live with thee exiled in the country?"

"The same," quoth Rosalynde.

"Then," quoth Gerismond, turning to Saladyne, "jolly forester be frolic, for thy fortunes are great, and thy desires excellent; thou hast got a princess as famous for her perfection, as exceeding in proportion."

"And she hath with her beauty won," quoth Saladyne, "an humble servant, as full of faith as she of amiable favor."

While every one was amazed with these comical events, Corydon came skipping in, and told them that the priest was at church, and tarried for their coming. With that Gerismond led the way, and the rest followed; where to the admiration of all the country swains in Arden their marriages were solemnly solemnized. As soon as the priest had finished, home they went with Alinda, where Corydon had made all things in readiness. Dinner was provided, and (the tables being spread, and the brides set down by Gerismond) Rosader, Saladyne, and Montanus that day were servitors; homely cheer they had, such as their country could afford, but to mend their fare they had mickle good chat, and many discourses of their loves and fortunes. About mid-dinner, to make them merry, Corydon came in with an old crowd,[1] and played them a fit of mirth, to which he sung this pleasant song:

Corydon's Song

A blithe and bonny country lass,
  heigh ho, the bonny lass!
Sate sighing on the tender grass
  and weeping said, will none come woo me.
A smicker boy, a lither swain,
  heigh ho, a smicker swain!
That in his love was wanton fain,
  with smiling looks straight came unto her.

[1] An old type of violin.

Whenas the wanton wench espied,
heigh ho, when she espied!
The means to make herself a bride,
she simpered smooth like Bonnybell:
The swain, that saw her squint-eyed kind,
heigh ho, squint-eyed kind!
His arms about her body twined,
and: "Fair lass, how fare ye, well?"

The country kit said: "Well, forsooth,
10 heigh ho, well forsooth!
But that I have a longing tooth,
a longing tooth that makes me cry."
"Alas," said he, "what gars thy grief?"
heigh ho, what gars thy grief?"
"A wound," quoth she, "without relief,
I fear a maid that I shall die."
"If that be all," the shepherd said,
heigh ho, the shepherd said!
"I'll make thee wive it gentle maid,
20 and so recure thy malady."

Hereon they kissed with many a oath,
heigh ho, with many an oath!
And fore God Pan did plight their troth,
and to the church they hied them fast.
And God send every pretty peat,[1]
heigh ho, the pretty peat!
That fears to die of this conceit,
so kind a friend to help at last.

Corydon having thus made them merry, as they
30 were in the midst of their jollity, word was brought in to Saladyne and Rosader that a brother of theirs, one Fernandyne, was arrived, and desired to speak with them. Gerismond overhearing this news, demanded who it was.

"It is, sir," quoth Rosader, "our middle brother, that lives a scholar in Paris; but what fortune hath driven him to seek us out I know not."

With that Saladyne went and met his brother, whom he welcomed with all courtesy, and Rosader

[1] Girl.

gave him no less friendly entertainment; brought he was by his two brothers into the parlor where they all sate at dinner. Fernandyne, as one that knew as many manners as he could points of sophistry, and was as well brought up as well lettered, saluted them all. But when he espied Gerismond, kneeling on his knee he did him what reverence belonged to his estate, and with that burst forth into these speeches:

"Although, right mighty prince, this day of my 10 brother's marriage be a day of mirth, yet time craves another course; and therefore from dainty cates rise to sharp weapons. And you, the sons of Sir John of Bordeaux, leave off your amours and fall to arms; change your loves into lances, and now this day show yourselves as valiant as hitherto you have been passionate. For know, Gerismond, that hard by at the edge of this forest the twelve peers of France are up in arms to recover thy right; and Torismond, trooped with a crew of desperate runagates, is ready 20 to bid them battle. The armies are ready to join; therefore show thyself in the field to encourage thy subjects; and you, Saladyne and Rosader, mount you, and show yourselves as hardy soldiers as you have been hearty lovers; so shall you, for the benefit of your country, discover the idea of your father's virtues to be stamped in your thoughts, and prove children worthy of so honorable a parent."

At this alarm, given by Fernandyne, Gerismond leaped from the board, and Saladyne and Rosader 30 betook themselves to their weapons.

"Nay," quoth Gerismond, "go with me; I have horse and armor for us all, and then, being well mounted, let us show that we carry revenge and honor at our falchions' points."

Thus they leave the brides full of sorrow, especially Alinda, who desired Gerismond to be good to her father. He, not returning a word because his haste was great, hied him home to his lodge, where he delivered Saladyne and Rosader horse and armor, and himself armed royally led the way; not having ridden two leagues before they discovered where in a valley both the battles were joined. Gerismond seeing the wing wherein the peers fought, thrust in there, and cried "Saint Denis!" Gerismond laying on such load upon his enemies, that he showed how highly he did estimate of a crown. When the peers perceived that their lawful king was there, they grew more eager; and Saladyne and Rosader so behaved themselves, that none durst stand in their way, nor abide the fury of their weapons. To be short, the peers were conquerors, Torismond's army put to flight, and himself slain in battle. The peers then gathered themselves together, and saluted their king, conducted him royally into Paris, where he was received with great joy of all the citizens. As soon as all was quiet and he had received again the crown, he sent for Alinda and Rosalynde to the court, Alinda being very passionate for the death of her father, yet brooking it with the more patience, in that she was contented with the welfare of her Saladyne.

Well, as soon as they were come to Paris, Gerismond made a royal feast for the peers and lords of his land, which continued thirty days, in which time summoning a parliament, by the consent of his nobles he created Rosader heir apparent to the kingdom; he restored Saladyne to all his father's land and gave him the Dukedom of Nameurs; he made Fernandyne principal secretary to himself; and that fortune might every way seem frolic, he made Montanus lord over all the forest of Arden, Adam Spencer Captain of the King's Guard, and Corydon master of Alinda's flocks.

Here, gentlemen, may you see in Euphues' Golden Legacy, that such as neglect their fathers' precepts, incur much prejudice; that division in nature, as it is a blemish in nurture, so 't is a breach of good fortunes; that virtue is not measured by birth but by action; that younger brethren, though inferior in years, yet may be superior to honor; that concord is the sweetest conclusion, and amity betwixt brothers more forceable than fortune. If you gather any 10 fruits by this Legacy, speak well of Euphues for writing it, and me for fetching it. If you grace me with that favor, you encourage me to be more forward; and as soon as I have overlooked my labors, expect the Sailor's Calendar.

T. LODGE.

THOMAS NASHE

THE UNFORTUNATE TRAVELLER OR THE LIFE OF JACK WILTON

THOMAS NASHE matriculated at St. John's College, Cambridge, October 13, 1582, received a B. A. in March, 1585-6, and left for London, it seems, in 1588. There he became a prolific hack writer and was probably engaged to help defend the bishops' power in the Martin Mar-prelate controversy. In *Pierce Penniless*, the most popular of his volumes in his own time, he attacked rich men who failed to support wits. While the plague was raging in London, Nashe took refuge with his patron, Sir George Carey, on the Isle of Wight, where he wrote part of *The Unfortunate Traveller* and also *Christ's Tears*, which attacked the merchant class and thereby got Nashe into trouble. After his return to London, some of his pamphlets were considered seditious. His lodgings were searched in 1596, and he was forced to flee to Yarmouth, where he stayed while making his peace with the authorities. In gratitude for hospitality, he wrote *Lenten Stuff* in praise of the red herring to which the town owed its prosperity, a volume which contains some of his best narrative and liveliest prose. Nashe seems to have been alive in 1600, but was dead the next year.

The Unfortunate Traveller is a typical picaresque novel, recounting the adventures of a wandering rogue but also bringing in familiar names and making sport of customs and foibles of the day. It is the first important realistic novel in English. The background of the book was taken from various chronicles, but Nashe was careless of chronology and freely mixed events to suit his convenience. He steps from one battle to an insurrection that actually happened nineteen years later and ends the volume at the Field of the Cloth of Gold, fourteen years before some of the events treated earlier in the book. It is hard to believe that he had ever looked at a map of Europe since his itineraries skip about in strange fashion. He does not seem to know that Venice is built on canals, but he shares the common belief of his day that Italy was a sink of every conceivable iniquity. Nevertheless his unquenchable humor and skill at burlesque, his love of low life, and his forceful handling of the terrible have kept his book alive and interesting.

THE UNFORTUNATE TRAVELLER

About that time that the terror of the world and fever quartan of the French, Henry the Eighth (the only true subject of chronicles), advanced his standard against the two hundred and fifty towers of Turnay and Terwin and had the Emperor and all the nobility of Flanders, Holland, and Brabant as mercenary attendants on his full-sailed fortune, I, Jack Wilton (a gentleman at least), was a certain kind of an appendix or page, belonging or apper-
10 taining in or unto the confines of the English court, where what my credit was, a number of my creditors that I cozened can testify. *Coelum petimus stultitia;* which of us all is not a sinner? Be it known to as many as will pay money enough to peruse my story, that I followed the camp or the court, or the court

and the camp when Terwin lost her maidenhead and opened her gates to more than Jane Trosse did. There did I (soft! let me drink before I go any further) reign sole king of the cans and black jacks, prince of the pygmies, county palatine of clean straw and provant, and to conclude, lord high regent of rashers of the coals and red herring cobs. *Paulo maiora canamus.*

Well, to the purpose! What stratagemical acts 10 and monuments do you think an ingenious infant of my age might enact? You will say it were sufficient if he slur a die, pawn his master to the utmost penny, and minister the oath on the pantoufle artificially. These are signs of good education, I must confess, and arguments of In grace and virtue to proceed. Oh, but *aliquid latet quod non patet*; there's a farther path I must trace; examples confirm. List, lordings, to my proceedings. Whosoever is acquainted with the state of a camp understands 20 that in it be many quarters and yet not so many as on London Bridge. In those quarters are many companies, much company, much knavery; as true as that old adage, "Much courtesy, much subtlety." Those companies, like a great deal of corn, do yield some chaff; the corn are cormorants, the chaff are good fellows, which are quickly blown to nothing with bearing a light heart in a light purse.

Amongst this chaff was I winnowing my wits to live merrily, and by my troth, so I did. The prince 30 could command men spend their blood in his service; I could make them spend all the money they had for my pleasure. But poverty in the end parts friends; though I was prince of their purses and exacted of my unthrift subjects as much liquid allegiance as any Kaiser in the world could do, yet, where it is not to be had, the king must lose his right; want can not be withstood, men can do no more than they can do; what remained, then, but the fox's case must help, when the lion's skin is out at the elbows?

There was a lord in the camp; let him be a Lord of Misrule if you will, for he kept a plain alehouse without welt or guard of any ivy bush,[1] and sold cider and cheese by pint and by pound to all that came (at the very name of cider I can but sigh; there is so much of it in Rhenish wine nowadays). Well, *tendit ad sidera virtus;* there's great virtue belongs (I can tell you) to a cup of cider, and very good men have sold it, and at sea it is *aqua coelestis.* But that's neither here nor there; if it had no other patron but this peer of quart pots to authorize it, it were sufficient. This great lord, this worthy lord, this noble lord, thought no scorn (Lord have mercy upon us!) to have his great velvet breeches larded with the droppings of this dainty liquor, and yet he was an old servitor, a cavalier of an ancient house, as it might appear by the arms of his ancestors drawn very amiably in chalk on the inside of his tent door.

He and no other was the man I chose out to damn with a lewd, moneyless device. For, coming to him on a day as he was counting his barrels and setting the price in chalk on the head of every one of them, I did my duty very devoutly and told his aley honor I had matters of some secrecy to impart unto him if it pleased him to grant me private audience.

"With me, young Wilton?" quoth he. "Marry and shalt. Bring us a pint of cider of a fresh tap into the Three Cups here; wash the pot."

So into a back room he led me, where after he had spit on his finger and picked off two or three motes of his old moth-eaten velvet cap and sponged and wrung all the rheumatic drivel from his ill-favored goat's-beard, he bade me declare my mind,

[1] The sign of an inn.

and thereupon he drank to me on the same. I up with a long circumstance, alias, a cunning shift of the seventeens, and discoursed unto him what entire affection I had borne him time out of mind, partly for the high descent and lineage from whence he sprung, and partly for the tender care and provident respect he had of poor soldiers. That, whereas the vastity of that place (which afforded them no indifferent supply of drink or of victuals) might humble
10 them to some extremity and so weaken their hands, he vouchsafed in his own person to be a victualler to the camp (a rare example of magnificence and honorable courtesy), and diligently provided that without far travel every man might for his money have cider and cheese his belly full; nor did he sell his cheese by the whey only, or his cider by the great, but abased himself by his own hands to take a shoemaker's knife (a homely instrument for such a high personage to touch) and cut it out equally, like
20 a true justiciary, in little pennyworths that it would do a man good for to look upon. So likewise of his cider, the poor man might have his moderate draught of it (as there is a moderation in all things) as well for his doit or his dandiprat as the rich man for his half-sous or his denier.

"Not so much," quoth I, "but this tapster's linen apron, which you wear to protect your apparel from the imperfections of the spigot, most amply bewrays your lowly mind. I speak it with tears; too few such
30 humble-spirited noble men have we, that will draw drink in linen aprons. Why, you are every child's fellow; any man that comes under the name of a soldier and a good fellow, you will sit and bear company to the last pot; yea, and you take in as good part the homely phrase of 'Mine host, here's to you!' as if one saluted you with all the titles of your barony. These considerations, I say, which the

world suffers to slip by in the channel of carelessness, have moved me in ardent zeal of your welfare to forewarn you of some dangers that have beset you and your barrels."

At the name of *dangers* he start up and bounced with his fist on the board so hard that his tapster, overhearing him, cried, "Anon, anon, sir! By and by!" and came in and made a low leg and asked him what he lacked. He was ready to have stricken his
10 tapster for interrupting him in attention of this his so much desired relation, but for fear of displeasing me he moderated his fury and only sending him for the other fresh pint, willed him to look to the bar and come when he is called, "with a devil's name!" Well, at his earnest importunity, after I had moistened my lips to make my lie run glib to his journey's end, forward I went as followeth.

"It chanced me the other night, amongst other pages, to attend where the King, with his lords and
20 many chief leaders, sat in council. There amongst sundry serious matters that were debated and intelligences from the enemy given up, it was privily informed (no villains to these privy informers!) that you—even you that I now speak to, had—(O, would I had no tongue to tell the rest; by this drink, it grieves me so I am not able to repeat it!)"

Now was my drunken lord ready to hang himself for the end of the full point, and over my neck he throws himself very lubberly, and entreated me, as
30 I was a proper young gentleman and ever looked for pleasure at his hands, soon to rid him out of this hell of suspense and resolve him of the rest. Then fell he on his knees, wrung his hands, and I think, on my conscience, wept out all the cider that he had drunk in a week before, to move me to have pity on him; he rose and put his rusty ring on my finger, gave me his greasy purse with that single money that was in

it, promised to make me his heir, and a thousand more favors if I would expire the misery of his unspeakable tormenting uncertainty.

I, being by nature inclined to mercy (for indeed I knew two or three good wenches of that name), bade him harden his ears and not make his eyes abortive before their time, and he should have the inside of my breast turned outward, hear such a tale as would tempt the utmost strength of life to attend
10 it, and not die in the midst of it.

"Why," quoth I, "myself that am but a poor childish well-willer of yours, with the very thought that a man of your desert and state by a number of peasants and varlets should be so injuriously abused in hugger-mugger, have wept all my urine upward. The wheel under our city bridge carries not so much water over the city as my brain hath welled forth gushing streams of sorrow. I have wept so immoderately and lavishly that I thought verily my palate
20 had been turned to Pissing Conduit in London. My eyes have been drunk, outrageously drunk, with giving but ordinary intercourse through their sea-circled islands to my distilling dreariment. What shall I say? That which malice hath said is the mere overthrow and murder of your days. Change not your color; none can slander a clear conscience to itself; receive all your fraught of misfortune in at once.

"It is buzzed in the King's head that you are a secret friend to the enemy, and under pretence of
30 getting a license to furnish the camp with cider and such-like provant, you have furnished the enemy, and in empty barrels sent letters of discovery and corn innumerable."

I might well have left here, for by this time his white liver had mixed itself with the white of his eye, and both were turned upwards, as if they had offered themselves a fair white for death to shoot at.

The truth was, I was very loath mine host and I should part to heaven with dry lips, wherefore the best means that I could imagine to wake him out of his trance, was to cry loud in his ear, "Ho, host, what's to pay? Will no man look to the reckoning here?" And in plain verity, it took expected effect, for with the noise he started and bustled, like a man that had been scared with fire out of his sleep, and ran hastily to his tapster, and all to belabored him about the ears, for letting gentlemen call so long and not look in to them. Presently he remembered himself, and had like to have fallen into his memento again, but that I met him half ways and asked his lordship what he meant to slip his neck out of the collar so suddenly and, being revived, strike his tapster so rashly.

"Oh," quoth he, "I am bought and sold for doing my country such good service as I have done. They are afraid of me because my good deeds have brought me into such estimation with the commonalty. I see, I see, it is not for the lamb to live with the wolf."

"The world is well amended," thought I, "with your cidership; such another forty years' nap together as Epimenides had would make you a perfect wise man."

"Answer me," quoth he, "my wise young Wilton, is it true that I am thus underhand dead and buried by these bad tongues?"

"Nay," quoth I, "you shall pardon me, for I have spoken too much already; no definitive sentence of death shall march out of my well-meaning lips; they have but lately sucked milk, and shall they so suddenly change their food and seek after blood?"

"Oh but," quoth he, "a man's friend is his friend (fill the other pint, tapster); what said the King? Did he believe it when he heard it? I pray thee say;

I swear to thee by my nobility, none in the world shall be made privy that I received any light of this matter from thee."

"That firm affiance," quoth I, "had I in you before, or else I would never have gone so far over the shoes, to pluck you out of the mire. Not to make many words (since you will needs know), the King says flatly, you are a miser and a snudge, and he never hoped better of you."

10 "Nay, then," quoth he, "questionless some planet that loves not cider hath conspired against me."

"Moreover, which is worse, the King hath vowed to give Terwin one hot breakfast only with the bungs that he will pluck out of your barrels. I cannot stay at this time to report each circumstance that passed, but the only counsel that my long cherished kind inclination can possibly contrive, is now in your old days to be liberal; such victuals or provisions as you have, presently distribute it frankly amongst poor 20 soldiers; I would let them burst their bellies with cider and bathe in it, before I would run into my prince's ill opinion for a whole sea of it. The hunter pursuing the beaver for his stones, he bites them off, and leaves them behind for him to gather up, whereby he lives quiet. If greedy hunters and hungry tell-tales pursue you, it is for a little pelf that you have; cast it behind you, neglect it, let them have it, lest it breed a further inconvenience. Credit my advice; you shall find it prophetical—and thus 30 I have discharged the part of a poor friend."

With some few like phrases of ceremony, "Your Honor's suppliant," and so forth, and "Farewell, my good youth, I thank thee and will remember thee," we parted.

But the next day I think we had a dole of cider: cider in bowls, in scuppets, in helmets; and to conclude, if a man would have filled his boots full, there he might have had it; provant thrust itself into poor soldiers' pockets whether they would or no. We made five peals of shot into the town together of nothing but spigots and faucets of discarded empty barrels; every underfoot soldier had a distenanted tun, as Diogenes had his tub, to sleep in. I myself got as many confiscated tapsters' aprons as made me a tent as big as any ordinary commander's in the field.

10 But in conclusion my well-beloved baron of double beer got him humbly on his mary-bones to the King and complained he was old and stricken in years and had never an heir to cast at a dog, wherefore if it might please his Majesty to take his lands into his hands, and allow him some reasonable pension to live on, he should be marvelous well pleased; as for the wars, he was weary of them; yet as long as Highness should venture his own person, he would not flinch a foot, but make his withered body a buck-
20 ler to bear off any blow that should be advanced against him.

The King, marveling at this strange alteration of his great merchant of cider (for so he would often pleasantly term him), with a little farther talk bolted out the whole complotment. Then was I pitifully whipped for my holyday lie though they made themselves merry with it many a fair winter's evening after. Yet, notwithstanding, his good ass-headed honor, mine host, persevered in his former
30 simple request to the King to accept the surrender of his lands and allow him a beadsmanry or out-brothership of brachet; which at length through his vehement instancy took effect, and the King jestingly said, since he would needs have it so, he would distrain on part of his land for impost of cider which he was behindhand with him and never paid.

This was one of my famous achievements, insomuch as I never light upon the like famous fool but I have done a thousand better jests if they had been booked in order as they were begotten. It is pity posterity should be deprived of such precious records; and yet there is no remedy—and yet there is too, for when all fails, well fare a good memory. Gentle readers (look you be gentle, now since I have called you so), as freely as my knavery was mine own, it shall be yours to use in the way of honesty.

Wilton has various other adventures, some at Münster, Germany.

10 With the tragical catastrophe of this Munsterian conflict did I cashier the new vocation of my cavaliership. There was no more honorable wars in Christendom then towards, wherefore after I had learned to be half an hour in bidding a man *bon jour* in German synonyms, I traveled along the country towards England as fast as I could.

What with wagons and bare ten toes having attained to Middleborough (good Lord, see the changing chances of us knight-arrant infants!), I met 20 with the right honorable Lord Henry Howard, Earl of Surrey, my late master. Jesu, I was persuaded I should not be more glad to see heaven than I was to see him! Oh, it was a right noble lord, liberality itself (if in this iron age there were any such creature as liberality left on the earth), a prince in content because a poet without a peer.

Destiny never defames herself but when she lets an excellent poet die. If there be any spark of Adam's paradised perfection yet embered up in the 30 breasts of mortal men, certainly God hath bestowed that, his perfectest image, on poets. None come so near to God in wit, none more contemn the world, *vatis avarus non temere est animus,* saith Horace, *versus amat, hoc studet unum*: seldom have you seen any poet possessed with avarice; only verses he loves, nothing else he delights in; and as they contemn the world, so, contrarily, of the mechanical world are none more contemned. Despised they are of the world, because they are not of the world; their thoughts are exalted above the world of ignorance and all earthly conceits.

As sweet angelical choristers, they are continually
10 conversant in the heaven of arts. Heaven itself is but the highest height of knowledge; he that knows himself and all things else, knows the means to be happy; happy, thrice happy are they whom God hath doubled his spirit upon and given a double soul unto, to be poets.

My heroical master exceeded in this supernatural kind of wit; he entertained no gross earthly spirit of avarice nor weak womanly spirit of pusillanimity and fear that are fained to be of the water, but admi-
20 rable, airy, and fiery spirits, full of freedom, magnanimity, and bountihood. Let me not speak any more of his accomplishments for fear I spend all my spirits in praising him and leave myself no vigor of wit or effects of a soul to go forward with my history.

Having thus met him I so much adored, no interpleading was there of opposite occasions, but back I must return and bear half-stakes with him in the lottery of travel. I was not altogether unwilling
30 to walk along with such a good purse-bearer; yet, musing what changeable humor had so suddenly seduced him from his native soil to seek out needless perils in those parts beyond sea, one night very boldly I demanded of him the reason that moved him thereto.

"Ah," quoth he, "my little page, full little canst thou perceive how far metamorphosed I am from myself since I last saw thee. There is a little god called Love that will not be worshiped of any leaden brains, one that proclaims himself sole king and emperor of piercing eyes and chief sovereign of soft hearts. He it is that, exercising his empire in my eyes, hath exorcised and clean conjured me from my content.

"Thou knowest stately Geraldine, too stately, I fear, for me to do homage to her statue or shrine. 10 She it is that is come out of Italy to bewitch all the wise men of England. Upon Queen Katherine Dowager she waits, that hath a dowry of beauty sufficient to make her wooed of the greatest kings in Christendom. Her high exalted sunbeams have set the Phœnix-nest of my breast on fire, and I myself have brought Arabian spiceries of sweet passions and praises, to furnish out the funeral flame of my folly. Those who were condemned to be smothered to death by sinking down into the soft bottom of an 20 high-built bed of roses, never died so sweet a death as I should die, if her rose-colored disdain were my deathsman.

"Oh, thrice-imperial Hampton Court, Cupid's enchanted castle, the place where I first saw the perfect omnipotence of the Almighty expressed in mortality, 'tis thou alone that, tithing all other men solace in thy pleasant situation, affordest me nothing but an excellent-begotten sorrow out of the chief treasury of all thy recreations!

30 "Dear Wilton, understand that there it was where I first set eye on my more than celestial Geraldine. Seeing her, I admired her; all the whole receptacle of my sight was unhabited with her rare worth. Long suit and uncessant protestations got me the grace to be entertained. Did never unloving servant so prenticelike obey his never pleased mistress as I

did her. My life, my wealth, my friends, had all their destiny depending on her command.

"Upon a time I was determined to travel, the fame of Italy and an especial affection I had unto poetry, my second mistress, for which Italy was so famous, had wholly ravished me into it. There was no dehortment from it, but needs thither I would; wherefore coming to my mistress as she was then walking with other ladies of estate in Paradise at Hampton 10 Court, I most humbly besought her of favor that she would give me so much gracious leave to absent myself from her service as to travel a year or two into Italy.

"She very discreetly answered me that if my love were so hot as I had often avouched, I did very well to apply the plaster of absence unto it, for absence, as they say, causeth forgetfulness: 'yet nevertheless, since it is Italy, my native country, you are so desirous to see, I am the more willing to make my will 20 yours. *I pete Italiam;* go and seek Italy with Aeneas, but be more true than Aeneas; I hope that kind, wit-cherishing climate will work no change in so witty a breast. No country of mine shall it be more, if it conspire with thee in any new love against me. One charge I will give thee, and let it be rather a request than a charge: when thou comest to Florence (the fair city from whence I fetched the pride of my birth), by an open challenge defend my beauty against all comers.

30 " 'Thou hast that admirable carriage in arms, that it shall be no discredit for me to bequeath all the glory of my beauty to thy well-governed arm. Fain would I be known where I was born; fain would I have thee known where Fame sits in her chiefest theatre. Farewell; forget me not; continued deserts will eternize me unto thee; thy full wishes shall be expired when thy travel shall be once ended.'

"Here did tears step out before words and intercepted the course of my kind-conceived speech, even as wind is allayed with rain. With heart-scalding sighs I confirmed her parting request, and vowed myself hers while living heat allowed me to be mine own. *Hinc illae lachrymae*: here hence proceedeth the whole cause of my peregrination."

Not a little was I delighted with this unexpected love story, especially from a mouth out of which was
10 nought wont to march but stern precepts of gravity and modesty. I swear unto you, I thought his company the better by a thousand crowns, because he had discarded those nice terms of chastity and continency. Now I beseech God love me so well as I love a plain-dealing man. Earth is earth, flesh is flesh; earth will to earth and flesh unto flesh. Frail earth, frail flesh, who can keep you from the work of your creation?

Dismissing this fruitless annotation *pro et contra*,
20 towards Venice we progressed and took Rotterdam in our way that was clean out of our way. There we met with aged learning's chief ornament, that abundant and superingenious clerk Erasmus, as also with merry Sir Thomas More, our countryman, who was come purposely over a little before us to visit the said grave father Erasmus. What talk, what conference we had then, it were here superfluous to rehearse; but this I can assure you, Erasmus in all his speeches seemed so much to mislike the indiscretion
30 of princes in preferring of parasites and fools that he decreed with himself to swim with the stream and write a book forthwith in commendation of folly. Quick-witted Sir Thomas More travelled in a clean contrary province; for he, seeing most commonwealths corrupted by ill custom, and that principalities were nothing but great piracies which, gotten by violence and murder, were maintained by private

undermining and bloodshed; that in the chiefest flourishing kingdoms there was no equal or well-divided weal one with another, but a manifest conspiracy of rich men against poor men, procuring their own unlawful commodities under the name and interest of the commonwealth. He concluded with himself to lay down a perfect plot of a commonwealth or government which he would entitle his *Utopia*.

So left we them to prosecute their discontented 10 studies and make our next journey to Wittenberg.

Wilton goes to Italy, where he separates from Surrey and takes a courtesan. He is in Rome during the plague.

During this time of visitation there was a Spaniard, one Esdras of Granado, a notable bandetto authorized by the Pope because he had assisted him in some murders. This villain colleagued with one Bartol, a desperate Italian, practised to break into those rich men's houses in the night, where the plague had most reigned, and if there were none but the mistress and maid left alive, to ravish them both and bring away all the wealth they could fasten on. 20 In an hundred chief citizens' houses where the hand of God had been, they put this outrage in use. Though the women so ravished cried out, none durst come near them for fear of catching their deaths by them, and some thought they cried out only with the tyranny of the malady.

Amongst the rest, the house where I lay he invaded, where all being snatched up by sickness but the good wife of the house, a noble and chaste matron called Heraclide, and her zany, and I and my 30 courtesan, he, knocking at the door late in the night, ran in to the matron and left me and my love to the mercy of his companion. Who, finding me in bed (as the time required) ran at me full with his rapier, thinking I would resist him, but as good luck was, I escaped him and betook me to my pistol in the window uncharged. He, fearing it had been charged, threatened to run her through if I once offered but to aim at him. Forth the chamber he dragged her, holding his rapier at her heart, whilst I still cried out, "Save her, kill me, and I'll ransom her with a thousand ducats!" But lust prevailed; no prayers 10 would be heard.

Into my chamber I was locked, and watchmen charged (as he made semblance when there was none there) to knock me down with their halberds if I stirred but a foot down the stairs. So threw I myself pensive again on my pallet and dared all the devils in hell now I was alone to come and fight with me one after another in defense of that detestable rape. I beat my head against the walls and called them bawds because they would see such a 20 wrong committed and not fall upon him.

To return to Heraclide below, whom the ugliest of all bloodsuckers, Esdras of Granado, had under shrift. First he assailed her with rough means and slew her zany at her foot, that stepped before her in rescue. Then when all armed resist was put to flight, he assayed her with honey speech and promised her more jewels and gifts than he was able to pilfer in an hundred years after. He discoursed unto her how he was countenanced and borne out by the 30 Pope, and how many execrable murders with impunity he had executed on them that displeased him.

"This is the eight-score house," quoth he, "that hath done homage unto me, and here I will prevail, or I will be torn in pieces!"

"Ah," quoth Heraclide, with a heartrending sigh, "art thou ordained to be a worse plague to me than the plague itself? Have I escaped the hands of God to fall into the hands of man? Hear me, Jehovah, and be merciful in ending my misery! Dispatch me incontinent, dissolute homicide, death's usurper! Here lies my husband, stone cold on the dewy floor. If thou beest of more power than God, to strike me speedily, strike home, strike deep, send me to heaven with my husband. Ay me, it is the spoil of my honor thou seekest in my soul's troubled departure; thou art some devil sent to tempt me. Avoid from 10 me, Satan; my soul is my Savior's; to Him I have bequeathed it; from Him can no man take it. Jesu, Jesu! Spare me undefiled for thy spouse. Jesu, Jesu! Never fail those that put their trust in thee."

With that she fell in a swoon, and her eyes in their closing seemed to spawn forth in their outward sharp corners new-created seed-pearl which the world before never set eye on. Soon he rigorously revived her and told her that he had a charter above Scripture; she must yield; she should yield; see who durst 20 remove her out of his hands.

Twixt life and death thus she faintly replied, "How thinkest thou; is there a power above thy power? If there be, he is here present in punishment, and on thee will take present punishment if thou persistest in thy enterprise. In the time of security every man sinneth, but when death substitutes one friend his special bailey to arrest another by infection and disperseth his quiver into ten thousand hands at once, who is it but looks about him? 30 A man that hath an inevitable huge stone hanging only by a hair over his head, which he looks every Paternoster-while to fall and bash him in pieces, will not he be submissively sorrowful for his transgressions, refrain himself from the least thought of folly, and purify his spirit with contrition and penitence? God's hand like a huge stone hangs inevitably over thy head; what is the plague, but Death

playing the Provost Marshal, to execute all those that will not be called home by any other means? This my dear knight's body is a quiver of his arrows which already are shot into thee invisible. Even as the age of goats is known by the knots on their horns, so think the anger of God apparently visioned or shown unto thee in the knitting of my brows. A hundred have I buried out of my house, at all whose departures I have been present; a hundred's infec-
10 tion is mixed with my breath; lo, now I breathe upon thee, a hundred deaths come upon thee. Repent betimes; imagine there is a hell, though not a heaven; that hell thy conscience is thoroughly acquainted with, if thou hast murdered half so many as thou unblushingly braggest. As Mæcenas in the latter end of his days was seven years without sleep, so these seven weeks have I took no slumber. My eyes have kept continual watch upon the devil my enemy; death I deemed my friend (friends fly from
20 us in adversity); death, the devil, and all the ministering spirits of temptation are watching about thee to entrap thy soul, by my abuse, to eternal damnation. It is thy soul only mayst thou save by saving mine honor. Death will have thy body infallibly for breaking into my house that he had selected for his private habitation. If thou ever camest of a woman or hopst to be saved by the seed of a woman, spare a woman! Deers, oppressed with dogs, when they cannot take soil, run to men for succor; to whom
30 should women in their disconsolate and desperate state run but to men like the deer for succor and sanctuary? If thou be a man, thou wilt succor me; but if thou be a dog and a brute beast, thou wilt spoil me, defile me, and tear me. Either renounce God's image or renounce the wicked mind that thou barest!"

These words might have moved a compound heart

of iron and adamant, but in his heart they obtained no impression, for he sitting in his chair of state against the door all the while that she pleaded, leaning his overhanging gloomy eye-brows on the pommel of his unsheathed sword, he never looked up or gave her a word. But when he perceived she expected his answer of grace or utter perdition, he start up and took her currishly by the neck and asked her how long he should stay for her ladyship.

10 "Thou tellest me," quoth he, "of the plague and the heavy hand of God and thy hundred infected breaths in one; I tell thee I have cast the dice an hundred times for the galleys in Spain, and yet still missed the ill chance. Our order of casting is this: If there be a general or captain new come home from the wars and hath some four or five hundred crowns overplus of the King's in his hand and his soldiers all paid, he makes proclamation that whatsoever two resolute men will go to dice for it and win the bridle 20 or lose the saddle, to such a place let them repair and it shall be ready for them. Thither go I and find another such needy squire resident. The dice run, I win, he is undone. I winning have the crowns; he losing is carried to the galleys. This is our custom, which a hundred times and more hath paid me custom of crowns when the poor fellows have gone to Gehenna, had coarse bread and whipping-cheer all their life after.

"Now, thinkest thou that I who so oft have es- 30 caped such a number of hellish dangers, only depending upon the turning of a few pricks, can be scare-budged with the plague? What plague canst thou name worse than I have had: whether diseases, imprisonment, poverty, banishment,—I have passed through them all. My own mother gave I a box of the ear to and brake her neck down a pair of stairs because she would not go in to a gentleman when I bade her; my sister I sold to an old Leno to make his best of her; any kinswoman that I have—knew I she were not a whore—myself should make her one! Thou art a whore; thou shalt be a whore in spite of religion or precise ceremonies."

Therewith he flew upon her and threatened her with his sword, but it was not that he meant to wound her with. He grasped her by the ivory throat and shook her as a mastiff would shake a 10 young bear, swearing and staring he would tear out her weasand if she refused. Not content with that savage restraint, he slipped his sacrilegious hand from her lily, lawn-skinned neck and inscarfed it in her long silver locks, which with struggling were unrolled. Backward he dragged her, even as a man backward would pluck a tree down by the twigs, and then, like a traitor that is drawn to execution on a hurdle, he traileth her up and down the chamber by those tender untwisted braids, and setting his bar- 20 barous foot on her bare snowy breast, bade her yield or have her wind stamped out.

She cried, "Stamp, stifle me in my hair, hang me up by it on a beam and so let me die, rather than I should go to heaven with a beam in my eye!"

"No," quoth he, "nor stamped, nor stifled, nor hanged, nor to heaven shalt thou go till I have had my will of thee! Thy busy arms in these silken fetters I'll enfold!"

Dismissing her hair from his fingers and pinioning 30 her elbows therewithal; she struggled, she wrested, but all was in vain. So struggling and so resisting, her jewels did sweat, signifying there was poison coming towards her. On the hard boards he threw her and used his knee as an iron ram to beat ope the two-leaved gate of her chastity. Her husband's dead body he made a pillow to his abomination.

Conjecture the rest; my words stick fast in the

mire and are clean tired—would I had never undertook this tragical tale! Whatsoever is born, is born to have an end. Thus ends my tale; his boorish lust was glutted, his beastly desire satisfied; what in the house of any worth was carriageable, he put up, and went his way.

Let not your sorrow die, you that have read the proem of the narration of this elegiacal history. Show you have quick wits in sharp conceit of com-
10 passion. A woman that hath viewed all her children sacrificed before her eyes, and after the first was slain, wiped the sword with her apron to prepare it for the cleanly murder of the second, and so on forward till it came to the empiercing of the seventeenth of her loins—will you not give her great allowance of anguish? This woman, this matron, this forsaken Heraclide, having buried fourteen children in five days whose eyes she howlingly closed and caught many wrinkles with funeral kisses, be-
20 sides having her husband within a day after laid forth as a comfortless corse, a carrionly block that could neither eat with her, speak with her, nor weep with her, is she not to be borne withal though her body swell with a tympany of tears, though her speech be as impatient as unhappy Hecuba's, though her head raves and her brain dote? Devise with yourselves that you see a corse rising from his hearse after he is carried to church, and such another suppose Heraclide to be, rising from the couch of en-
30 forced adultery.

Her eyes were dim, her cheeks bloodless, her breath smelt earthy, her countenance was ghastly. Up she rose after she was deflowered, but loath she arose as a reprobate soul rising to the Day of Judgment. Looking on the one side as she rose, she spied her husband's body lying under her head. Ah, then she bewailed, as Cephalus when he had killed Procris unwittingly, or Œdipus when ignorantly he had slain his own father and known his mother incestuously. This was her subdued reason's discourse.

"Have I lived to make my husband's body the bier to carry me to hell? Had filthy pleasure no other pillow to lean upon but his spreaded limbs? On thy flesh my fault shall be imprinted at the Day of Resurrection! O Beauty, the bait ordained to ensnare the irreligious! Rich men are robbed for their wealth; women are dishonested for being too fair. No blessing is beauty, but a curse; cursed be the time that ever I was begotten; cursed be the time that my mother brought me forth to tempt! The serpent in Paradise did no more; the serpent in Paradise is damned sempiternally—why should not I hold myself damned (if predestination's opinions be true) that am predestinate to this horrible abuse? The hog dieth presently if he loseth an eye; with the hog have I wallowed in the mire; I have lost my eye of honesty; it is clean plucked out with a strong hand of unchastity; what remaineth but I die? Die I will, though life be unwilling; no recompense is there for me to redeem my compelled offence but with a rigorous compelled death. Husband, I'll be thy wife in heaven. Let not thy pure deceasing spirit despise me when we meet because I am tyrannously polluted. The Devil, the belier of our frailty and common accuser of mankind, cannot accuse me though he would of unconstrained submitting. If any guilt be mine, this is my fault, that I did not deform my face ere it should so impiously allure!"

Having passioned thus awhile, she hastily ran and looked herself in the glass to see if her sin were not written on her forehead. With looking, she blushed though none looked upon her but her own reflected image. Then began she again, *"Heu quam difficile est crimen non prodere vultu;* how hard it

is not to bewray a man's fault by his forehead! Myself do but behold myself, and yet I blush; then God beholding me, shall not I be ten times more ashamed? The angels shall hiss at me, the saints and martyrs fly from me; yea, God himself shall add to the Devil's damnation, because he suffered such a wicked creature to come before him. Agamemnon, thou wert an infidel; yet when thou wentst to the Trojan War, thou leftst a musician at home with thy
10 wife who by playing the foot *spondaeus* till thy return, might keep her in chastity. My husband, going to war with the Devil and his enticements, when he surrendered left no musician with me but mourning and melancholy; had he left any, as Ægisthus killed Agamemnon's musician ere he could be successful, so surely would he have been killed ere this Ægisthus surceased. My distressed heart, as the hart whenas he loseth his horns is astonied and sorrowfully runneth to hide himself, so be thou afflicted
20 and distressed! Hide thyself under the Almighty's wing of mercy! Sue, plead, entreat; grace is never denied to them that ask. It may be denied; I may be a vessel ordained to dishonor.

"The only repeal we have from God's undefinite chastisement, is to chastise ourselves in this world,—and so I will. Nought but death be my penance! Gracious and acceptable may it be; my hand and my knife shall manumit me out of the horror of mind I endure. Farewell, life, that hast lent me nothing but
30 sorrow! Farewell, sin-sowed flesh, that hast more weeds than flowers, more woes than joys. Point, pierce! Edge, enwiden!—I patiently afford thee a sheath. Spur forth my soul to mount post to heaven! Jesu, forgive me, Jesu, receive me!"

So, throughly stabbed, fell she down, and knocked her head against her husband's body: wherewith he, not having been aired his full four and twenty hours, start as out of a dream; whiles I through a cranny of my upper chamber unsealed had beheld all this sad spectacle. Awaking, he rubbed his head to and fro, and wiping his eyes with his hand, began to look about him. Feeling something lie heavy on his breast, he turned it off, and, getting upon his legs, lighted a candle.

Here beginneth my purgatory. For he, good man, 10 coming into the hall with the candle and spying his wife with her hair about her ears, defiled and massacred, and his simple zany, Campestrano, run through, took a halberd in his hand and running from chamber to chamber to search who in his house was likely to do it, at length found me lying on my bed, the door locked to me on the outside, and my rapier unsheathed in the window, wherewith he straight conjectured it was I. And calling the neighbors hard by, said I had caused myself to be 20 locked into my chamber after that sort, sent away my courtesan whom I called my wife, and made clean my rapier because I would not be suspected.

Upon this was I laid in prison; should have been hanged; was brought to the ladder; had made a ballad for my farewell in a readiness, called *Wilton's Wantonness*—and yet for all that, scaped dancing in a hempen circle. He that hath gone through many perils and returned safe from them makes but a merriment to dilate them. I had the knot under my 30 ear; there was fair play; the hangman had one halter; another about my neck which was fastened to the gallows. The riding device was almost thrust home and his foot on my shoulder to press me down, when I made my saint-like confession you have heard before,—that such and such men at such an hour brake into the house, slew the zany, took my courtesan, locked me into my chamber, ravished Heraclide, and finally how she slew herself.

Present at the execution was there a banished English Earl, who, hearing that a countryman of his was to suffer for such a notable murder, came to hear his confession and see if he knew him. He had not heard me tell half of that I have recited, but he craved audience and desired the execution might be stayed.

10 "Not two days since it is, gentlemen and noble Romans," said he, "since, going to be let blood in a barber's shop against the infection, all on a sudden in a great tumult and uproar was there brought in one Bartol, an Italian, grievously wounded and bloody. I, seeming to commiserate his harms, courteously questioned him with what ill debtors he had met, or how or by what casualty he came to be so arrayed. 'Oh,' quoth he, 'long have I lived sworn brothers in sensuality with one Esdras of Granado; 20 five hundred rapes and murders have we committed betwixt us. When our iniquities were grown to the height and God had determined to countercheck our amity, we came to the house of Johannas de Imola,' (whom this young gentleman hath named); there did he justify all those rapes in manner and form as the prisoner here hath confessed. But lo, an accident after, which neither he nor this audience is privy to: Esdras of Granado, not content to have ravished the matron Heraclide and robbed her, after 30 he had betook him from thence to his heels, lighted on his companion Bartol with his courtesan, whose pleasing face he had scarce winkingly glanced on, but he picked a quarrel with Bartol to have her from him. On this quarrel they fought; Bartol was wounded to the death, Esdras fled, and the fair dame left to go whither she would. This Bartol in the barber's shop freely acknowledged, as both the

barber and his man and other here present can amply depose."

Wilton leaves Rome.

We, careless of these mischances, held on our flight, and saw no man come after us but we thought had pursued us. A thief, they say, mistakes every bush for a true man; the wind rattled not in any bush by the way as I rode, but I straight drew my rapier. To Bologna with a merry gale we posted, where we lodged ourselves in a blind street out of 10 the way, and kept secret many days. But when we perceived we sailed in the haven, that the wind was laid and no alarum made after us, we boldly came abroad; and one day, hearing of a more desperate murderer than Cain that was to be executed, we followed the multitude, and grudged not to lend him our eyes at his last parting.

Who should it be but one Cutwolf, a wearish, dwarfish, writhen-faced cobbler, brother to Bartol the Italian that was confederate to Esdras of Gra- 20 nado and at that time stole away my courtesan when he ravished Heraclide.

It is not so natural for me to epitomize his impiety as to hear him in his own person speak upon the wheel where he was to suffer. Prepare your ears and your tears, for never till this, thrust I any tragical matter upon you. Strange and wonderful are God's judgments; here shine they in their glory. Chaste Heraclide, thy blood is laid up in heaven's treasury; not one drop of it was lost but lent out to 30 usury; water poured forth sinks down quietly into the earth, but blood spilt on the ground sprinkles up to the firmament. Murder is wide-mouthed and will not let God rest till he grant revenge. Not only the blood of the slaughtered innocent, but the soul ascendeth to His throne and there cries out and exclaims for justice and recompense. Guiltless souls that live every hour subject to violence and with your despairing fears do much impair God's providence, fasten your eyes on this spectacle that will add to your faith. Refer all your oppressions, afflictions and injuries to the even-balanced eye of the Almighty. He it is that, when your patience sleepeth, will be most exceeding mindful of you.

This is but a gloss upon the text; thus Cutwolf 10 begins his insulting oration:

"Men and people that have made holiday to behold my pained flesh toil on the wheel, expect not of me a whining penitent slave, that shall do nothing but cry and say his prayers, and so be crushed in pieces. My body is little, but my mind is as great as a giant's; the soul which is in me is the very soul of Julius Caesar by reversion. My name is Cutwolf, neither better nor worse by occupation, but a poor cobbler of Verona—cobblers are men, and kings are 20 no more. The occasion of my coming hither at this present, is to have a few of my bones broken (as we are all born to die) for being the death of the Emperor of Homicides, Esdras of Granado.

"About two years since, in the streets of Rome, he slew the only and eldest brother I had, named Bartol, in quarreling about a courtezan. The news brought to me as I was sitting in my shop under a stall, knocking in of tacks, I think I raised up my bristles, sold pritch-awl, sponge, blacking tub and 30 punching iron, bought me rapier and pistol, and to go I went. Twenty months later, I pursued him, from Rome to Naples, from Naples to Caieta passing over the river, from Caieta to Siena, from Siena to Florence, from Florence to Parma, from Parma to Pavia, from Pavia to Sion, from Sion to Geneva, from Geneva back again towards Rome;

where in the way it was my chance to meet him here at Bologna as I will tell you how.

"I saw a great fray in the streets as I passed along and many swords walking, whereupon drawing nearer and inquiring who they were, answer was returned me that it was that notable bandetto, Esdras of Granado. Oh, so I was tickled in the spleen with that word, my heart hopped and danced, my elbows itched, my fingers frisked, I wist not what should 10 become of my feet nor knew what I did for joy. The fray parted. I thought it not convenient to single him out, being a sturdy knave, in the street, but to stay till I had got him at more advantage. To his lodging I dogged him, lay at his door all night where he entered for fear he should give me the slip anyway. Betimes in the morning I rung the bell and craved to speak with him. Up to his chamber door I was brought where, knocking, he rose in his shirt and let me in; and when he was entered, 20 bade me lock the door and declare my errand, and so he slipped to bed again.

"'Marry, this,' quoth I, 'is my errand. Thy name is Esdras of Granado, is it not? Most treacherously thou slewest my brother Bartol about two years ago in the streets of Rome; his death am I come to revenge. In quest of thee, ever since, above three thousand miles have I traveled. I have begged, to maintain me the better part of the way, only because I would intermit no time from my pursuit in 30 going back for money. Now have I got thee naked in my power; die thou shalt, though my mother and my grandmother dying did entreat for thee. I have promised the devil thy soul within this hour; break my word I will not: in thy breast I intend to bury a bullet! Stir not, quinch not, make no noise; for if thou dost it will be worse for thee!'

"Quoth Esdras, 'Whatever thou beest at whose

mercy I lie, spare me, and I will give thee as much gold as thou wilt ask. Put me to any pains, my life reserved, and I willingly will sustain them: cut off my arms and legs, and leave me as a lazar to some loathsome spittle, where I may but live a year to pray and repent me! For thy brother's death the despair of mind that hath ever since haunted me, the guilty gnawing worm of conscience I feel may be sufficient penance. Thou canst not send me to 10 such a hell as already there is in my heart. To dispatch me presently is no revenge, it will soon be forgotten; let me die a lingering death, it will be remembered a great deal longer. A lingering death may avail my soul, but it is the illest of ills that can misfortune my body. For my soul's health I beg my body's torment! Be not thou a devil to torment my soul and send me to eternal damnation. Thy overhanging sword hides heaven from my sight; I dare not look up lest I embrace my death's-20 wound unawares. I cannot pray to God and plead to thee both at once. Ay me, already I see my life buried in the wrinkles of thy brows; say but I shall live though thou meanest to kill me. Nothing confounds like to sudden terror; it thrusts every sense out of office. Poison wrapped up in sugared pills is but half a poison; the fear of death's looks are more terrible than his stroke. The whilst I view death, my faith is deaded; where a man's fear is, there his heart is. Fear never engenders hope; how 30 can I hope that heaven's Father will save me from the hell everlasting when he gives me over to the hell of thy fury?

"'Heraclide, now think I on thy tears sown in the dust—thy tears that my bloody mind made barren. In revenge of thee, God hardens this man's heart against me. Yet I did not slaughter thee, though hundreds else my hand hath brought to the shambles. Gentle sir, learn of me what it is to clog your conscience with murder, to have your dreams, your sleeps, your solitary walks troubled and disquieted with murder; your shadow by day will affright you; you will not see a weapon unsheathed but immediately you will imagine it is predestinate for your destruction. This murder is a house divided within itself; it suborns a man's own soul to inform against him: his soul, being his accuser, 10 brings forth his two eyes as witnesses against him, and the least eye-witness is unrefutable. Pluck out my eyes if thou wilt, and deprive my traitorous soul of her two best witnesses. Dig out my blasphemous tongue with thy dagger! Both tongue and eyes will I gladly forego, to have a little more time to think on my journey to heaven.

"'Defer a while thy resolution. I am not at peace with the world, for even but yesterday I fought, and in my fury threatened further venge- 20 ance. Had I face to face asked forgiveness, I should think half my sins were forgiven. A hundred devils haunt me daily for my horrible murders; the devils when I die will be loath to go to hell with me, for they desired of Christ He would not send them to hell before their time; if they go not to hell, into thee they will go and hideously vex thee for turning them out of their habitation. Wounds I contemn; life I prize light; it is another world's tranquility which makes me so timorous; everlast- 30 ing damnation, everlasting howling and lamentation! It is not from death I request thee to deliver me but from this terror of torment's eternity. Thy brother's body only I pierced unadvisedly; his soul meant I no harm to at all. My body and soul both shalt thou cast away quite if thou dost at this instant what thou mayest. Spare me, spare me, I beseech thee! By thy own soul's salvation I desire thee seek not my soul's utter perdition! In destroying me, thou destroyest thyself and me.'

"Eagerly I replied after this long suppliant oration, 'Though I knew God would never have mercy upon me except I had mercy on thee, yet of thee no mercy would I have. Revenge in our tragedies continually is raised from hell; of hell do I esteem better than heaven if it afford me revenge. There is no heaven but revenge. I tell thee I would not 10 have undertook so much toil to gain heaven as I have done in pursuing thee for revenge. Divine revenge, of which as of the joys above there is no fullness or satiety! Look how my feet are blistered with following thee from place to place! I have riven my throat with overstraining it to curse thee. I have ground my teeth to powder with grating and grinding them together for anger when any hath named thee. My tongue with vain threats is bolen[1] and waxen too big for my mouth; my eyes have 20 broken their strings with staring and looking ghastly as I stood devising how to frame or set my countenance when I met thee. I have near spent my strength in imaginary acting on stone walls, what I determined to execute on thee. Entreat not; a miracle may not reprieve thee; villain, thus march I with my blade into thy bowels!'

"'Stay, stay!' exclaimed Esdras, 'and hear me but one word further. Though neither for God nor man thou carest, but placest thy whole felicity in 30 murder, yet of thy felicity learn how to make a greater felicity. Respite me a little from thy sword's point, and set me about some execrable enterprise that may subvert the whole state of Christendom and make all men's ears tingle that hear of it. Command me to cut all my kindred's throats, to burn men, women and children in their beds in millions,

[1] Swollen.

by firing their cities at midnight. Be it Pope, Emperor or Turk that displeaseth thee, he shall not breathe on the earth. For thy sake will I swear and forswear, renounce my baptism and all the interest I have in any other sacrament. Only let me live, how miserable soever, be it in a dungeon amongst toads, serpents, and adders, or set up to the neck in dung. No pains I will refuse, however prorogued, to have a little respite to purify my spirit. Oh hear 10 me, hear me, and thou canst not be hardened against me!'

"At this his importunity I paused a little, not as retiring from my wreakful resolution, but going back to gather more forces of vengeance. With myself I devised how to plague him double in his base mind. My thoughts traveled in quest of some notable new Italianism whose murderous platform might not only extend on his body but his soul also. The groundwork of it was this: that whereas he 20 had promised for my sake to swear and forswear, and commit Julian-like violence on the highest seals of religion, if he would but thus far satisfy me, he should be dismissed from my fury. First and foremost he should renounce God and His laws and utterly disclaim the whole title or interest he had in any covenant of salvation. Next, he should curse Him to His face, as Job was willed by his wife, and write an absolute firm obligation of his soul to the devil without condition or exception. Thirdly and 30 lastly, having done this, he should pray to God fervently never to have mercy upon him, or pardon him.

"Scarce had I propounded these articles unto him, but he was beginning his blasphemous abjurations. I wonder the earth opened not and swallowed us both, hearing the bold terms he blasted forth in contempt of Christianity; heaven hath thundered

when half less contumelies against it have been uttered. Able they were to raise saints and martyrs from their graves, and pluck Christ Himself from the right hand of His Father. My joints trembled and quaked with attending them, my hair stood upright, and my heart was turned wholly to fire. So affectionately and zealously did he give himself over to infidelity, as if Satan had gotten the upper hand of our High Maker. The vein in his left hand that
10 is derived from the heart with no faint blow he pierced, and with the blood that flowed from it writ a full obligation of his soul to the devil; yea, he more earnestly prayed unto God never to forgive it his soul, than many Christians do to save their souls.

"These fearful ceremonies brought to an end, I bade him ope his mouth and gape wide. He did so, as what will not slaves do for fear? Therewith I made no more ado, but shot him full into
20 the throat with my pistol; no more spake he after; so did I shoot him that he might never speak after or repent him. His body, being dead, looked black as a toad; the devil presently branded it for his own.

"This is the fault that hath called me hither. No true Italian but will honor me for it. Revenge is the glory of arms and the highest performance of valor; revenge is whatsoever we call law or justice. The farther we wade in revenge, the nearer come we to the throne of the Almighty. To His scepter
30 it is properly ascribed; His scepter he lends unto man when he lets one man scourge another. All true Italians imitate me in revenging constantly and dying valiantly. Hangman, to thy task, for I am ready for the utmost of thy rigor."

Herewithal the people, outrageously incensed, with one conjoined outcry yelled mainly, "Away with him, away with him! Executioner, torture him! Tear him! Or we will tear thee in pieces if thou spare him!"

The executioner needed no exhortation hereunto, for of his own nature was he hackster good enough; old-excellent he was at a bone-ache. At the first chop with his wood-knife would he fish for a man's heart and fetch it out as easily as a plum from the bottom of a porridge-pot. He would crack necks as fast as a cook cracks eggs; a fiddler cannot turn 10 his pin so soon as he would turn a man off the ladder.

Bravely did he drum on this Cutwolf's bones, not breaking them outright, but like a saddler knocking in of tacks, jarring on them quaveringly with his hammer a great while together. No joint about him but, with a hatchet he had for the nonce, he disjointed half, and then with boiling lead soldered up the wounds from bleeding. His tongue he pulled out, lest he should blaspheme in his torment; 20 venomous stinging worms he thrust into his ears to keep his head ravingly occupied. With cankers scruzed to pieces he rubbed his mouth and his gums; no limb of his but was lingeringly splintered in shivers.

In this horror left they him on the wheel as in hell, where yet living he might behold his flesh legacied amongst the fowls of the air. Unsearchable is the book of our destinies; one murder begetteth another; was never yet bloodshed barren 30 from the beginning of the world to this day.

Mortifiedly abjected and daunted was I with this truculent tragedy of Cutwolf and Esdras. To such straight life did it thenceforward incite me that ere I went out of Bologna I married my courtesan, performed many alms-deeds, and hasted so fast out of the Sodom of Italy that within forty days I arrived at the King of England's camp twixt Ardes and Guines in France, where he with great triumphs met and entertained the Emperor and the French King and feasted many days.

And so as my story began with the King at Turnay and Turwin, I think meet here to end it with the King at Ardes and Guines. All the conclusive epilogue I will make is this, that if herein I have pleased any, it shall animate me to more pains in this kind.

10 Otherwise I will swear upon an English
Chronicle never to be outlandish
Chronicler more while I live. Fare-
well as many as wish me well.

June 27, 1593

THOMAS DELONEY

JACK OF NEWBURY

Thomas Deloney, another representative of Elizabethan realism, was exceedingly popular in his time, but until recently has been overlooked, for the most part, by students of the novel. Little is known of his life. He was originally a silk weaver of Norwich and probably sprang from a French Huguenot family. By 1583, he had begun writing, and by 1586 we find him settled, as a married man, in London. At first, no doubt, combining literature with weaving, Deloney gained much vogue as a ballad writer. He must have been in close touch with the life of the masses for whom he wrote, and he evidently wandered much through the English countryside. With *Jack of Newbury* in 1597, he turned to novel writing, as a result, possibly, of his having been compelled by hard times to give up his weaving. He died in 1600.

Deloney is preëminently the representative of the working

classes. He chooses most of his characters from their ranks, holds similar ideals, and in politics champions the cause of industry. Of his three novels, *Jack of Newbury* and *Thomas of Reading* treat weavers; *The Gentle Craft*, a work in two parts, deals with shoemakers.

Deloney, as a novelist, is a direct descendant of the popular literature of preceding epochs. In fact numerous episodes in his novels, such as the trick on the old woman in this selection, are of the sort found in jest books, but, except in *The Gentle Craft*, he gives his work a rough unity by means of a central character. Deloney likewise made use of material from various chronicles and from local traditions picked up during his wandering. In *Jack of Newbury* the hero is an actual person who died in that town in 1519.

Apart from their graphic depiction of Elizabethan manners, Deloney's novels are true in characterization and racy in dialogue.

JACK OF NEWBURY

Jack Winchcombe of Newbury, a poor boy who has become a master weaver, has recently married a girl of humble parentage for his second wife. She is here receiving a visitor.

"Truly, gossip, you are welcome. I pray you to sit down and we will have a morsel of something by and by."

"Nay, truly, gossip, I cannot stay," quoth she; "in troth I must be gone, for I did but even step in to see how you did."

"You shall not choose but stay a while," quoth Mistress Winchcombe; and with that a fair napkin was laid upon the little table in the parlor, hard by 10 the fireside, whereon was set a good, cold capon with a great deal of other good cheer with ale and wine plenty.

"I pray you, good gossip, eat, and I beshrew you if you spare," quoth the one.

"I thank you heartily, good gossip," saith the other. "But, good gossip, I pray you tell me, doth your husband love you well and make much of you?"

"Yes truly, I thank God," quoth she.

"Now by my troth," said the other, "it were a shame for him if he should not, for though I say it before your face, though he had little with you, you were worthy to be as good a man's wife as his."

"Trust me, I would not change my John for my lord marquis," quoth she. "A woman can be but well, for I live at heart's ease and have all things at will, and truly he will not see me lack anything."

10 "Marry, God's blessing on his heart," quoth her gossip. "It is a good hearing. But I pray you, tell me; I heard say your husband is chosen for our burgess in the Parliament house. Is it true?"

"Yes, verily," quoth his wife. "I wis it is against his will, for it will be no small charges unto him."

"Tush, woman, what talk you of that? Thanks be to God, there is never a gentleman in all Berkshire that is better able to bear it. But hear you, gossip, shall I be so bold to ask you one question 20 more?"

"Yes, with all my heart," quoth she.

"I heard say that your husband would now put you in your hood and silk gown; I pray you, is it true?"

"Yes in truth," quoth Mistress Winchcombe, "but far against my mind, gossip. My French hood is bought already, and my silk gown is a-making; likewise the goldsmith hath brought home my chain and bracelets; but I assure you, gossip, if you will 30 believe me, I had rather go an hundred miles than wear them; for I shall be so ashamed that I shall not look upon any of my neighbors for blushing."

"And why, I pray you?" quoth her gossip. "I tell you, dear woman, you need not be anything abashed or blush at the matter, especially seeing your husband's estate is able to maintain it. Now trust me truly, I am of opinion you will become it singular well."

"Alas," quoth Mistress Winchcombe, "having never been used to such attire, I shall not know where I am nor how to behave myself in it, and besides my complexion is so black that I shall carry but an ill-favored countenance under a hood."

"Now without doubt," quoth her gossip, "you are to blame to say so. Beshrew my heart if I 10 speak it to flatter, you are a very fair and well-favored young woman as any is in Newbury. And never fear your behavior in your hood, for I tell you true, as old and withered as I am myself, I could become a hood well enough and behave myself as well in such attire as any other whatsoever, and I would not learn of never a one of them all. What, woman, I have been a pretty wench in my days and seen some fashions. Therefore you need not to fear, seeing both your beauty and comely personage 20 deserves no less than a French hood, and be of good comfort. At the first, possible, folks will gaze something at you, but be not you abashed for that. It is better they should wonder at your good fortune than lament at your misery; but when they have seen you two or three times in that attire, they will afterward little respect it, for every new thing at the first seems rare, but being once a little used, it grows common."

"Surely, gossip, you say true," quoth she, "and I 30 am but a fool to be so bashful. It is no shame to use God's gifts for our credits, and well might my husband think me unworthy to have them if I would not wear them; and though I say it, my hood is a fair one as any woman wears in this country, and my gold chain and bracelets are none of the worst sort, and I will show them you because you shall give your opinion upon them," and therewithal she stepped into her chamber and fetched them forth.

When her gossip saw them, she said, "Now beshrew my fingers but these are fair ones indeed. And when do you mean to wear them, gossip?"

"At Whitsuntide," quoth she, "if God spare me life."

"I wish that well you may wear them," said her gossip, "and I would I were worthy to be with you 10 when you dress yourself. It should be never the worse for you. I would order the matter so that you should set everything about you in such sort as never a gentlewoman of them all should stain you."

Mistress Winchcombe gave her great thanks for her favor, saying that if she needed her help, she would be bold to send for her.

Then began her gossip to turn her tongue to another tune and now to blame her for her great 20 house-keeping. And thus she began: "Gossip, you are but a young woman and one that hath had no great experience of the world; in my opinion you are something too lavish in expenses. Pardon me, good gossip, I speak but for good will, and because I love you I am the more bold to admonish you. I tell you plain, were I the mistress of such a house, having such large allowance as you have, I would save twenty pound a year that you spend to no purpose."

30 "Which way might that be?" quoth Mistress Winchcombe. "Indeed I confess I am but a green housewife, and one that hath had but small trial in the world; therefore I would be very glad to learn anything that were for my husband's profit and my commodity."

"Then listen to me," quoth she. "You feed your folks with the best of the beef and the finest of the wheat, which in my opinion is a great oversight, neither do I hear of any knight in this country that doth it. And to say the truth, how were they able to bear that port which they do if they saved it not by some means? Come thither, and I warrant you that you shall see but brown bread on the board; if it be wheat and rye mingled together, it is a great matter and the bread highly commended, but most commonly they eat either barley bread or rye 10 mingled with peas and such like coarse grain which is doubtless but of small price, and there is no other bread allowed except at their own board. And in like manner for their meat; it is well known that necks and points of beef is their ordinary fare, which because it is commonly lean, they seethe therewith now and then a piece of bacon or pork, whereby they make their pottage fat and therewith drives out the rest with more content. And thus must you learn to do. And beside that, the midriffs of the oxen, 20 and the cheeks, the sheeps' heads and the gathers, which you give away at your gate, might serve them well enough, which would be a great sparing to your other meat, and by this means you would save in the year much money, whereby you might the better maintain your hood and silk gown. Again, you serve your folks with such superfluities that they spoil in a manner as much as they eat. Believe me, were I their dame, they should have things more sparingly, and then they would think it more dainty."

30 "Trust me, gossip," quoth Mistress Winchcombe, "I know your words in many things to be true, for my folks are so corn fed that we have much ado to please them in their diet. One doth say, 'This is too salt,' and another saith, 'This is too gross; this is too fresh; and that too fat,' and twenty faults they will find at their meals. I warrant you, they make such parings of their cheese and keep such

chipping of their bread that their very orts would serve two or three honest folks to their dinner."

"And from whence, I pray you, proceeds that," quoth her gossip, "but of too much plenty? But i'faith, were they my servants, I would make them glad of the worst crumbs they cast away, and thereupon I drink to you, and I thank you for my good cheer with all my heart."

"Much good may it do you, gossip," said Mistress Winchcombe, "and I pray you when you come this way, let us see you."

"That you shall verily," quoth she, and so away she went.

After this, Mistress Winchcombe took occasion to give her folks shorter commons and coarser meat than they were wont to have, which at length being come to the good man's ear, he was very much offended therewith, saying, "I will not have my people thus pinched of their victuals. Empty platters makes greedy stomachs, and where scarcity is kept, hunger is nourished; and therefore, wife, as you love me, let me have no more of this doings."

"Husband," quoth she, "I would they should have enough, but it is sin to suffer and a shame to see the spoil they make. I could be very well content to give them their bellies full and that which is sufficient, but it grieves me, to tell you true, to see how coy they are, and the small care they have in the wasting of things, and I assure you the whole town cries shame of it, and it hath bred me no small discredit for looking no better to it. Trust me no more if I was not checked in my own house about this matter, when my ears did burn to hear what was spoken."

"Who was it that checked thee, I pray thee tell me. Was it not your old gossip, Dame Dainty, Mistress Trip and Go? I believe it was."

"Why, man, if it were she, you know she hath been an old house-keeper and one that hath known the world, and that she told me was for good will."

"Wife," quoth he, "I would not have thee to meddle with such light-brained housewives, and so I have told thee a good many times, and yet I cannot get you to leave her company."

"Leave her company? Why, husband, so long as she is an honest woman, why should I leave her company? She never gave me hurtful counsel in her life but hath always been ready to tell me things for my profit though you take it not so. Leave her company? I am no girl, I would you should well know, to be taught what company I should keep. I keep none but honest company, I warrant you. Leave her company, quotha? Alas, poor soul, this reward she hath for her good will. I wis, I wis, she is more your friend than you are your own."

"Well let her be what she will," said her husband, "but if she come any more in my house, she were as good no. And therefore take this for a warning, I would advise you," and so away he went.

There was one Randall Pert, a draper, dwelling in Watling Street, that owed Jack of Newbury five hundred pounds at one time, who in the end fell greatly to decay, in so much that he was cast in prison and his wife with her poor children turned out of doors. All his creditors except Winchcombe had a share of his goods, never releasing him out of prison so long as he had one penny to satisfy them. But when this tidings was brought to Jack of Newbury's ear, his friends counseled him to lay his action against him.

"Nay," quoth he, "if he be not able to pay me when he is at liberty, he will never be able to pay me in prison; and therefore it were as good for me to forbear my money without troubling him as to add more sorrow to his grieved heart and be never the nearer. Misery is trodden down by many, and once brought low, they are seldom or never relieved; therefore he shall rest for me untouched, and I would to God he were clear of all other men's debts so that I gave him mine to begin the world again."

Thus lay the poor draper a long time in prison, in which space his wife, which before for daintiness would not foul her fingers nor turn her head aside for fear of hurting the set of her neckenger,[1] was glad to go about and wash bucks at the Thames' side and to be a charwoman in rich men's houses; her soft hand was now hardened with scouring, and instead of gold rings upon her lily fingers, they were now filled with chaps, provoked by the sharp lye and other drudgeries.

At last Master Winchcombe, being, as you heard, chosen against the Parliament a burgess for the town of Newbury and coming up to London for the same purpose, when he was alighted at his inn, he left one of his men there to get a porter to bring his trunk up to the place of his lodging. Poor Randall Pert, which lately before was come out of prison, having no other means of maintenance, became a porter to carry burthens from one place to another, having an old ragged doublet and a torn pair of breeches with his hose out at the heels, and a pair of old broken slip shoes on his feet, a rope about his middle instead of a girdle, and on his head an old greasy cap which had so many holes in it that his hair started through it, who, as soon as he heard one call for a porter, made answer straight, "Here, master, what is it that you would have carried?"

"Marry," quoth he, "I would have this trunk borne to the Spread Eagle at Iuiebridge."

[1] Neckerchief.

"You shall, master," quoth he, "but what will you give me for my pains?"

"I will give thee two pence."

"A penny more and I will carry it," said the porter; and so being agreed, away he went with his burthen till he came to the Spread Eagle door, where on a sudden espying Master Winchcombe standing, he cast down the trunk and ran away as hard as ever he could.

10 Master Winchcombe, wondering what he meant thereby, caused his man to run after him and so fetch him again, but when he saw one pursue him, he ran then the faster; and in running, he lost one of his slip shoes and then another, ever looking behind him like a man pursued with a deadly weapon, fearing every twinkling of an eye to be thrust through. At last his breech, being tied but with one point, what with the haste he made and the weakness of the thong, fell about his heels, which so 20 shackled him that down he fell in the street all along, sweating and blowing, being quite worn out of breath; and so by this means the serving-man overtook him, and taking him by the sleeve, being as windless as the other, stood blowing and puffing a great while ere they could speak one to another.

"Sirrah," quoth the serving-man, "you must come to my master. You have broken his trunk all to pieces by letting it fall."

"Oh for God's sake," quoth he, "let me go; for 30 Christ's sake, let me go, or else Master Winchcombe of Newbury will arrest me, and then I am undone forever."

Now by this time Jack of Newbury had caused his trunk to be carried into the house, and then he walked along to know what the matter was; and when he heard the porter say that he would arrest him, he wondered greatly, and having quite forgot

Pert's favor, being so greatly changed by imprisonment and poverty, he said, "Wherefore should I arrest thee? Tell me, good fellow; for my own part I know no reason for it."

"O sir," quoth he, "I would to God I knew none neither."

Then asking him what his name was, the poor man, falling down on his knees, said, "Good Master Winchcombe, bear with me, and cast me not into 10 prison. My name is Pert, and I do not deny but that I owe you five hundred pound; yet for the love of God, take pity upon me."

When Master Winchcombe heard this, he wondered greatly at the man and did as much pity his misery though as yet he made it not known, saying, "Passion of my heart, man, you will never pay me thus. Never think being a porter to pay five hundred pound debt. But this hath your prodigality brought you to, your thriftless neglecting of your 20 business, that set more by your pleasure than your profit." Then looking better upon him, he said, "What, never a shoe to thy foot, hose to thy leg, band to thy neck, nor cap to thy head? Oh Pert, this is strange, but wilt thou be an honest man and give me a bill of thy hand for my money?"

"Yes, sir, with all my heart," quoth Pert.

"Then come to the scrivener's," quoth he, "and dispatch it, and I will not trouble thee."

Now when they were come thither with a great 30 many following them at their heels, Master Winchcombe said, "Hearest thou, scrivener? This fellow must give me a bill of his hand for five hundred pounds; I pray thee make it as it should be."

The scrivener, looking upon the poor man and seeing him in that case, said to Master Winchcombe, "Sir, you were better to let it be a bond and have some sureties bound with him."

"Why, scrivener," quoth he, "dost thou think this is not a sufficient man of himself for five hundred pound?"

"Truly, sir," said the scrivener, "if you think him so, you and I are of two minds."

"I'll tell thee what," quoth Master Winchcombe, "were it not that we are all mortal, I would take his word as soon as his bill or bond. The honesty of a man is all."

10 "And we in London," quoth the scrivener, "do trust bonds far better than honesty. But, sir, when must this money be paid?"

"Marry, scrivener, when this man is Sheriff of London."

At that word the scrivener and the people standing by laughed heartily, saying, "In truth, sir, make no more ado, but forgive it him; as good to do the one as the other."

"Nay, believe me," quoth he, "not so; therefore 20 do as I bid you."

Whereupon the scrivener made the bill to be paid when Randall Pert was Sheriff of London and thereunto set his own hand for a witness, and twenty persons more that stood by set to their hands likewise.

Then he asked Pert what he should have for carrying his trunk.

"Sir," quoth he, "I should have three pence, but seeing I find you so kind, I will take but two pence 30 at this time."

"Thanks, good Pert," quoth he, "but for thy three pence, there is three shillings; and look thou come to me tomorrow morning betimes."

The poor man did so, at what time Master Winchcombe had provided him out of Burchin Lane a fair suit of apparel, merchant like, with a fair black cloak and all other things fit to the same. Then he took him a shop in Canweek Street and furnished the same shop with a thousand pounds' worth of cloth, by which means and other favors that Master Winchcombe did him, he grew again into great credit and in the end became so wealthy that while Master Winchcombe lived, he was chosen sheriff, at what time he paid five hundred pounds every penny, and after died an alderman of the city.

Upon a time it came to pass when Master Winch-
10 combe was far from home and his wife gone abroad, that Mistress Many Better, Dame Tittle Tattle, Gossip Pintpot, according to her old custom, came to Mistress Winchcombe's house, perfectly knowing of the good man's absence and little thinking the good wife was from home; where knocking at the gate, Tweedle stepped out and asked who was there, where hastily opening the wicket, he suddenly discovered the full proportion of this foul beast who demanded if their mistress were within.

20 "What, Mistress Frank," quoth he, "in faith welcome. How have you done a great while? I pray you come in."

"Nay, I cannot stay," quoth she. "Notwithstanding I did call to speak a word or two with your mistress. I pray you tell her that I am here."

"So I will," quoth he, "so soon as she comes in."

Then said the woman, "What, is she abroad? Why then, farewell, good Tweedle."

"Why what haste, what haste, Mistress Frank?"
30 quoth he. "I pray you stay and drink ere you go. I hope a cup of new sack will do your old belly no hurt."

"What," quoth she, "have you new sack already? Now by my honesty, I drunk none this year, and therefore I do not greatly care if I take a taste before I go;" and with that she went into the wine cellar with Tweedle, where first he set before her a piece of powdered beef as green as a leek. And then going into the kitchen, he brought her a piece of roasted beef, hot from the spit.

Now certain of the maidens of the house and some of the young men, who had long before determined to be revenged of this prattling housewife, came into the cellar one after another, one of them bringing a great piece of a gammon of bacon in his hand; and every one bade Mistress Frank welcome. And first one drunk to her and then another, and so the third, the fourth, and the fifth; so that Mistress Frank's brains waxed as mellow as a pippin at Michaelmas, and so light that sitting in the cellar, she thought the world ran round. They, seeing her to fall into merry humors, whetted her on in merriment as much as they could, saying, "Mistress Frank, spare not, I pray you, but think yourself as welcome as any woman in all Newbury, for we have cause to love you because you love our mistress so well."

"Now by my troth," quoth she, lisping in her speech (her tongue waxing somewhat too big for her mouth), "I love your mistress well indeed as if she were mine own daughter."

"Nay, but hear you," quoth they, "she begins not to deal well with us now."

"No, my lambs," quoth she, "why so?"

"Because," quoth they, "she seeks to bar us of our allowance, telling our master that he spends too much in house-keeping."

"Nay, then," quoth she, "your mistress is both an ass and a fool; and though she go in her hood, what care I? She is but a girl to me. Twittle, twattle, I know what I know. Go to, drink to me! Well, Tweedle, I drink to thee with all my heart. Why, thou whoreson, when wilt thou be married? Oh that I were a young wench for thy sake, but 'tis no matter. Though I be but a poor woman, I am a true woman. Hang dogs, I have dwelt in this town these thirty winters."

"Why then," quoth they, "you have dwelt here longer than our master."

"Your master?" quoth she. "I knew your master a boy when he was called Jack of Newbury. Ay Jack, I knew him called plain Jack; and your 10 mistress, now she is rich and I am poor, but it's no matter. I knew her a draggle tail girl, mark ye."

"But now," quoth they, "she takes upon her lustily and hath quite forgot what she was."

"Tush, what will you have of a green thing?" quoth she. "Here I drink to you so long as she goes where she list agossiping; and it's no matter; little said is soon amended. But hear you, my masters, though Mistress Winchcombe go in her hood, I am as good as she, I care not who tell it her. I 20 spend not my husband's money in cherries and codlings. Go to, go to, I know what I say well enough. I thank God I am not drunk. Mistress Winchcombe, mistress? No, Nan Winchcombe I will call her name, plain Nan. What, I was a woman when she was, sir-reverence, a paltry girl though now she goes in her hood and chain of gold. What care I for her? I am her elder, and I know more of her tricks. Nay, I warrant you, I know what I say. 'Tis no matter. Laugh at me, and spare not. 30 I am not drunk, I warrant," and with that, being scant able to hold open her eyes, she began to nod and to spill the wine out of her glass; which they perceiving, let her alone, going out of the cellar till she was sound asleep, and in the mean space they devised how to finish this piece of knavery.

At last they all consented to lay her forth at the back side of the house, half a mile off, even at the foot of a stile that whosoever came next over might find her. Notwithstanding Tweedle stayed hard to see the end of this action. At last comes a notable clown from Greenham, taking his way to Newbury; who, coming hastily over the stile, stumbled at the woman and fell down clean over her. But in his starting up, seeing it was a woman, cried out, "Alas, alas!"

"How now, what is the matter?" quoth Tweedle.

10 "Oh," quoth he, "here lies a dead woman."

"A dead woman?" quoth Tweedle. "That's not so, I trow," and with that he tumbled her about.

"Bones of me," quoth Tweedle, "'tis a drunken woman and one of the town undoubtedly; in troth it is a great pity she should lie here."

"Why, do you know her?" quoth the clown.

"No, not I," quoth Tweedle; "nevertheless I will give thee half a groat, and take her in thy basket, and carry her throughout the town, and see if any-20 body know her."

"Then," said the other, "let me see the money, and I will. For, by the mass, che earned not half a groat this great while."

"There it is," quoth Tweedle. Then the fellow put her in his basket and so lifted her upon his back.

"Now by the mass, she stinks vilely of drink or wine or something. But tell me, what shall I say when I come into the town," quoth he.

"First," quoth Tweedle, "I would have thee so 30 soon as ever thou canst get to the town's end, with a lusty voice to cry, 'O yes,' and then say, 'Who knows this woman, who?' And though possible some will say, 'I know her' and 'I know her,' yet do not thou set her down till thou comest to the Market Cross, and there use the like words. And if any be so friendly to tell thee where she dwells, then just before her door, cry so again. And if thou perform this bravely, I will give thee half a groat more."

"Master Tweedle," quoth he, "I know you well enough. You dwell with Master Winchcombe, do you not? I' faith if I do it not in the nick, give me never a penny."

And so away he went till he came to the town's end, and there he cries out as boldly as any bailiff's man, "O yes, who knows this woman, who?"

10 Then said the drunken woman in the basket, her head falling first on one side and then on the other side, "Who co me, who?"

Then said he again, "Who knows this woman, who?"

"Who co me, who?" quoth she, and look how oft he spoke the one, she spoke the other, saying still, "Who co me, who co me, who?" Whereat all the people in the street fell into such a laughter that the tears ran down again.

20 At last one made answer saying, "Good fellow, she dwells in the North Brook Street, a little beyond Master Winchcombe's."

The fellow, hearing that, goes down thither in all haste, and there in the hearing of a hundred people cries, "Who knows this woman, who?"

Whereat her husband comes out saying, "Marry, that do I too well, God help me."

Then said the clown, "If you know her, take her, for I know her not but for a drunken beast."

30 And as her husband took her out of the basket, she gave him a sound box on the ear, saying, "What, you queans, do you mock me?" and so was carried in.

But the next day when her brain was quiet and her head cleared of these foggy vapors, she was so ashamed of herself that she went not forth of her doors a long time after; and if anybody did say unto her, "Who co me, who?" she would be so mad and furious that she would be ready to draw her knife and stick them and scold as if she strove for the best game at the cucking stool. Moreover her prattling to Mistress Winchcombe's folks of their mistress made her on the other side to fall out with her in such sort that she troubled them no more, either with her company or her counsel.

OVERBURY AND EARLE CHARACTERS

CHARACTER writing was not unknown in early English literature, but the seventeenth century saw an enthusiastic outbreak of charactery as a special and separate form of writing. The immediate cause was probably Isaac Casaubon's translation into Latin of Theophrastus, a Greek writer of characters who lived in the fourth century. This appeared in 1592; an English version followed it the next year. Bacon's *Essays* possibly furnished another example for the crisp, condensed, acute style suited to charactery. The first Englishman to publish a volume of these sketches avowedly modeled on Theophrastus was Bishop Hall, whose *Characters of Virtues and Vices* appeared in 1608. He differs from the Greek, however, in that his work is full of moralizing; his characters are meant to do for a large audience what his sermons presumably did for a limited one.

Sir Thomas Overbury, who imitated Theophrastus more closely than Hall had done, was born in 1581, entered Queen's College, Oxford, in 1595, and received his B. A. three years later. To finish his education, he studied and traveled on the Continent. From his youth a friend of Robert Carr, Earl of Somerset, he opposed that gentleman's match with the Countess of Essex. The lady in revenge managed to have Sir Thomas imprisoned in the Tower and finally had him poisoned. He died there on September 15, 1613. The Earl of Somerset married Lady Essex, but suspicion of Overbury's murder fell on them; they were tried and acquitted, but her ladyship's tools, who seem to have performed the crime, were executed.

Overbury's volume of characters was first published posthumously in 1614, but the manuscript may have been circulated among his friends before his death. It went at once into edition after edition, its popularity perhaps enhanced by its author's mysterious fate. By the time it reached the sixteenth in 1638, the number of sketches had been greatly increased. It is now impossible to tell which are by Overbury himself and which by his friends. These characters describe the foibles and manners of persons seen in everyday life. They lack Hall's moralizing, and they show a pretty wit in style and observation.

John Earle, perhaps the best of the character writers, attended Christ Church College, Oxford, whence he graduated in 1619; became a fellow of Merton next year; and was made Doctor of Divinity in 1640. He was, throughout his life, a pious and devoted clergyman of the Church of England. Having suffered for his royalist principles during the Puritan régime, at the restoration of Charles II he was made Dean of Westminster in 1660, Bishop of Worcester in 1662, and the next year Bishop of Salisbury. He accompanied the court in its flight to Oxford from the plague in London and died there in 1665.

Earle's *Microcosmography* was printed in 1628, but the sixth edition in 1633 was the first to contain all his characters. Naturally they are ethical in their purpose, but they betray close observation of the persons about Earle in the university town where they were written. Furthermore, they strike at motives beneath externals and portray them with sympathetic humor. The fundamental kindliness and humanity which made the bishop treat his Puritan foes generously in their downfall is manifest in the young scholar's attitude toward those he saw about him at Oxford.

SIR THOMAS OVERBURY: CHARACTERS

An Affected Traveller

is a speaking fashion; he hath taken pains to be ridiculous and hath seen more than he hath perceived. His attire speaks French or Italian, and his gait cries, "Behold me". He censures all things

by countenances, and shrugs, and speaks his own language with shame and lisping; he will choke rather than confess beer good drink; and his pick-tooth is a main part of his behaviour. He chooseth rather to be counted a spy than not a politician and maintains his reputation by naming great men familiarly. He chooseth rather to tell lies than not wonders, and talks with men singly; his discourse sounds big but means nothing, and his boy is bound
10 to admire him howsoever. He comes still from great personages but goes with mean. He takes occasion to shew jewels given him in regard of his virtue, that were bought in St. Martin's, and, not long after having with a mountebank's method pronounced them worth thousands, impawneth them for a few shillings. Upon festival days he goes to court and salutes without resaluting; at night in an ordinary he canvasseth the business in hand and seems as conversant with all intents and plots as if
20 he begot them. His extraordinary account of men is first to tell them the ends of all matters of consequence and then to borrow money of them; he offereth courtesies to shew them, rather than himself, humble. He disdains all things above his reach and preferreth all countries before his own. He imputeth his wants and poverty to the ignorance of the time, not his own unworthiness, and concludes his discourse with half a period or a word, and leaves the rest to imagination. In a word, his religion is
30 fashion, and both body and soul are governed by fame; he loves most voices above truth.

An Elder Brother

is a creature born to the best advantage of things without him,—that hath the start at the beginning but loiters it away before the ending. He looks like his land, as heavily and dirtily, as stubbornly. He dares do anything but fight and fears nothing but his father's life, and minority. The first thing he makes known is his estate, and the loadstone that draws him is the upper end of the table. He wooeth by a particular, and his strongest argument is the jointure. His observation is all about the fashion, and he commends partlets [1] for a rare device. He speaks no language but smells of dogs or hawks, and 10 his ambition flies justice-height. He loves to be commended, and he will go into the kitchen but he'll have it. He loves glory but is so lazy as he is content with flattery. He speaks most of the precedency of age and protests fortune the greatest virtue. He summoneth the old servants and tells what strange acts he will do when he reigns. He verily believes house-keepers the best commonwealths men and therefore studies baking, brewing, greasing and such, as the limbs of goodness. He judgeth it 20 no small sign of wisdom to talk much; his tongue therefore goes continually his errand but never speeds. If his understanding were not honester than his will, no man should keep good conceit by him, for he thinks it no theft to sell all he can to opinion. His pedigree and his father's seal-ring are the stilts of his crazed disposition. He had rather keep company with the dregs of men than not to be the best man. His insinuation is the inviting of men to his house, and he thinks it a great modesty to com- 30 prehend his cheer under a piece of mutton and a rabbit; if he by this time be not known, he will go home again; for he can no more abide to have himself concealed than his land; yet he is (as you see) good for nothing except to make a stallion to maintain the race.

[1] Ruffs worn by women.

A Fair and Happy Milk-Maid

is a country wench that is so far from making herself beautiful by art that one look of hers is able to put all face-physic out of countenance. She knows a fair look is but a dumb orator to commend virtue, therefore minds it not. All her excellencies stand in her so silently as if they had stolen upon her without her knowledge. The lining of her apparel (which is her self) is far better than out sides of tissue, for though she be not arrayed in the spoil of the silk-worm, she is decked in innocence, a far better wearing. She doth not, with lying long abed, spoil both her complexion and conditions; nature hath taught her too immoderate sleep is rust to the soul. She rises therefore with chanticleer, her dame's cock, and at night makes the lamb her curfew. In milking a cow and straining the teats through her fingers, it seems that so sweet a milk-press makes the milk the whiter or sweeter, for never came almond glove or aromatic ointment on her palm to taint it. The golden ears of corn fall and kiss her feet when she reaps them, as if they wished to be bound and led prisoners by the same hand that felled them. Her breath is her own, which scents all the year long of June, like a new-made hay-cock. She makes her hand hard with labour and her heart soft with pity; and when winter evenings fall early (sitting at her merry wheel) she sings a defiance to the giddy wheel of fortune. She doth all things with so sweet a grace it seems ignorance will not suffer her to do ill, being her mind is to do well. She bestows her year's wages at next fair, and in choosing her garments counts no bravery i' th' world like decency. The garden and bee-hive are all her physic and chirurgery, and she lives the longer for 't. She

dare go alone and unfold sheep i' th' night and fears no manner of ill, because she means none; yet to say truth, she is never alone, for she is still accompanied with old songs, honest thoughts, and prayers, but short ones; yet they have their efficacy in that they are not palled with ensuing idle cogitations. Lastly, her dreams are so chaste that she dare tell them; only a Friday's dream is all her superstition; that she conceals for fear of anger. Thus lives
10 she, and all her care is she may die in the springtime, to have store of flowers stuck upon her winding-sheet.

JOHN EARLE: MICROCOSMOGRAPHY

A Child

is a man in a small letter, yet the best copy of Adam before he tasted of Eve or the apple; and he is happy whose small practice in the world can only write his character. He is nature's fresh picture newly drawn in oil, which time and much handling dims and defaces. His soul is yet a white paper unscribbled with observations of the world, where-
20 with at length it becomes a blurred note-book. He is purely happy, because he knows no evil nor hath made means by sin to be acquainted with misery. He arrives not at the mischief of being wise nor endures evils to come, by foreseeing them. He kisses and loves all, and when the smart of the rod is past, smiles on his beater. Nature and his parents alike dandle him and tice him on with a bait of sugar to a draught of wormwood. He plays yet, like a young prentice the first day, and is not come
30 to his task of melancholy. All the language he speaks yet is tears, and they serve him well enough

to express his necessity. His hardest labour is his tongue as if he were loth to use so deceitful an organ, and he is best company with it when he can but prattle. We laugh at his foolish sports, but his game is our earnest, and his drums, rattles, and hobby-horses but the emblems and mocking of men's business. His father hath writ him as his own little story, wherein he reads those days of his life that he cannot remember and sighs to see what innocence 10 he has out-lived. The elder he grows, he is a stair lower from God and, like his first father, much worse in his breeches. He is the Christian's example and the old man's relapse: the one imitates his pureness, and the other falls into his simplicity. Could he put off his body with his little coat, he had got eternity without a burthen and exchanged but one heaven for another.

A Flatterer

is the picture of a friend, and, as pictures flatter many times, so he oft shews fairer than the true sub- 20 stance; his look, conversation, company, and all the outwardness of friendship more pleasing by odds, for a true friend dare take the liberty to be sometimes offensive, whereas he is a great deal more cowardly and will not let the least hold go, for fear of losing you. Your mere sour look affrights him and makes him doubt his cashiering. And this is one sure mark of him, that he is never first angry but ready, though upon his own wrong, to make satisfaction. Therefore he is never yoked with a 30 poor man or any that stands on lower ground, but whose fortunes may tempt his pains to deceive him. Him he learns first, and learns well, and grows perfitter in his humours than himself, and by this door enters upon his soul, of which he is able at

last to take the very print and mark, and fashion his own by it like a false key to open all your secrets. All his affections jump even with yours; he is beforehand with your thoughts and able to suggest them unto you. He will commend to you first what he knows you like, and has always some absurd story or other of your enemy and then wonders how your two opinions should jump in that man. He will ask your counsel sometimes as a man of deep
10 judgment, and has a secret of purpose to disclose you, and whatsoever you say, is persuaded. He listens to your words with great attention, and sometimes will object that you may confute him, and then protests he never heard so much before. A piece of wit bursts him with an overflowing laughter, and he remembers it for you to all companies, and laughs again in the telling. He is one never chides you but for your virtues, as, "You are too good, too honest, too religious", when his chiding may
20 seem but the earnester commendation, and yet would fain chide you out of them too, for your vice is the thing he has use of and wherein you may best use him, and he is never more active than in the worst diligences. Thus at last he possesses you from yourself and then expects but his hire to betray you. And it is a happiness not to discover him; for, as long as you are happy, you shall not.

A Coward

is the man that is commonly most fierce against the coward and labouring to take off this suspicion from
30 himself, for the opinion of valour is a good protection to those that dare not use it. No man is valianter than he in civil company and where he thinks no danger may come on it, and is the readiest man to fall upon a drawer and those that must not

strike again. Wonderful exceptious and choleric where he sees men are loth to give him occasion, and you cannot pacify him better than by quarreling with him. The hotter you grow, the more temperate man is he; he protests he always honored you, and, the more you rail upon him, the more he honors you, and you threaten him at last into a very honest quiet man. The sight of a sword wounds him more sensibly than the stroke, for before that 10 come, he is dead already. Every man is his master that dare beat him, and every man dares that knows him. And he that dare do this is the only man can do much with him; for his friend he cares not for, as a man that carries no such terror as his enemy, which for this cause only is more potent with him of the two. And men fall out with him of purpose to get courtesies from him and be bribed again to a reconcilement. A man in whom no secret can be bound up, for the apprehension of each danger 20 loosens him and makes him bewray both the room and it. He is a Christian merely for fear of hell of fire, and, if any religion could fright him more, would be of that.

A Young Raw Preacher

is a bird not yet fledged that hath hopped out of his nest to be chirping on a hedge and will be straggling abroad at what peril soever. His backwardness in the university hath set him thus forward; for, had he not truanted there, he had not been so hasty a divine. His small standing and time hath made him 30 a proficient only in boldness, out of which and his tablebook he is furnished for a preacher. His collections of study are the notes of sermons, which, taken up at St. Mary's, he utters in the country. And if he

write brachygraphy,[1] his stock is so much the better. His writing is more than his reading, for he reads only what he gets without book. Thus accomplished, he comes down to his friends, and his first salutation is grace and peace out of the pulpit. His prayer is conceited, and no man remembers his college more at large. The pace of his sermon is a full career, and he runs wildly over hill and dale till the clock stop him. The labor of it is chiefly in his
10 lungs. And the only thing he has made in it himself is the faces. He takes on against the Pope without mercy and has a jest still in lavender for Bellarmine. Yet he preaches heresy, if it comes in his way, though with a mind, I must needs say, very orthodox. His action is all passion, and his speech interjections; he has an excellent faculty in bemoaning the people and spits with a very good grace. His style is compounded of twenty several men's; only his body imitates someone extraordinary. He
20 will not draw his handkercher out of his place nor blow his nose without discretion. His commendation is that he never looks upon book, and indeed he was never used to it. He preaches but once a year, though twice a Sunday; for the stuff is still the same, only the dressing a little altered. He has more tricks with a sermon than a tailor with an old cloak,—to turn it, and piece it, and at last quite disguise it with a new preface. If he have waded further in his profession and would shew reading of
30 his own, his authors are postils [2] and his school-divinity a catechism. His fashion and demure habit gets him in with some town-precisian and makes him a guest on Friday nights. You shall know him by his narrow velvet cape, and serge facing, and his ruff, next his hire, the shortest thing about him.

[1] Shorthand.
[2] Glosses.

The companion of his walk is some zealous tradesman, whom he astonisheth with strange points, which they both understand alike. His friends and much painfulness may prefer him to thirty pounds a year, and this means to a chambermaid,—with whom we leave him now in the bonds of wedlock. Next Sunday you shall have him again.

An Old College Butler

is none of the worst students in the house, for he keeps the set hours at his book more duly than any.
10 His authority is great over men's good names, which he charges many times with shrewd aspersions, which they hardly wipe off without payment. His box and counters prove him to be a man of reckoning; yet he is stricter in his accounts than a usurer and delivers not a farthing without writing. He doubles the pains of *Gallobelgicus*, for his books go out once a quarter, and they are much in the same nature—brief notes and sums of affairs—and are out of request as soon. His comings in are like a
20 tailor's,—from the shreds of bread, the chippings, and remnants of the broken crust, excepting his vails from the barrel, which poor folks buy for their hogs but drink themselves. He divides a halfpenny loaf with more subtlety than Keckermann and subdivides the *a primo ortum* [1] so nicely that a stomach of great capacity can hardly apprehend it. He is a very sober man, considering his manifold temptations of drink and strangers, and, if he be overseen,[2] 'tis within his own liberties, and no man ought to
30 take exception. He is never so well pleased with his place as when a gentleman is beholding to him for shewing him the buttery, whom he greets with

[1] The result of the first division.
[2] Drunk.

a cup of single beer and sliced manchet and tells him, "'Tis the fashion of the college". He domineers over freshmen when they first come to the hatch, and puzzles them with strange language of Q's and C's[1] and some broken Latin which he has learned at his bin. His faculties extraordinary is the warming of a pair of cards and telling out a dozen of counters for post and pair, and no man is more methodical in these businesses. Thus he 10 spends his age, till the tap of it is run out, and then a fresh one is set abroach.

ROGER BOYLE, EARL OF ORRERY

PARTHENISSA

ROGER BOYLE was born in Ireland in 1621 and received at Trinity College, Dublin, and at Oxford, the education fitted to a gentleman's son. After making the grand tour on the continent, he became an officer in the army, taking a prominent part on the king's side in the Irish wars, later supporting Cromwell in his Irish campaigns, and finally helping to seize the island for Charles II. He died in 1679.

Lord Orrery was a versatile and prolific writer besides a soldier and statesman. Among his works are treatises on war, volumes of poetry and numerous dramas as well as the long chivalric romance, *Parthenissa.* This last is the most important English work in the tradition of the seventeenth century French romances in which the love of countless beautiful ladies and the battles and tournaments of their gallant knights had been traced through interminable pages. In England, groups of gentlefolk met to read these works aloud, to discuss the abstract problems they gave rise to, and even to call one another by romantic names and to find pretended resemblances between their own lives and those of their favorite heroes and heroines. Boyle belonged to the group centering around Katherine Phillips, "the match-

[1] Small portions of bread and beer.

less Orinda." The first part of his novel appeared in 1654; a more complete version came in 1665, but *Parthenissa,* after proceeding eight hundred pages without beginning its main plot, was suffered to remain unfinished. In its own day it was popular although so keen an observer as Dorothy Osborne could write of it, "'Tis handsome language; you would know it to be writ by a person of good quality though you were not told it; but on the whole I am not very much taken with it. All the stories have too near a resemblance with those of other romances." Indeed she is quite right; the theme of the incident quoted here also appears in the *Arcadia* and in the Spanish form of the earlier romance, *Amadis of Gaul,* whence Sidney probably took it.

PARTHENISSA

Artabanes, a prince of Parthia who fell in love at first sight with Parthenissa, the daughter of a Parthian general, is telling his story to Callimachus, priest of Aphrodite's temple at Hieropolis in Syria. He narrates how the King Arsaces held a tilting to celebrate the anniversary of his coronation.

The exercises of it were to last three days, and Fortune, to evince her blindness, had permitted me the two first to remain victorious. But as I was coming out of the lists, attended by the acclamations and company of my friends, we heard a great noise of trumpets and clarions, which imposed on us a general stop and silence; the king, too, and all the court at so unexpected music returned to their seats to learn the cause of it. Their curiosity was soon 10 satisfied by the appearing of four and twenty blackamoor pages richly clothed and well horsed, who carried each of them at the end of an ebony stick tipped with gold the several picture of some excellent beauty. These were followed by their master who was advantageously mounted, and whose helmet, being opened, discovered a face more capable to create fear than any other passion; and yet even in those barbarous features there was an ample evidence of a resembling courage and magnanimity. As soon as he was come near the highest scaffold, he sent one of the six pages which followed him, to enquire where the king was, who having obeyed and satisfied his lord, he himself immediately advanced toward Arsaces and made him a salutation much after the rate of these ensuing words. "Sir," said he, "I am of that Arabia which is called the happy and am in some degree allied to the king of 10 that country. I adored a beauty there which had no defect but her cruelty, and though that soon ended with her life, yet my passion, instead of dying with the object of it, did the contrary; for it increased to such a height that it seemed all those flames with which she set so many hearts on fire flew into mine as the seat of the greatest and perfectest empire. And though time be the common cure of most misfortunes, yet it proved the increase of mine; for the more I reflected on my loss, the greater I always 20 found it, and at last the operation of so just a grief reduced me to so deep a melancholy that my king came to visit me and, to cure my passion, spoke so many impious things against the perfection that had created it (which he injuriously said was equaled by many) that not daring to expiate his offense with his life, because of his character, I publicly vowed never to continue in his dominions, and that I would visit all the courts of Asia to justify that none but my own king durst say any beauty was comparable 30 to that of the fair Mizalinza's. To effect this, I instantly abandoned the place of my birth and published my design and the conditions of my combat (if any were so vain as to undertake it) which were: that whosoever should defend the object of his passion by equaling it to her that created mine, in case I became victorious, he should give me the picture of his mistress, which I ever after carried with me

and hung up as a trophy. These four and twenty several beauties had the ill fortune to be compared to Mizalinza's, and by the death or conquest of those which adored them are now to wait upon her whom their deluded lovers equaled them to. The fame of this great meeting has drawn me, sir, to your court where, if any be so presumptuous as to justify such a folly, I will not with my lance alone (which I understand is the only arms of this tilting)
10 but with my sword maintain a truth which Mizalinza's eyes more than the defeat of the greatest courages in the world hath abundantly justified. But perhaps," he continued, "that the sight of this charming beauty will produce a confession which may exempt my sword from that trouble."

Thereupon with a deep reverence he drew out the copy of so glorified an original, and having exposed it to all our views, he further added that, if any durst undertake to lessen her beauty by a compari-
20 son, that the next morning he would appear on the same place he was then on to manifest to the offender that nothing but his blood was capable to wash away his crime. Then without staying for any answer, he retired to his lodgings and left us in as great an astonishment at his insolence as at his passion. But Arsaces, who was a prince that in his youth had been blest with a high valor, did so exceedingly resent the impudence of Ambixules (for so this Arabian prince was called,) that he publicly
30 professed, if none in his court had the courage to fight with him, he would do it for the defense of an imaginary mistress rather than suffer an affront to be done unto the Parthians as great even as the insolency with which it was committed. There is no doubt but that Orodes's [1] court was then replen-

[1] Orodes and Arsaces are the same man, Arsaces being a family name that has almost become a title.

ished with men who apprehended nothing in dangers but that they were not great enough. Yet at that instant the loves of the major part were so unhappy that they durst not acknowledge the objects of them, and 'twas upon that score only this Arabian had like to have engrossed an honor, without drawing his sword, greater than ever he had obtained by it. The same misfortune had then an influence over me, and I dare truly profess, if I had any uncertainty 10 in the undertaking to punish Ambixules' insolence, it proceeded not from my apprehension of him but Parthenissa, for whom I durst hardly acknowledge openly I had a passion till she in private had approved it. But I thought the crime of that presumption would not equal that of the tacit confession any beauty transcended hers, and that I had less title to her anger by discovering my flame to defend her right than expose that to any apparent injury by a concealment of it. Neither was it impossible but 20 I might return from the combat without receiving any such wounds whose cure might necessitate my discovery, in which case I was resolved to conceal myself and not acknowledge my passion, till she to whom it was addressed would bless me with the reception of it.

'Twas with these and many such reasons that I assumed a resolution to become the protector of an excellency which had no misfortune but that it needed one, or that it had one so unworthy that 30 honor as Artabanes. I kept this determination exceeding private, lest if it had been discovered, my friends might have denied my first assay in arms to have been against so known a conqueror. I had some difficulty, too, to fit myself with armour, for that I had made use of the two precedent days was too publicly known to have been used the third. But I remembered that the prince Sillaces, my most particular friend and who merited abundantly to be so, had an excellent one which he had made for that solemnity, but being unfortunately troubled with an ague, he was necessitated to decline shewing his skill and gallantry, which indeed I apprehended more than any others. These arms I sent privately to borrow of his servant, who, knowing his prince could not possibly use them, sent them to me; and I found that they were very fit, our shapes and heights being as resembling as our friendships. I will not amuse myself to tell you how impatiently I passed the night, nor how early I came to the assignation lest some others should have prevented me. I shall only let you know that I was there before any that might have had my design and before Ambixules, too, whom I did not long expect, and how at his entry into the lists, managed his horse with so much art and grace that he attracted all the eyes of the assistants. After he had ended, I began the same exercise to show him I was not ignorant of it. But not to dress a true story in clothes of a romance, I will pass by the descriptions of our arms, devices, mottoes, and all things of so low a nature, to acquaint you that Ambixules having repaid me the civility of looking on his horse's manage, demanded of me the sight of my mistress's picture: to which I told him that the excellency I adored would not be what it was if it lay in the power of art to represent it, but that the original being present, I would conduct him to it; where his justice must be as blind as she herself is painted if he did not adore what he came to injure.

"Come," said Ambixules, smiling, "I will go see this beauty to convince you by a demonstration that he which hath seen Mizalinza's eyes can be conquered by no others. But," he continued, "though contrary to my practice, I am content to begin the combat before I see your mistress's picture; yet you must oblige yourself that some friend for you after your death will let me have the reward of it."

This insolence did not a little offend me, but being resolved to repair the wrong with nobler arms than those which had committed it, I only told him I was confident to give him the recompense of his victory before he won it, since it was impossible to see Parthenissa without carrying away her image. 10 By this time we were come so near her that I went to the scaffold she was on, and without lifting up my helmet (to continue my disguise) I saluted her with a respect equal to my passion and told her, "Madam, if I have the confidence to beg your permission to vindicate your beauty, 'tis out of the certainty that the success of so just a dispute cannot but prove as fortunate as that it needs not any defense. Neither do I draw my sword to justify that you are the perfectest of your sex, but to punish Am- 20 bixules for not acknowledging it."

Whilst I was speaking these few words, she was in some disorder, yet it was so innocent a one that it rather was a friend than any enemy to her beauty, but she quickly suppressed it to answer me. "Whosoever you are that to give a long proof of your courage, gives as little one of your judgment, I shall conjure you not to undertake a defense where the injustice of the quarrel may give your enemy an advantage which I believe he would hardly obtain 30 on a contrary score."

"Madam," I replied, "I know how to distinguish betwixt your modesty and your justice and consequently to attribute what you now speak, to the first; but if you have so partial a character to the fair Parthenissa, I will convince her by an experiment how much she has injured herself and my election."

Thereupon saluting her with an infinite humility,

but without staying for any reply, I desired Ambixules to return to the place of combat and to hasten a decision of it; but he was so intent and ravished in the consideration of Parthenissa's beauties that to interrupt his thoughts, I was forced to tell him, "Ambixules, I fear if you continue longer in the employment you are in, I shall have but little honor in my victory, having to deal with one who will have lost his heart."

10 This truth made him ashamed of what he should rather have gloried in; so that turning about his horse, he rid with me where the judges attended us and by the way assured me that my mistress had so much of Mizalinza in her that, having vanquished me, he would desire no other picture of her but that he carried in his memory. This antedated victory I excused upon the same score that I had the former, being by this time come where it was no time to talk. I will pass by acquainting you with the joy 20 Arsaces had to perceive this Arabian was not altogether unlike to escape unpunished, the general wonder of all the court who I was, and the secret repining of many beauties to perceive Parthenissa's could find a protector when none of theirs had any; to tell you that the three first courses we broke our lances with equal advantage, and perceiving they were too civil weapons for our designs, we both, as if it had been by mutual consent, drew out our swords and soon made each other feel of what tem- 30 per they were; but Ambixules having given me a furious reverse which I was endeavoring to repay in the same kin, his horse unexpectedly rose before so that what I intended for his master fell upon him, and the blow being given with all my strength and lighting upon his head, cleft it in two. I was extremely troubled at this misfortune, and having begged Ambixules' pardon for an undesigned

wrong, I trotted some seventy paces from him, and lighting off my horse, I returned again, and told him that to manifest I would take no advantage over him but what I had by the goodness of my quarrel, and that what I had done was unintended, I came to offer him, if he thought he had any odds in fighting on horse-back, to send for a fresh one,—that then he should make choice of that or of mine; or if he esteemed himself in as good a condition on foot, 10 I was ready so to finish what we had begun.

The Arabian replied that he knew his courage gave him sufficient advantage over me in whatsoever posture he was in, and since I had killed his horse, he would not so long a time suspend his revenge as that which must be spent in sending for another. This rudeness so incensed me that I repaid it with some dangerous wounds, but at the last, finding his fury more than his strength made him continue the combat, I retired two or three paces with intention 20 to preserve a valor I could not but esteem though I had received some dangerous effects of it, and told him, "You see, Ambixules, the power of justice which has reduced you to a condition of acknowledging rather than persevering in your error, and that advantage which the goodness of my cause hath given me I desire only to employ to obtain a confession from your tongue which your weakness has already made."

"Nor my weakness nor my tongue," said he, "shall 30 ever confess you have any advantage over me, and whilst I hold my sword, you shall find me a subject fitter to create your fear than your pity."

Thereupon he renewed the fight with much more strength than I thought he had left him; yet for a while I only defended myself, but when I perceived his blows were so brisk that my charity might prove my ruin, and that he had so much vigor as I might kill him without a stain, I cried out to him, "Since my civility cannot make you acknowledge what your justice should, your death shall."

Finishing these words, I made him soon feel the punishment of a fault which might have had a milder reparation, if the continuance of his insolency had not rendered him unworthy of it. But to conclude this tragedy, as soon as he fell, he told me, "Whosoever thou art, I forgive thee that death
10 which, by my being worsted, is rather my joy than my trouble, and though I scorn to beg my life, (were it in thy power to save, which I thank the gods it is not) yet I do not,—to conjure thee, to assure that beauty which to have fought against does more afflict me than to be reduced to what I am, that 'twas her eyes which inspired thy arm and weighed down mine, and that had not shame been more prevalent with me than truth, I had been her champion and not her adversary. Conjure her to pardon a crime
20 which I expiate with my blood, and which my hand should have punished for her if thine had not." He would have continued his recantation by which I perceived I had not only killed an enemy but a rival, had he not found that his tongue began to falter, which made him, though with much difficulty, turn himself towards the place where Parthenissa was, and not having the strength to speak to her, he lifted up his hands to implore that pardon his hasty summons hindered him to express.

30 As soon as Ambixules was dead, all his pages came and presented me those pictures which had been the rewards of their prince's former combats and desired me that they might have his body to carry into Arabia, which I yielded unto; and then, taking all the consequents of my victory, I went with them to Parthenissa's scaffold, where I found her, by an excess of goodness, weeping the death of

her enemy, which made me envy what I had deplored and forced me to think my success a misfortune, since it created the fair Parthenissa's tears, who judging of my disorder by my silence, wiped them away and thereby gave me the confidence to present her with all those fair captives and to tell her that the originals of them could no more complain against their servant's unhappy defense since thereby they had the honor to be hers, which was a felicity greater
10 than any could have attended their success.

APHRA BEHN

OROONOKO OR THE ROYAL SLAVE

Aphra Amis, who was to become the celebrated Mrs. Behn, was baptized at Wye, Kent, on July 10, 1640. She seems to have been the daughter of a barber and to have been later adopted by a man named Johnson. With him apparently—for there is some difference of opinion on these points—she went to Surinam in South America and resided there for several years. Returning to Europe she acted as an English spy in Antwerp from August, 1666, to the following January. Numerous love affairs in that city, ascribed to her by an early biographer, have now been proved fictitious. During her political correspondence, she used the pseudonym of Astrea. Back in England once more, she suffered a short imprisonment for debt but soon turned to writing for the theater. After the first presentation of one of her plays in 1670, she pursued a successful dramatic career, composing likewise fiction and verse. Mrs. Behn is considered the first Englishwoman to earn her living by the pen. She died in April, 1689.

Mrs. Behn's handful of short novels, serious and humorous, are of different types,—the most important being *Oroonoko* and *The Fair Jilt*. Both these, compared to the long-winded French romances, are realistic, though, of course, far less so than the average modern novel. They are representatives of the tales developing from the Italian *novella*, the chief type of realism from 1660 to the end of the century. Both attempt to reënforce the sense of actuality, as did many such tales, by having the authoress a witness of at least part of the happenings. In *Oroonoko*, furthermore, Mrs. Behn developed her realistic background by borrowing numerous facts from a contemporary account of Surinam. The court life of Oroonoko's native land, moreover, reflects somewhat the loose morals of English high society after the Restoration.

Though in general unlike the French romances, *Oroonoko* betrays certain of their influences in the soft language of the eyes and the frequent blushing, in the great valor of Oroonoko and his immense prowess in battle. To conclude, *Oroonoko* is additionally interesting in that it heralds two favorite ideas of later periods; first, the idealization of life of primitive people and, secondly, pity for oppressed individuals.

OROONOKO OR THE ROYAL SLAVE

I do not pretend, in giving you the history of this royal slave, to entertain my Reader with the adventures of a feigned hero, whose life and fortunes fancy may manage at the poet's pleasure, nor, in relating the truth, design to adorn it with any accidents, but such as arrived in earnest to him; and it shall come simply into the world, recommended by its own proper merits, and natural intrigues, there being enough of reality to support it and to render 10 it diverting, without the addition of invention.

I was myself an eye-witness to a great part of what you will find here set down; and what I could not be witness of, I received from the mouth of the chief actor in this history, the hero himself, who gave us the whole transactions of his youth; and I shall omit, for brevity's sake, a thousand little accidents of his life, which, however pleasant to us, where history was scarce and adventures very rare, yet might prove tedious and heavy to my reader, in a world where he finds diversions for every minute, new and strange. But we who were perfectly charmed with the character of this great man were curious to gather every circumstance of his life.

The scene of the last part of his adventures lies in a colony in America, called Surinam, in the West Indies.

But before I give you the story of this gallant slave, it is fit I tell you the manner of bringing them 10 to these new colonies; those they make use of there, not being natives of the place; for those we live with in perfect amity, without daring to command them, but, on the contrary, caress them with all the brotherly and friendly affection in the world; trading with them for their fish, venison, buffaloes' skins, and little rarities; as marmosets, a sort of monkey, as big as a rat or weasel, but of a marvellous and delicate shape, having face and hands like a human creature; and cousheries, a little beast in the form and fashion 20 of a lion, as big as a kitten, but so exactly made in all parts like that noble beast, that it is it in miniature; then for little parrakeetoes, great parrots, mackaws, and a thousand other birds and beasts of wonderful and surprising forms, shapes, and colours; for skins of prodigious snakes, of which there are some three-score yards in length; as is the skin of one that may be seen at his Majesty's Antiquary's, where are also some rare flies of amazing forms and colours presented to them by myself, some 30 as big as my fist, some less, and all of various excellences, such as art cannot imitate. Then we trade for feathers, which they order into all shapes, make themselves little short habits of them, and glorious wreaths for their heads, necks, arms and legs, whose tinctures are inconceivable. I had a set of these presented to me, and I gave them to the King's Theatre; it was the dress of the Indian Queen,

infinitely admired by persons of quality; and was
unimitable. Besides these, a thousand little knacks,
and rarities in nature, and some of art, as their
baskets, weapons, aprons, etc. We dealt with them
with beads of all colours, knives, axes, pins, and
needles, which they used only as tools to drill holes
with in their ears, noses, and lips, where they hang
a great many little things; as long beads, bits of tin,
brass or silver beat thin, and any shining trinket.
10 The beads they weave into aprons about a quarter
of an ell long and of the same breadth; working
them very prettily in flowers of several colours of
beads, which aprons they wear just before them, as
Adam and Eve did the fig-leaves; the men wearing a
long stripe of linen, which they deal with us for.
They thread these beads also on long cotton-threads,
and make girdles to tie their aprons to, which come
twenty times, or more, about the waist, and then
cross, like a shoulder-belt, both ways, and round
20 their necks, arms and legs. This adornment, with
their long black hair, and the face painted in little
specks or flowers here and there, makes them a
wonderful figure to behold. Some of the beauties,
which indeed are finely shaped, as almost all are, and
who have pretty features, are very charming and
novel; for they have all that is called beauty, except
the colour, which is a reddish yellow; or after a new
oiling, which they often use to themselves, they are
of the colour of a new brick, but smooth, soft and
30 sleek. They are extreme modest and bashful, very
shy, and nice of being touched. And though they
are all thus naked, if one lives for ever among them,
there is not to be seen an indecent action, or glance;
and being continually used to see one another so
unadorned, so like our first parents before the fall, it
seems as if they had no wishes, there being nothing
to heighten curiosity; but all you can see, you see at

once and every moment see, and where there is no
novelty, there can be no curiosity. Not but I have
seen a handsome young Indian, dying for love of a
very beautiful young Indian maid; but all his courtship was to fold his arms, pursue her with his eyes,
and sighs were all his language; while she, as if no
such lover were present or rather as if she desired
none such, carefully guarded her eyes from beholding him and never approached him, but she looked
10 down with all the blushing modesty I have seen in
the most severe and cautious of our world. And
these people represented to me an absolute idea of
the first state of innocence, before man knew how
to sin: and 'tis most evident and plain, that simple
Nature is the most harmless, inoffensive, and virtuous mistress. It is she alone, if she were permitted,
that better instructs the world than all the inventions
of man; religion would here but destroy that tranquillity they possess by ignorance, and laws would
20 but teach them to know offences, of which now they
have no notion. They once made mourning and
fasting for the death of the English Governor, who
had given his hand to come on such a day to them
and neither came nor sent; believing when, once a
man's word was past, nothing but death could or
should prevent his keeping it; and when they saw he
was not dead, they asked him what name they had
for a man who promised a thing he did not do. The
Governor told them such a man was a liar, which was
30 a word of infamy to a gentleman. Then one of them
replied, "Governor, you are a liar and guilty of that
infamy." They have a native justice, which knows
no fraud; and they understand no vice, or cunning,
but when they are taught by the white men. They
have plurality of wives, which when they grow old,
they serve those that succeed them, who are young,
but with a servitude easy and respected; and unless

they take slaves in war, they have no other attendants.

Those on that continent where I was, had no King; but the oldest War-Captain was obeyed with great resignation.

A War-Captain is a man who has led them on to battle with conduct and success; of whom I shall have occasion to speak more hereafter, and of some other of their customs and manners, as they fall in 10 my way.

With these people, as I said, we live in perfect tranquillity and good understanding, as it behooves us to do; they knowing all the places where to seek the best food of the country and the means of getting it; and for very small and unvaluable trifles, supplying us with what it is almost impossible for us to get; for they do not only in the woods and over the savannahs, in hunting, supply the parts of hounds, by swiftly scouring through those almost 20 impassable places, and by the mere activity of their feet run down the nimblest deer and other eatable beasts; but in the water, one would think they were gods of the rivers or fellow-citizens of the deep; so rare an art they have in swimming, diving, and almost living in water; by which they command the less swift inhabitants of the floods. And then for shooting, what they cannot take or reach with their hands, they do with arrows; and have so admirable an aim that they will split almost a hair; and at any 30 distance that an arrow can reach, they will shoot down oranges, and other fruit and only touch the stalk with the dart's point, that they may not hurt the fruit. So that, they being on all occasions very useful to us, we find it absolutely necessary to caress them as friends and not to treat them as slaves; nor dare we do otherwise, their numbers so far surpassing ours in that continent.

Those then whom we make use of to work in our plantations of sugar are Negroes, black-slaves altogether, who are transported thither in this manner.

Those who want slaves make a bargain with a master or a captain of a ship, and contract to pay him so much apiece, a matter of twenty pounds a head, for as many as he agrees for, and to pay for them when they shall be delivered on such a plantation; so that when there arrives a ship laden with slaves, they 10 who have so contracted go aboard and receive their number by lot; and perhaps in one lot that may be for ten, there may happen to be three or four men, the rest women and children. Or be there more or less of either sex, you are obliged to be contented with your lot.

Coramantien, a country of blacks so called, was one of those places in which they found the most advantageous trading for these slaves, and thither most of our great traders in that merchandise traffic; 20 for that nation is very warlike and brave; and having a continual campaign, being always in hostility with one neighbouring Prince or other, they had the fortune to take a great many captives; for all they took in battle were sold as slaves,—at least those common men who could not ransom themselves. Of these slaves so taken, the General only has all the profit, and of these Generals our captains and masters of ships buy all their freights.

The King of Coramantien was of himself a man 30 of an hundred and odd years old and had no son, though he had many beautiful black wives; for most certainly there are beauties that can charm of that colour. In his younger years he had had many gallant men to his sons, thirteen of which died in battle, conquering when they fell; and he had only left him, for his successor, one grandchild, son to one of these dead victors, who, as soon as he could bear

a bow in his hand and a quiver at his back, was sent into the field to be trained up by one of the oldest Generals to war; where, from his natural inclination to arms and the occasions given him, with the good conduct of the old General, he became, at the age of seventeen, one of the most expert Captains and bravest soldiers that ever saw the field of Mars; so that he was adored as the wonder of all that world, and the darling of the soldiers. Besides, he was 10 adorned with a native beauty, so transcending all those of his gloomy race, that he struck an awe and reverence, even into those that knew not his quality; as he did into me, who beheld him with surprise and wonder, when afterwards he arrived in our world.

He had scarce arrived at his seventeenth year, when, fighting by his side, the General was killed with an arrow in his eye, which the Prince Oroonoko (for so was this gallant Moor called) very narrowly avoided; nor had he, if the General who saw the 20 arrow shot, and perceiving it aimed at the Prince, had not bowed his head between, on purpose to receive it in his own body, rather than it should touch that of the Prince, and so saved him.

It was then, afflicted as Oroonoko was, that he was proclaimed General in the old man's place; and then it was, at the finishing of that war, which had continued for two years, that the Prince came to Court, where he had hardly been a month together, from the time of his fifth year to that of seventeen; and it 30 was amazing to imagine where it was he learned so much humanity, or to give his accomplishments a juster name, where it was he got that real greatness of soul, those refined notions of true honour, that absolute generosity, and that softness that was capable of the highest passions of love and gallantry, whose objects were almost continually fighting men or those mangled or dead, who heard no sounds but those of war and groans. Some part of it we may attribute to the care of a Frenchman of wit and learning, who finding it turn to a very good account to be a sort of royal tutor to this young black and perceiving him very ready, apt, and quick of apprehension, took a great pleasure to teach him morals, language and science; and was for it extremely beloved and valued by him. Another reason was, he loved, when he came from war, to see all the English 10 gentlemen that traded thither, and did not only learn their language, but that of the Spaniard also, with whom he traded afterwards for slaves.

I have often seen and conversed with this great man and been a witness to many of his mighty actions, and do assure my reader, the most illustrious Courts could not have produced a braver both for greatness of courage and mind, a judgment more solid, a wit more quick, and a conversation more sweet and diverting. He knew almost as much as if 20 he had read much; he had heard of and admired the Romans; he had heard of the late Civil Wars in England, and the deplorable death of our great Monarch; and would discourse of it with all the sense and abhorrence of the injustice imaginable. He had an extreme good and graceful mien and all the civility of a well-bred great man. He had nothing of barbarity in his nature, but in all points addressed himself as if his education had been in some European Court.

30 This great and just character of Oroonoko gave me an extreme curiosity to see him, especially when I knew he spoke French and English, and that I could talk with him. But though I had heard so much of him, I was as greatly surprised when I saw him, as if I had heard nothing of him; so beyond all report I found him. He came into the room and addressed himself to me and some other women

with the best grace in the world. He was pretty tall, but of a shape the most exact that can be fancied; the most famous statuary could not form the figure of a man more admirably turned from head to foot. His face was not of that brown rusty black which most of that nation are, but a perfect ebony or polished jet. His eyes were the most awful that could be seen and very piercing, the white of them being like snow, as were his teeth. His nose was rising
10 and Roman, instead of African and flat; his mouth the finest shaped that could be seen, far from those great turned lips which are so natural to the rest of the Negroes. The whole proportion and air of his face was so nobly and exactly formed, that, bating his colour, there could be nothing in nature more beautiful, agreeable and handsome. There was no one grace wanting, that bears the standard of true beauty. His hair came down to his shoulders, by the aids of art, which was by pulling it out with a quill
20 and keeping it combed, of which he took particular care. Nor did the perfections of his mind come short of those of his person; for his discourse was admirable upon almost any subject; and whoever had heard him speak, would have been convinced of their errors, that all fine wit is confined to the white men, especially to those of Christendom, and would have confessed that Oroonoko was as capable even of reigning well, and of governing as wisely, had as great a soul, as politic maxims, and was as sensible
30 of power, as any Prince civilised in the most refined schools of humanity and learning or the most illustrious courts.

This Prince, such as I have described him, whose soul and body were so admirably adorned, was (while yet he was in the Court of his grandfather, as I said) as capable of love, as it was possible for a brave and gallant man to be; and in saying that, I have named the highest degree of love, for sure great souls are most capable of that passion.

I have already said the old General was killed by the shot of an arrow, by the side of this Prince, in battle, and that Oroonoko was made General. This old dead hero had one only daughter left of his race, a beauty, that to describe her truly, one need say only, she was female to the noble male, the beautiful black Venus to our young Mars, as charming in her person as he and of delicate virtues. I have seen a hundred white men sighing after her and making a thousand vows at her feet, all in vain and unsuccessful. And she was indeed too great for any but a prince of her own nation to adore.

Oroonoko coming from the wars, which were now ended, after he had made his Court to his grandfather, he thought in honour he ought to make a visit to Imoinda, the daughter of his foster-father, the dead General; and to make some excuses to her, because his preservation was the occasion of her father's death; and to present her with those slaves that had been taken in this last battle, as the trophies of her father's victories. When he came, attended by all the young soldiers of any merit, he was infinitely surprised at the beauty of this fair Queen of Night, whose face and person were so exceeding all he had ever beheld, that lovely modesty with which she received him, that softness in her look and sighs, upon the melancholy occasion of this honour that was done by so great a man as Oroonoko, and a Prince of whom she had heard such admirable things; the awfulness wherewith she received him, and the sweetness of her words and behaviour while he stayed, gained a perfect conquest over his fierce heart, and made him feel the victor could be subdued. So that having made his first compliments and presented her an hundred and fifty slaves in fetters, he told her with his eyes that he was not insensible of her charms; while Imoinda, who wished for nothing more than so glorious a conquest, was pleased to believe she understood that silent language of newborn love, and, from that moment, put on all her additions to beauty.

The Prince returned to Court with quite another humour than before; and though he did not speak much of the fair Imoinda, he had the pleasure to hear all his followers speak of nothing but the charms of that maid, insomuch that, even in the presence of the old King, they were extolling her and heightening, if possible, the beauties they had found in her; so that nothing else was talked of, no other sound was heard in every corner where there were whisperers, but *Imoinda! Imoinda!*

It will be imagined Oroonoko stayed not long before he made his second visit; nor, considering his quality, not much longer before he told her he adored her. I have often heard him say that he admired by what strange inspiration he came to talk things so soft and so passionate, who never knew love nor was used to the conversation of women; but, to use his own words, he said, "Most happily, some new, and, till then, unknown power instructed his heart and tongue in the language of love; and at the same time, in favour of him, inspired Imoinda with a sense of his passion." She was touched with what he said, and returned it all in such answers as went to his very heart, with a pleasure unknown before. Nor did he use those obligations ill that love had done him, but turned all his happy moments to the best advantage; and as he knew no vice, his flame aimed at nothing but honour, if such a distinction may be made in love; and especially in that country, where men take to themselves as many as they can maintain, and where the only crime and sin with woman is to turn her off, to abandon her to want, shame, and misery; such ill morals are only practised in Christian countries, where they prefer the bare name of religion and, without virtue or morality, think that sufficient. But Oroonoko was none of those professors; but as he had right notions of honour, so he made her such propositions as were not only and barely such; but, contrary to the custom of his country, he made her vows she should be the only woman he would possess while he lived, that no age or wrinkles should incline him to change; for her soul would be always fine and always young, and he should have an eternal idea in his mind of the charms she now bore and should look into his heart for that idea, when he could find it no longer in her face.

After a thousand assurances of his lasting flame and her eternal empire over him, she condescended to receive him for her husband, or rather, received him as the greatest honour the gods could do her.

There is a certain ceremony in these cases to be observed, which I forgot to ask him how performed; but it was concluded on both sides that in obedience to him the grandfather was to be first made acquainted with the design; for they pay a most absolute resignation to the monarch, especially when he is a parent also.

On the other side, the old King, who had many wives and many concubines, wanted not court-flatterers to insinuate into his heart a thousand tender thoughts for this young beauty, and who represented her to his fancy as the most charming he had ever possessed in all the long race of his numerous years. At this character, his old heart, like an extinguished brand, most apt to take fire, felt new sparks of love, and began to kindle; and now grown to his second childhood, longed with impatience to behold this gay thing, with whom, alas, he could but innocently play.

But how he should be confirmed she was this wonder, before he used his power to call her to Court, (where maidens never came, unless for the King's private use) he was next to consider; and while he was so doing, he had intelligence brought him that Imoinda was most certainly mistress to the Prince Oroonoko. This gave him some chagrin; however, it gave him also an opportunity, one day when the Prince was a hunting, to wait on a man of quality, as his slave 10 and attendant, who should go and make a present to Imoinda, as from the Prince; he should then, unknown, see this fair maid and have an opportunity to hear what message she would return the Prince for his present, and from thence gather the state of her heart and degree of her inclination. This was put in execution, and the old monarch saw and burned; he found her all he had heard and would not delay his happiness, but found he should have some obstacle to overcome her heart; for she expressed her 20 sense of the present the Prince had sent her, in terms so sweet, so soft and pretty, with an air of love and joy that could not be dissembled, insomuch that it was past doubt whether she loved Oroonoko entirely. This gave the old King some affliction; but he salved it with this, that the obedience the people pay their King was not at all inferior to what they paid their gods; and what love would not oblige Imoinda to do, duty would compel her to.

He was therefore no sooner got into his apartment, 30 but he sent the Royal Veil to Imoinda; that is the ceremony of invitation. He sends the lady he has a mind to honour with his bed, a veil, with which she is covered and secured for the King's use; and it is death to disobey, besides held a most impious disobedience.

It is not to be imagined the surprise and grief that seized this lovely maid at this news and sight. However, as delays in these cases are dangerous and pleading worse than treason, trembling and almost fainting, she was obliged to suffer herself to be covered and led away.

They brought her thus to Court; and the King, who had caused a very rich bath to be prepared, was led into it, where he sat under a canopy in state, to receive this longed-for virgin; whom he having commanded to be brought to him, they, after disrobing her, led her to the bath, and making fast the doors, left her to descend. The King, without more courtship, bade her throw off her mantle and come to his arms. But Imoinda, all in tears, threw herself on the marble, on the brink of the bath, and besought him to hear her. She told him, as she was a maid, how proud of the divine glory she should have been of having it in her power to oblige her King; but as by the laws he could not and from his Royal goodness would not take from any man his wedded wife, so she believed she should be the occasion of making him commit a great sin, if she did not reveal her state and condition, and tell him she was another's and could not be so happy to be his.

The King, enraged at this delay, hastily demanded the name of the bold man that had married a woman of her degree without his consent. Imoinda, seeing his eyes fierce and his hands tremble (whether with age or anger, I know not, but she fancied the last), almost repented she had said so much, for now she feared the storm would fall on the Prince; she therefore said a thousand things to appease the raging of his flame and to prepare him to hear who it was with calmness; but before she spoke, he imagined who she meant, but would not seem to do so, but commanded her to lay aside her mantle and suffer herself to receive his caresses, or, by his gods he swore, that happy man whom she was going to name should die, though it were even Oroonoko himself. "Therefore," said he, "deny this marriage, and swear thyself a maid." "That," replied Imoinda, "by all our powers I do; for I am not yet known to my husband." "It is enough," said the King, "it is enough to satisfy both my conscience and my heart." And rising from his seat, he went and led her into the bath, it being in vain for her to resist.

In this time, the Prince, who was returned from 10 hunting, went to visit his Imoinda but found her gone; and not only so, but heard she had received the Royal Veil. This raised him to a storm, and in his madness, they had much ado to save him from laying violent hands on himself. Force first prevailed and then reason; they urged all to him that might oppose his rage, but nothing weighed so greatly with him as the King's old age, uncapable of injuring him with Imoinda. He would give way to that hope, because it pleased him most and flattered 20 best his heart. Yet this served not altogether to make him cease his different passions, which sometimes raged within him, and sometimes softened into showers. It was not enough to appease him, to tell him his grandfather was old and could not that way injure him, while he retained that awful duty which the young men are used there to pay to their grave relations. He could not be convinced he had no cause to sigh and mourn for the loss of a mistress he could not with all his strength and courage re-30 trieve, and he would often cry, "Oh, my friends! were she in walled cities or confined from me in fortifications of the greatest strength, did enchantments or monsters detain her from me, I would venture through any hazard to free her; but here, in the arms of a feeble old man, my youth, my violent love, my trade in arms, and all my vast desire of glory, avail me nothing. Imoinda is as irrecoverably lost to me as if she were snatched by the cold arms of death. Oh! she is never to be retrieved. If I would wait tedious years till fate should bow the old King to his grave, even that would not leave me Imoinda free; but still that custom that makes it so vile a crime for a son to marry his father's wives or mistresses would hinder my happiness, unless I would either ignobly set an ill precedent to my successors or abandon my country and fly with her to some unknown world who never heard our story."

But it was objected to him that his case was not the same; for Imoinda being his lawful wife by solemn contract, it was he was the injured man and might, if he so pleased, take Imoinda back, the breach of the law being on his grandfather's side; and that if he could circumvent him and redeem her from the Otan, which is the Palace of the King's Women, a sort of Seraglio, it was both just and lawful for him so to do.

This reasoning had some force upon him, and he should have been entirely comforted but for the thought that she was possessed by his grandfather. However, he loved so well that he was resolved to believe what most favoured his hope and to endeavour to learn from Imoinda's own mouth what only she could satisfy him in,—whether she was robbed of that blessing which was only due to his faith and love. But as it was very hard to get a sight of the women (for no men ever entered into the Otan but when the King went to entertain himself with some one of his wives or mistresses, and it was death, at any other time, for any other to go in); so he knew not how to contrive to get a sight of her.

While Oroonoko felt all the agonies of love and suffered under a torment the most painful in the world, the old King was not exempted from his share of affliction. He was troubled for having been forced, by an irresistible passion, to rob his son of a treasure, he knew, could not but be extremely dear to him, since she was the most beautiful that ever had been seen and had besides all the sweetness and innocence of youth and modesty, with a charm of wit surpassing all. He found that however she was forced to expose her lovely person to his withered arms, she could only sigh and weep there and think of Oroonoko; and oftentimes could not forbear speaking of him, though her life were, by custom, forfeited by owning her passion. But she spoke not of a lover only but of a Prince dear to him to whom she spoke; and of the praises of a man, who, till now, filled the old man's soul with joy at every recital of his bravery or even his name. And it was this dotage on our young hero that gave Imoinda a thousand privileges to speak of him without offending, and this condescension in the old King that made her take the satisfaction of speaking of him so very often.

Besides, he many times inquired how the Prince bore himself; and those of whom he asked, being entirely slaves to the merits and virtues of the Prince, still answered what they thought conduced best to his service; which was, to make the old King fancy that the Prince had no more interest in Imoinda and had resigned her willingly to the pleasure of the King; that he diverted himself with his mathematicians, his fortifications, his officers, and his hunting.

This pleased the old lover, who failed not to report these things again to Imoinda, that she might, by the example of her young lover, withdraw her heart and rest better contented in his arms. But, however she was forced to receive this unwelcome news, in all appearance, with unconcern and content, her heart was bursting within, and she was only happy when she could get alone, to vent her griefs and moans with sighs and tears.

What reports of the Prince's conduct were made to the King, he thought good to justify, as far as possibly he could by his actions; and when he appeared in the presence of the King, he showed a face not at all betraying his heart: so that in a little time, the old man, being entirely convinced that he was no longer a lover of Imoinda, he carried him with him, in his train to the Otan, often to banquet with his mistresses. But as soon as he entered, one day, into the apartment of Imoinda with the King, at the first glance from her eyes notwithstanding all his determined resolution he was ready to sink in the place where he stood, and had certainly done so, but for the support of Aboan, a young man who was next to him; which, with his change of countenance, had betrayed him, had the King chanced to look that way. And I have observed, it is a very great error in those who laugh when one says, "A Negro can change colour"; for I have seen them as frequently blush and look pale, and that as visibly as ever I saw in the most beautiful white. And it is certain that both these changes were evident, this day, in both these lovers. And Imoinda, who saw with some joy the change in the Prince's face and found it in her own, strove to divert the King from beholding either, by a forced caress, with which she met him; which was a new wound in the heart of the poor dying Prince. But as soon as the King was busied in looking on some fine thing of Imoinda's making, she had time to tell the Prince, with her angry but love-darting eyes, that she resented his coldness and bemoaned her own miserable captivity. Nor were his eyes silent but answered hers again, as much as eyes could do, instructed by the most tender and most passionate heart that ever loved; and they spoke so

well and so effectually, as Imoinda no longer doubted
but she was the only delight and the darling of that
soul she found pleading in them its right of love,
which none was more willing to resign than she.
And it was this powerful language alone that in an
instant conveyed all the thoughts of their souls to
each other, that they both found there wanted but
opportunity to make them both entirely happy. But
when he saw another door opened by Onahal, a
10 former old wife of the King's who now had charge
of Imoinda, and saw the prospect of a bed of state
made ready, with sweets and flowers for the dalli-
ance of the King, who immediately led the trembling victim from his sight into that prepared repose,
what rage! what wild frenzies seized his heart!
which forcing to keep within bounds and to suffer
without noise, it became the more insupportable and
rent his soul with ten thousand pains. He was
forced to retire to vent his groans, where he fell
20 down on a carpet and lay struggling a long time and
only breathing now and then, "Oh Imoinda!" When
Onahal had finished her necessary affair within,
shutting the door she came forth, to wait till the
King called; and hearing some one sighing in the
other room, she passed on and found the Prince in
that deplorable condition, which she thought needed
her aid. She gave him cordials, but all in vain; till
finding the nature of his disease by his sighs and
naming Imoinda, she told him he had not so much
30 cause as he imagined to afflict himself; for if he
knew the King so well as she did, he would not lose
a moment in jealousy, and that she was confident
that Imoinda bore, at this minute, part in his affliction. Aboan was of the same opinion, and both
together persuaded him to re-assume his courage;
and all sitting down on the carpet, the Prince said
so many obliging things to Onahal that he half per-

suaded her to be of his party, and she promised him she would thus far comply with his just desires, that she would let Imoinda know how faithful he was, what he suffered, and what he said.

This discourse lasted till the King called, which gave Oroonoko a certain satisfaction, and with the hope Onahal had made him conceive, he assumed a look as gay as it was possible a man in his circumstances could do; and presently after, he was called in with the rest who waited without. The King commanded music to be brought and several of his young wives and mistresses came all together by his command to dance before him; where Imoinda performed her part with an air and grace so passing all the rest, as her beauty was above them, and received the present ordained as a prize. The Prince was every moment more charmed with the new beauties and graces he beheld in this fair one; and while he gazed and she danced, Onahal was retired to a window with Aboan.

This Onahal, as I said, was one of the cast-mistresses of the old King; and it was these, now past their beauty, that were made guardians or governantes to the new and the young ones, and whose business it was to teach them all those wanton arts of love, with which they prevailed and charmed heretofore in their turn; and who now treated the triumphing happy-ones with all the severity, as to liberty and freedom, that was possible, in revenge of the honours they rob them of; envying them those satisfactions, those gallantries and presents, that were once made to themselves, while youth and beauty lasted, and which they now saw pass, as it were regardless by, and paid only to the bloomings. And certainly, nothing is more afflicting to a decayed beauty than to behold in itself declining charms that were once adored, and to find those caresses paid to new beauties, to which once she laid a claim; to hear them whisper, as she passes by that once was a delicate woman. Those abandoned ladies therefore endeavour to revenge all the despites and decays of time on these flourishing happy-ones. And it was this severity that gave Oroonoko a thousand fears he should never prevail with Onahal to see Imoinda. But, as I said, she was now retired to a window with Aboan.

10 This young man was not only one of the best quality but a man extremely well made and beautiful; and coming often to attend the King to the Otan, he had subdued the heart of the antiquated Onahal, which had not forgot how pleasant it was to be in love. And though she had some decays in her face, she had none in her sense and wit; she was there agreeable still, even to Aboan's youth, so that he took pleasure in entertaining her with discourses of love. He knew, also, that to make his court to these 20 she-favourites was the way to be great, these being the persons that do all affairs and business at Court. He had also observed that she had given him glances more tender and inviting than she had done to others of his quality. And now, when he saw that her favour could so absolutely oblige the Prince, he failed not to sigh in her ear and look with eyes all soft upon her and gave her hope that she had made some impressions on his heart. He found her pleased at this and making a thousand advances to 30 him; but the ceremony ending and the King departing, broke up the company for that day and his conversation.

Aboan failed not that night to tell the Prince of his success and how advantageous the service of Onahal might be to his amour with Imoinda. The Prince was overjoyed with this good news and besought him, if it were possible, to caress her so as to engage her entirely, which he could not fail to do if he complied with her desires; "For then," said the Prince, "her life lying at your mercy, she must grant you the request you make in my behalf." Aboan understood him and assured him he would make love so effectually that he would defy the most expert mistress of the art to find out whether he dissembled it or had it really. And it was with impatience they waited the next opportunity of going to the Otan.

10 The wars came on; the time of taking the field approached; and it was impossible for the Prince to delay his going at the head of his Army to encounter the enemy, so that every day seemed a tedious year till he saw his Imoinda, for he believed he could not live, if he were forced away without being so happy. It was with impatience, therefore, that he expected the next visit the King would make, and, according to his wish, it was not long.

The parley of the eyes of these two lovers had not 20 passed so secretly, but an old jealous lover could spy it, or rather, he wanted not flatterers who told him they observed it; so that the Prince was hastened to the camp, and this was the last visit he found he should make to the Otan; he therefore urged Aboan to make the best of this last effort and to explain himself so to Onahal, that she, deferring her enjoyment of her young lover no longer, might make way for the Prince to speak to Imoinda.

The whole affair being agreed on between the 30 Prince and Aboan, they attended the King, as the custom was, to the Otan; where, while the whole company was taken up in beholding the dancing and antic postures the Women-Royal made to divert the King, Onahal singled out Aboan, whom she found most pliable to her wish. When she had him where she believed she could not be heard, she sighed to him and softly cried, "Ah, Aboan! When will you be sensible of my passion? I confess it with my mouth, because I would not give my eyes the lie, and you have but too much already perceived they have confessed my flame; nor would I have you believe that because I am the abandoned mistress of a King, I esteem myself altogether divested of charms. No, Aboan, I have still a rest of beauty enough engaging and have learned to please too well, not to be desirable. I can have lovers still, but will have none but Aboan." "Madam," replied the half-feigning youth, "you have already, by my eyes, found you can still conquer, and I believe it is in pity of me you condescend to this kind confession. But, Madam, words are used to be so small a part of our country-courtship that it is rare one can get so happy an opportunity as to tell one's heart, and those few minutes we have are forced to be snatched for more certain proofs of love than speaking and sighing, and such I languish for."

He spoke this with such a tone that she hoped it true and could not forbear believing it; and being wholly transported with joy for having subdued the finest of all the King's subjects to her desires, she took from her ears two large pearls and commanded him to wear them in his. He would have refused them crying, "Madam, these are not the proofs of your love that I expect; it is opportunity, it is a lone hour only that can make me happy." But forcing the pearls into his hand, she whispered softly to him, "Oh! do not fear a woman's invention, when love sets her a thinking." And pressing his hand, she cried, "This night you shall be happy. Come to the gate of the orange-grove, behind the Otan, and I will be ready about midnight to receive you." It was thus agreed, and she left him that no notice might be taken of their speaking together.

The ladies were still dancing, and the King, laid

on a carpet, with a great deal of pleasure was beholding them, especially Imoinda, who that day appeared more lovely than ever, being enlivened with the good tidings Onahal had brought her of the constant passion the Prince had for her. The Prince was laid on another carpet at the other end of the room, with his eyes fixed on the object of his soul; and as she turned or moved, so did they; and she alone gave his eyes and soul their motions. Nor did 10 Imoinda employ her eyes to any other use than in beholding with infinite pleasure the joy she produced in those of the Prince. But while she was more regarding him than the steps she took, she chanced to fall and so near him, as that leaping with extreme force from the carpet, he caught her in his arms as she fell; and it was visible to the whole presence the joy wherewith he received her. He clasped her close to his bosom and quite forgot that reverence that was due to the mistress of a King and that punishment 20 that is the reward of a boldness of this nature. And had not the presence of mind of Imoinda, fonder of his safety than her own, befriended him in making her spring from his arms and fall into her dance again, he had at that instant met his death; for the old King, jealous to the last degree, rose up in rage, broke all the diversion, and led Imoinda to her apartment, and sent out word to the Prince to go immediately to the camp, and that if he were found another night in Court, he should suffer the death 30 ordained for disobedience to offenders.

You may imagine how welcome this news was to Oroonoko, whose unseasonable transport and caress of Imoinda was blamed by all men that loved him; and now he perceived his fault, yet cried, "That for such another moment he would be content to die."

All the Otan was in disorder about this accident, and Onahal was particularly concerned because on the Prince's stay depended her happiness, for she could no longer expect that of Aboan; so that ere they departed, they contrived it so that the Prince and he should both come that night to the grove of the Otan, which was all of oranges and citrons, and that there they would wait her orders.

They parted thus with grief enough till night, leaving the King in possession of the lovely maid. But nothing could appease the jealousy of the old lover; he would not be imposed on but would have it that Imoinda made a false step on purpose to fall into Oroonoko's bosom and that all things looked like a design on both sides; and it was in vain she protested her innocence; he was old and obstinate, and left her, more than half assured that his fear was true.

The King, going to his apartment, sent to know where the Prince was and if he intended to obey his command. The messenger returned and told him, he found the Prince pensive and altogether unpreparing for the campaign; that he lay negligently on the ground and answered very little. This confirmed the jealousy of the King and he commanded that they should very narrowly and privately watch his motions and that he should not stir from his apartment, but one spy or other should be employed to watch him; so that, the hour approaching wherein he was to go to the citron-grove, and taking only Aboan along with him, he leaves his apartment, and was watched to the very gate of the Otan; where he was seen to enter, and where they left him, to carry back the tidings to the King.

Oroonoko and Aboan were no sooner entered, but Onahal led the Prince to the apartment of Imoinda; who, not knowing any thing of her happiness, was laid in bed. But Onahal only left him in her chamber, to make the best of his opportunity, and took her dear Aboan to her own; where he showed the height of complaisance for his Prince, when, to give him an opportunity, he suffered himself to be caressed in bed by Onahal.

The Prince softly wakened Imoinda, who was not a little surprised with joy to find him there, and yet she trembled with a thousand fears. I believe he omitted saying nothing to this young maid that might persuade her to suffer him to seize his own
10 and take the rights of love. And I believe she was not long resisting those arms where she so longed to be; and having opportunity, night, and silence, youth, love, and desire, he soon prevailed, and ravished in a moment what his old grandfather had been endeavouring for so many months.

It is not to be imagined the satisfaction of these two young lovers, nor the vows she made him that she remained a spotless maid till that night and that what she did with his grandfather had robbed him
20 of no part of her virgin honour; the gods, in mercy and justice, having reserved that for her plighted lord, to whom of right it belonged. And it is impossible to express the transports he suffered, while he listened to a discourse so charming from her loved lips and clasped that body in his arms, for whom he had so long languished; and nothing now afflicted him but his sudden departure from her; for he told her the necessity and his commands, but should depart satisfied in this, that since the old King had
30 hitherto not been able to deprive him of those enjoyments which only belonged to him, he believed for the future he would be less able to injure him; so that, abating the scandal of the veil which was no otherwise so than that she was wife to another, he believed her safe, even in the arms of the King, and innocent; yet would he have ventured at the conquest of the world and have given it all to have

had her avoided that honour of receiving the Royal Veil. It was thus, between a thousand caresses, that both bemoaned the hard fate of youth and beauty, so liable to that cruel promotion; it was a glory that could well have been spared here, though desired and aimed at by all the young females of that kingdom.

But while they were thus fondly employed, forgetting how time ran on and that the dawn must
10 conduct him far away from his only happiness, they heard a great noise in the Otan and unusual voices of men; at which the Prince, starting from the arms of the frighted Imoinda, ran to a little battle-axe he used to wear by his side, and having not so much leisure as to put on his habit, he opposed himself against some who were already opening the door; which they did with so much violence, that Oroonoko was not able to defend it but was forced to cry out with a commanding voice, "Whoever ye are that have
20 the boldness to attempt to approach this apartment thus rudely, know, that I, the Prince Oroonoko, will revenge it with the certain death of him that first enters; therefore stand back and know this place is sacred to love and me this night; to-morrow 'tis the King's."

This he spoke with a voice so resolved and assured, that they soon retired from the door, but cried, "'Tis by the King's command we are come; and being satisfied by thy voice, O Prince, as much as if we
30 had entered, we can report to the King the truth of all his fears and leave thee to provide for thy own safety, as thou art advised by thy friends."

At these words they departed and left the Prince to take a short and sad leave of his Imoinda; who, trusting in the strength of her charms, believed she should appease the fury of a jealous King by saying she was surprised and that it was by force of arms he got into her apartment. All her concern now was for his life, and therefore she hastened him to the camp and with much ado prevailed on him to go. Nor was it she alone that prevailed; Aboan and Onahal both pleaded, and both assured him of a lie that should be well enough contrived to secure Imoinda. So that at last, with a heart sad as death, dying eyes, and sighing soul, Oroonoko departed and took his way to the camp.

10 It was not long after, the King in person came to the Otan, where beholding Imoinda, with rage in his eyes, he upbraided her wickedness and perfidy; and threatening her royal lover, she fell on her face at his feet, bedewing the floor with her tears and imploring his pardon for a fault which she had not with her will committed, as Onahal, who was also prostrate with her, could testify: that, unknown to her, he had broken into her apartment and ravished her. She spoke this much against her conscience, but to save 20 her own life, it was absolutely necessary she should feign this falsity. She knew it could not injure the Prince, he being fled to an army that would stand by him against any injuries that should assault him. However, this last thought of Imoinda's being ravished changed the measures of his revenge, and whereas before he designed to be himself her executioner, he now resolved she should not die. But as it is the greatest crime in nature amongst them to touch a woman after having been possessed by a son, 30 a father, or a brother, so now he looked on Imoinda as a polluted thing wholly unfit for his embrace, nor would he resign her to his grandson, because she had received the Royal Veil; he therefore removes her from the Otan, with Onahal; whom he put into safe hands, with the order they should be both sold off as slaves to another country, either Christian or heathen, it was no matter where.

This cruel sentence, worse than death, they implored might be reversed; but their prayers were vain, and it was put in execution accordingly, and that with so much secrecy that none, either without or within the Otan, knew anything of their absence or their destiny.

The old King nevertheless executed this with a great deal of reluctancy, but he believed he had made a very great conquest over himself, when he 10 had once resolved and had performed what he resolved. He believed now that his love had been unjust, and that he could not expect the gods, or Captain of the Clouds as they call the unknown power, would suffer a better consequence from so ill a cause. He now begins to hold Oroonoko excused and to say he had reason for what he did. And now every body could assure the King how passionately Imoinda was beloved by the Prince; even those confessed it now who said the contrary before his flame 20 was abated. So that the King being old and not able to defend himself in war and having no sons of all his race remaining alive but only this to maintain him on his throne, and looking on this as a man disobliged, first by the rape of his mistress or rather wife and now by depriving him wholly of her, he feared, might make him desperate and do some cruel thing, either to himself or his old grandfather the offender, he began to repent him extremely of the contempt he had, in his rage, put on Imoinda. Be- 30 sides, he considered he ought in honour to have killed her for this offence, if it had been one. He ought to have had so much value and consideration for a maid of her quality as to have nobly put her to death and not to have sold her like a common slave; the greatest revenge and the most disgraceful of any, and to which they a thousand times prefer death and implore it, as Imoinda did, but could not obtain that honour. Seeing therefore it was certain that Oroonoko would highly resent this affront, he thought good to make some excuse for his rashness to him; and to that end, he sent a messenger to the camp, with orders to treat with him about the matter, to gain his pardon, and endeavour to mitigate his grief; but that by no means he should tell him she was sold, but secretly put to death, for he knew he should never obtain his pardon for the other.

When the messenger came, he found the Prince upon the point of engaging with the enemy; but as soon as he heard of the arrival of the messenger, he commanded him to his tent, where he embraced him and received him with joy; which was soon abated by the downcast looks of the messenger, who was instantly demanded the cause by Oroonoko; who, impatient of delay, asked a thousand questions in a breath and all concerning Imoinda. But there needed little return; for he could almost answer himself of all he demanded, from his sight and eyes. At last the messenger casting himself at the Prince's feet and kissing them with all the submission of a man that had something to implore which he dreaded to utter, he besought him to hear with calmness what he had to deliver to him and to call up all his noble and heroic courage, to encounter with his words and defend himself against the ungrateful things he must relate. Oroonoko replied, with a deep sigh and a languishing voice, "I am armed against their worst efforts, for I know they will tell me, Imoinda is no more —— And after that, you may spare the rest." Then, commanding him to rise, he laid himself on a carpet, under a rich pavilion, and remained a good while silent and was hardly heard to sigh. When he was come a little to himself, the messenger asked him leave to deliver that part of his embassy which the Prince had not yet divined, and the Prince cried, "I permit thee." Then he told him the affliction the old King was in for the rashness he had committed in his cruelty to Imoinda and how he deigned to ask pardon for his offence and to implore the Prince would not suffer that loss to touch his heart too sensibly, which now all the gods could not restore him, but might recompense him in glory, which he begged he would pursue; and that death, that common revenger of all injuries, would soon even the account between him 10 and a feeble old man.

Oroonoko bade him return his duty to his lord and master; and to assure him there was no account of revenge to be adjusted between them; if there were, 'twas he was the aggressor and that death would be just and, maugre his age, would see him righted; and he was contented to leave his share of glory to youths more fortunate and worthy of that favour from the gods; that henceforth he would never lift a weapon or draw a bow but abandon the small re- 20 mains of his life to sighs and tears and the continual thoughts of what his lord and grandfather had thought good to send out of the world, with all that youth, that innocence and beauty.

After having spoken this, whatever his greatest officers and men of the best rank could do, they could not raise him from the carpet or persuade him to action and resolutions of life; but commanding all to retire, he shut himself into his pavilion all that day, while the enemy was ready to engage; and won- 30 dering at the delay, the whole body of the chief of the army then addressed themselves to him, and to whom they had much ado to get admittance. They fell on their faces at the foot of his carpet, where they lay and besought him with earnest prayers and tears to lead them forth to battle and not let the enemy take advantages of them, and implored him to have regard to his glory and to the world, that depended on his courage and conduct. But he made no other reply to all their supplications but this,—that he had now no more business for glory and for the world, it was a trifle not worth his care. "Go," continued he, sighing, "and divide it amongst you, and reap with joy what you so vainly prize, and leave me to my more welcome destiny."

They then demanded what they should do and whom he would constitute in his room, that the confusion of ambitious youth and power might not ruin their order and make them a prey to the enemy. He replied he would not give himself the trouble, but wished them to choose the bravest man amongst them, let his quality or birth be what it would; "For, oh my friends!" said he, "it is not titles make men brave or good, or birth that bestows courage and generosity or makes the owner happy. Believe this, when you behold Oroonoko the most wretched and abandoned by fortune of all the creation of the gods." So turning himself about, he would make no more reply to all they could urge or implore.

The army beholding their officers return unsuccessful, with sad faces and ominous looks that presaged no good luck, suffered a thousand fears to take possession of their hearts and the enemy to come even upon them before they would provide for their safety by any defence; and though they were assured by some who had a mind to animate them, that they should be immediately headed by the Prince and that in the mean time Aboan had orders to command as General, yet they were so dismayed for want of that great example of bravery that they could make but a very feeble resistance, and, at last, downright fled before the enemy, who pursued them to the very tents, killing them; nor could all Aboan's courage, which that day gained him immortal glory, shame them into a manly defence of themselves. The guards that were left behind about the Prince's tent, seeing the soldiers flee before the enemy and scatter themselves over the plain in great disorder, made such outcries as roused the Prince from his amorous slumber, in which he had remained buried for two days without permitting any sustenance to approach him. But, in spite of all his resolutions, he had not the constancy of grief to that degree as to make him insensible of the danger of his army; and in that instant he leaped from his couch and cried, "Come, if we must die; let us meet death the noblest way; and it will be more like Oroonoko to encounter him at an army's head, opposing the torrent of a conquering foe, than lazily on a couch to wait his lingering pleasure and die every moment by a thousand wrecking thoughts, or be tamely taken by an enemy, and led a whining, love-sick slave to adorn the triumphs of Jamoan, that young victor who already is entered beyond the limits I had prescribed him."

While he was speaking, he suffered his people to dress him for the field, and sallying out of his pavilion with more life and vigour in his countenance than ever he showed, he appeared like some Divine Power descended to save his country from destruction; and his people had purposely put him on all things that might make him shine with most splendour to strike a reverend awe into the beholders. He flew into the thickest of those that were pursuing his men; and being animated with despair, he fought as if he came on purpose to die and did such things as will not be believed that human strength could perform, and such as soon inspired all the rest with new courage and new order. And now it was that they began to fight indeed and so as if they would not be outdone even by their adored hero, who turning the tide of the victory, changing absolutely the fate of the day, gained an entire conquest; and Oroonoko having the good fortune to single out Jamoan, he took him prisoner with his own hand, having wounded him almost to death.

This Jamoan afterwards became very dear to him, being a man very gallant, and of excellent graces and fine parts; so that he never put him amongst the rank of captives as they use to do, without distinction, for the common sale or market, but kept him in his own court, where he retained nothing of the prisoner but the name and returned no more into his own country—so great an affection he took for Oroonoko—and, by a thousand tales and adventures of love and gallantry, flattered his disease of melancholy and languishment; which I have often heard him say had certainly killed him, but for the conversation of this prince and Aboan and the French Governor he had from his childhood, of whom I have spoken before and who was a man of admirable wit, great ingenuity, and learning, all which he had infused into his young pupil. This Frenchman was banished out of his own country for some heretical notions he held; and though he was a man of very little religion, yet he had admirable morals and a brave soul.

After the total defeat of Jamoan's army, which all fled or were left dead upon the place, they spent some time in the camp, Oroonoko choosing rather to remain awhile there in his tents than to enter into a place or live in a Court where he had so lately suffered so great a loss; the officers therefore, who saw and knew his cause of discontent, invented all sorts of diversions and sports to entertain their Prince; so that what with those amusements abroad and others at home—that is, within their tents—with the persuasions, arguments, and care of his friends and servants that he more peculiarly prized, he wore off in time a great part of that chagrin and torture of despair which the first efforts of Imoinda's death had given him; insomuch, as having received a thousand kind embassies from the King and invitation to return to Court, he obeyed, though with no little reluctancy; and when he did so, there was a visible change in him, and for a long time he was much more melancholy than before. But time lessens all extremes and reduces them to 10 mediums and unconcern; but no motives of beauties, though all endeavoured it, could engage him in any sort of amour, though he had all the invitations to it, both from his own youth and other ambitions and designs.

Oroonoko was no sooner returned from this last conquest and received at Court with all the joy and magnificence that could be expressed to a young victor, who was not only returned triumphant, but beloved like a deity, when there arrived in the port 20 an English ship.

This person had often before been in these countries and was very well known to Oroonoko, with whom he had trafficked for slaves and had used to do the same with his predecessors.

This commander was a man of a finer sort of address and conversation, better bred, and more engaging than most of that sort of men are; so that he seemed rather never to have been bred out of a Court, than almost all his life at sea. This captain, 30 therefore, was always better received at Court than most of the traders to those countries were; and especially by Oroonoko, who was more civilised, according to the European mode, than any other had been, and took more delight in the white nations, and, above all, men of parts and wit. To this captain he sold abundance of his slaves, and for the favour and esteem he had for him, made him

many presents and obliged him to stay at Court as long as possibly he could. Which the captain seemed to take as a very great honour done him, entertaining the Prince every day with globes and maps, and mathematical discourses and instruments; eating, drinking, hunting, and living with him with so much familiarity, that it was not to be doubted but he had gained very greatly upon the heart of this gallant young man. And the captain, in return
10 of all these mighty favours, besought the Prince to honour his vessel with his presence some day or other at dinner, before he should set sail; which he condescended to accept and appointed his day. The captain, on his part, failed not to have all things in a readiness, in the most magnificent order he could possibly; and the day being come, the captain, in his boat, richly adorned with carpets and velvet cushions, rowed to the shore to receive the Prince, with another long-boat, where was placed all his
20 music and trumpets, with which Oroonoko was extremely delighted; who met him on the shore, attended by his French Governor, Jamoan, Aboan, and about a hundred of the noblest of the youths of the Court; and after they had first carried the Prince on board, the boats fetched the rest off; where they found a very splendid treat, with all sorts of fine wines, and were as well entertained as it was possible in such a place to be.

The Prince having drunk hard of punch, and
30 several sorts of wine, as did all the rest (for great care was taken they should want nothing of that part of the entertainment), was very merry and in great admiration of the ship, for he had never been in one before, so that he was curious of beholding every place where he decently might descend. The rest, no less curious, who were not quite overcome with drinking, rambled at their pleasure fore and aft,

as their fancies guided them; so that the captain, who had well laid his design before, gave the word and seized on all his guests; they, clapping great irons suddenly on the Prince, when he was leaped down into the hold, to view that part of the vessel, and locking him fast down, secured him. The same treachery was used to all the rest; and all in one instant, in several places of the ship, were lashed fast in irons and betrayed to slavery. That great 10 design over, they set all hands at work to hoist sail; and with as treacherous and fair a wind they made from the shore with his innocent and glorious prize, who thought of nothing less than such an entertainment.

Some have commended this act as brave in the captain, but I will spare my sense of it and leave it to my reader to judge as he pleases. It may be easily guessed in what manner the Prince resented this indignity, who may be best resembled to a lion 20 taken in a toil; so he raged, so he struggled for liberty, but all in vain; and they had so wisely managed his fetters that he could not use a hand in his defence to quit himself of a life that would by no means endure slavery nor could he move from the place where he was tied to any solid part of the ship, against which he might have beat his head and have finished his disgrace that way. So that being deprived of all other means, he resolved to perish for want of food, and pleased at last with that thought 30 and toiled and tired by rage and indignation, he laid himself down and sullenly resolved upon dying and refused all things that were brought him.

This did not a little vex the captain, and the more so because he found almost all of them of the same humour; so that the loss of so many brave slaves, so tall and goodly to behold, would have been very considerable; he therefore ordered one to go from him (for he would not be seen himself) to Oroonoko, and to assure him he was afflicted for having rashly done so inhospitable a deed and which could not be now remedied, since they were far from shore; but since he resented it in so high a nature, he assured him he would revoke his resolution and set both him and his friends ashore on the next land they should touch at; and of this the messenger gave him his oath, provided he would resolve to live. And 10 Oroonoko, whose honour was such as he never had violated a word in his life himself, much less a solemn asseveration, believed in an instant what this man said; but replied he expected, for a confirmation of this, to have his shameful fetters dismissed. This demand was carried to the captain; who returned him answer that the offence had been so great which he had put upon the Prince that he durst not trust him with liberty while he remained in the ship, for fear lest, by a valour natural to him and a 20 revenge that would animate that valour, he might commit some outrage fatal to himself and the King his master, to whom the vessel did belong. To this Oroonoko replied he would engage his honour to behave himself in all friendly order and manner and obey the command of the captain, as he was lord of the King's vessel and General of those men under his command.

This was delivered to the still doubting captain, who could not resolve to trust a heathen, he said, 30 upon his parole, a man that had no sense or notion of the god that he worshipped. Oroonoko then replied he was very sorry to hear that the captain pretended to the knowledge and worship of any gods, who had taught him no better principles than not to credit as he would be credited. But they told him the difference of their faith occasioned that distrust, for the captain had protested to him upon the word of a Christian and sworn in the name of a great God, which if he should violate, he would expect eternal torments in the world to come. "Is that all the obligations he has to be just to his oath?" replied Oroonoko. "Let him know I swear by my honour, which to violate would not only render me contemptible and despised by all brave and honest men and so give myself perpetual pain, but it would be eternally offending and diseasing to all mankind, —harming, betraying, circumventing, and outraging all men. But punishments hereafter are suffered by one's self; and the world takes no cognizances whether this God have revenged them or not, it is done so secretly and deferred so long; while the man of no honour suffers every moment the scorn and contempt of the honester world and dies every day ignominiously in his fame, which is more valuable than life. I speak not this to move belief, but to show you how you mistake, when you imagine that he who will violate his honour, will keep his word with his gods." So, turning from him with a disdainful smile, he refused to answer him, when he urged him to know what answer he should carry back to his captain; so that he departed without saying any more.

The captain pondering and consulting what to do, it was concluded that nothing but Oroonoko's liberty would encourage any of the rest to eat, except the Frenchman, whom the captain could not pretend to keep prisoner but only told him he was secured, because he might act something in favour of the Prince, but that he should be freed as soon as they came to land. So that they concluded it wholly necessary to free the Prince from his irons, that he might show himself to the rest, that they might have an eye upon him, and that they could not fear a single man.

This being resolved, to make the obligation the greater, the captain himself went to Oroonoko; where, after many compliments and assurances of what he had already promised, he receiving from the Prince his parole and his hand for his good behaviour, dismissed his irons and brought him to his own cabin; where, after having treated and reposed him a while, for he had neither eaten nor slept in four days before, he besought him to visit 10 those obstinate people in chains who refused all manner of sustenance, and entreated him to oblige them to eat and assure them of their liberty the first opportunity.

Oroonoko, who was too generous not to give credit to his words, showed himself to his people who were transported with excess of joy at the sight of their darling Prince, falling at his feet, and kissing and embracing them, believing, as some divine oracle, all he assured them. But he besought them to bear their 20 chains with that bravery that became those whom he had seen act so nobly in arms, and that they could not give him greater proofs of their love and friendship, since it was all the security the captain, his friend, could have against the revenge, he said, they might possibly justly take for the injuries sustained by him. And they all, with one accord, assured him that they could not suffer enough, when it was for his repose and safety.

After this, they no longer refused to eat, but took 30 what was brought them and were pleased with their captivity, since by it they hoped to redeem the Prince, who, all the rest of the voyage, was treated with all the respect due to his birth, though nothing could divert his melancholy; and he would often sigh for Imoinda and think this a punishment due to his misfortune, in having left that noble maid behind him, that fatal night, in the Otan, when he fled to the camp.

Possessed with a thousand thoughts of past joys with this fair young person and a thousand griefs for her eternal loss, he endured a tedious voyage and at last arrived at the mouth of the River of Surinam, a colony belonging to the King of England and where they were to deliver some part of their slaves. There the merchants and gentlemen of the country
10 going on board to demand those lots of slaves they had already agreed on, and amongst those, the overseers of those plantations where I then chanced to be. The captain, who had given the word, ordered his men to bring up those noble slaves in fetters, whom I have spoken of; and having put them, some in one and some in other lots, with women and children (which they call pickaninnies), they sold them off as slaves to several merchants and gentlemen; not putting any two in one lot, because they would sepa-
20 rate them far from each other; not daring to trust them together, lest rage and courage should put them upon contriving some great action to the ruin of the colony.

Oroonoko was first seized on and sold to our overseer, who had the first lot, with seventeen more of all sorts and sizes, but not one of quality with him. When he saw this, he found what they meant—for, as I said, he understood English pretty well—and being wholly unarmed and defenceless, so as it was
30 in vain to make any resistance, he only beheld the captain with a look all fierce and disdainful, upbraiding him with eyes that forced blushes on his guilty cheeks; he only cried in passing over the side of the ship, "Farewell, sir, 'tis worth my suffering to gain so true a knowledge, both of you, and of your gods, by whom you swear." And desiring those that held him to forbear their pains and telling them he would

make no resistance, he cried, "Come, my fellow-slaves, let us descend, and see if we can meet with more honour and honesty in the next world we shall touch upon." So he nimbly leapt into the boat, and showing no more concern, suffered himself to be rowed up the river with his seventeen companions.

The gentleman that bought him was a young Cornish gentleman, whose name was Trefry; a man of great wit, and fine learning, and was carried into
10 those parts by the Lord ——, Governor, to manage all his affairs. He reflecting on the last words of Oroonoko to the captain and beholding the richness of his vest, no sooner came into the boat, but he fixed his eyes on him; and finding something so extraordinary in his face, his shape, and mien, a greatness of look, and haughtiness in his air, and finding he spoke English, had a great mind to be inquiring into his quality and fortune; which, though Oroonoko endeavoured to hide, by only confessing he was above
20 the rank of common slaves, Trefry soon found he was yet something greater than he confessed; and from that moment began to conceive so vast an esteem for him that he ever after loved him as his dearest brother and showed him all the civilities due to so great a man.

Trefry was a very good mathematician and a linguist, could speak French and Spanish; and in the three days they remained in the boat (for so long were they going from the ship to the plantation), he
30 entertained Oroonoko so agreeably with his art and discourse that he was no less pleased with Trefry than he was with the Prince; and he thought himself, at least fortunate in this, that since he was a slave, as long as he would suffer himself to remain so, he had a man of so excellent wit and parts for a master. So that before they had finished their voyage up the river, he made no scruple of declaring to Trefry all

his fortunes and most part of what I have here related and put himself wholly into the hands of his new friend, who, he found, resented all the injuries were done him and was charmed with all the greatnesses of his actions, which were recited with that modesty and delicate sense as wholly vanquished him and subdued him to his interest. And he promised him, on his word and honour, he would find the means to reconduct him to his own country
10 again; assuring him he had a perfect abhorrence of so dishonourable an action and that he would sooner have died than have been the author of such a perfidy. He found the Prince was very much concerned to know what became of his friends and how they took their slavery; and Trefry promised to take care about the inquiring after their condition, and that he should have an account of them.

Though, as Oroonoko afterwards said, he had little reason to credit the words of a *Backearary*, yet he
20 knew not why, but he saw a kind of sincerity and awful truth in the face of Trefry; he saw honesty in his eyes, and he found him wise and witty enough to understand honour; for it was one of his maxims, *A man of wit could not be a knave or villain.*

In their passage up the river, they put in at several houses for refreshment, and ever when they landed, numbers of people would flock to behold this man; not but their eyes were daily entertained with the sight of slaves, but the fame of Oroonoko was gone
30 before him, and all people were in admiration of his beauty. Besides, he had a rich habit on, in which he was taken, so different from the rest, and which the captain could not strip him of, because he was forced to surprise his person in the minute he sold him. When he found his habit made him liable, as he thought, to be gazed at the more, he begged Trefry to give him something more befitting a slave, which

he did and took off his robes; nevertheless, he shone through all, and his osenbrigs (a sort of brown Holland suit he had on) could not conceal the graces of his looks and mien, and he had no less admirers than when he had his dazzling habit on. The Royal Youth appeared in spite of the slave, and people could not help treating him after a different manner, without designing it. As soon as they approached him, they venerated and esteemed him; his eyes insensibly commanded respect, and his behaviour insinuated it into every soul. So that there was nothing talked of but this young and gallant slave, even by those who yet knew not that he was a prince.

I ought to tell you that the Christians never buy any slaves but they give them some name of their own, their native ones being likely very barbarous and hard to pronounce; so that Mr. Trefry gave Oroonoko that of Cæsar; which name will live in that country as long as that scarce more glorious one of the great Roman; for it is most evident he wanted no part of the personal courage of that Cæsar and acted things as memorable, had they been done in some part of the world replenished with people and historians that might have given him his due. But his misfortune was to fall in an obscure world that afforded only a female pen to celebrate his fame; though I doubt not but it had lived from others' endeavours, if the Dutch, who immediately after his time took that country, had not killed, banished, and dispersed all those that were capable of giving the world this great man's life, much better than I have done. And Mr. Trefry, who designed it, died before he began it and bemoaned himself for not having undertook it in time.

For the future, therefore, I must call Oroonoko Cæsar, since by that name only he was known in our western world, and by that name he was received on shore at Parham House, where he was destined a slave. But if the king himself (God bless him) had come ashore, there could not have been greater expectation by all the whole plantation and those neighbouring ones, than was on ours at that time; and he was received more like a governor than a slave; notwithstanding, as the custom was, they assigned him his portion of land, his house, and his business up in the plantation. But as it was more for form than any design to put him to his task, he endured no more of the slave but the name and remained some days in the house, receiving all visits that were made him, without stirring towards that part of the plantation where the negroes were.

At last, he would needs go view his land, his house, and the business assigned him. But he no sooner came to the houses of the slaves, which are like a little town by itself, the negroes all having left work, but they all came forth to behold him and found he was that Prince who had, at several times, sold most of them to these parts; and from a veneration they pay to great men, especially if they know them, and from the surprise and awe they had at the sight of him, they all cast themselves at his feet, crying out, in their language, "Live, O King! Long live, O King!" and, kissing his feet, paid him even divine homage.

Several English gentlemen were with him, and what Mr. Trefry had told them was here confirmed, of which he himself before had no other witness than Cæsar himself. But he was infinitely glad to find his grandeur confirmed by the adoration of all the slaves.

Cæsar, troubled with their over-joy and over-ceremony, besought them to rise and to receive him as their fellow-slave, assuring them he was no better. At which they set up with one accord a most terrible

and hideous mourning and condoling, which he and the English had much ado to appease; but at last they prevailed with them, and they prepared all their barbarous music, and every one killed and dressed something of his own stock (for every family has their land apart, on which, at their leisure times, they breed all eatable things) and clubbing it together, made a most magnificent supper, inviting their *Grandee Captain*, their *Prince*, to honour it with his
10 presence; which he did, and several English with him, where they all waited on him, some playing, others dancing before him all the time, according to the manners of their several nations, and with unwearied industry endeavouring to please and delight him.

While they sat at meat, Mr. Trefry told Cæsar that most of these young slaves were undone in love with a fine she-slave, whom they had had about six months on their land; the Prince, who never heard
20 the name of love without a sigh nor any mention of it without the curiosity of examining further into that tale which of all discourses was most agreeable to him, asked how they came to be so unhappy, as to be all undone for one fair slave. Trefry, who was naturally amorous, and loved to talk of love as well as anybody, proceeded to tell him they had the most charming black that ever was beheld on their plantation, about fifteen or sixteen years old, as he guessed; that for his part he had done nothing but
30 sigh for her ever since she came; and that all the white beauties he had seen never charmed him so absolutely as this fine creature had done; and that no man, of any nation, ever beheld her, that did not fall in love with her; and that she had all the slaves perpetually at her feet; and the whole country resounded with the fame of Clemene, for so (said he) we have christened her; but she denies us all with

such a noble disdain that 'tis a miracle to see, that she who can give such eternal desires should herself be all ice and all unconcern. She is adorned with the most graceful modesty that ever beautified youth; the softest sigher——that, if she were capable of love, one would swear she languished for some absent happy man, and so retired as if she feared a rape even from the God of Day or that the breezes would steal kisses from her delicate mouth. Her task of work, some sighing lover every day makes it his petition to perform for her; which she accepts blushing and with reluctancy, for fear he will ask her a look for a recompense, which he dares not presume to hope so great an awe she strikes into the hearts of her admirers. "I do not wonder," replied the Prince, "that Clemene should refuse slaves, being, as you say, so beautiful; but wonder how she escapes those that can entertain her as you can do, or why, being your slave, you do not oblige her to yield?" "I confess," said Trefry, "when I have, against her will, entertained her with love so long as to be transported with my passion even above decency, I have been ready to make use of those advantages of strength and force nature has given me. But, oh! she disarms me with that modesty and weeping, so tender and so moving, that I retire and thank my stars she overcame me." The company laughed at his civility to a slave, and Cæsar only applauded the nobleness of his passion and nature, since that slave might be noble, or, what was better, have true notions of honour and virtue in her. Thus passed they this night, after having received from the slaves all imaginable respect and obedience.

The next day, Trefry asked Cæsar to walk when the heat was allayed and designedly carried him by the cottage of the fair slave and told him she whom he spoke of last night lived there retired. "But," says he, "I would not wish you to approach, for I am sure you will be in love as soon as you behold her." Cæsar assured him he was proof against all the charms of that sex, and that if he imagined his heart could be so perfidious to love again after Imoinda, he believed he should tear it from his bosom. They had no sooner spoken, but a little shock-dog that Clemene had presented her, which she took great delight in, ran out; and she, not knowing anybody was there, ran to get it in again and bolted out on those who were just speaking of her; when seeing them, she would have run in again, but Trefry caught her by the hand and cried, "Clemene, however you fly a lover, you ought to pay some respect to this stranger," pointing to Cæsar. But she, as if she had resolved never to raise her eyes to the face of a man again, bent them the more to the earth, when he spoke, and gave the Prince the leisure to look the more at her. There needed no long gazing or consideration to examine who this fair creature was; he soon saw Imoinda all over her; in a minute he saw her face, her shape, her air, her modesty, and all that called forth his soul with joy at his eyes, and left his body destitute of almost life; it stood without motion, and for a minute knew not that it had a being; and, I believe, he had never come to himself, so oppressed he was with over-joy, if he had not met with this allay, that he perceived Imoinda fall dead in the hands of Trefry. This awakened him, and he ran to her aid and caught her in his arms, where by degrees she came to herself; and it is needless to tell with what transports, what ecstasies of joy, they both a while beheld each other, without speaking, then snatched each other to their arms, then gazed again, as if they still doubted whether they possessed the blessing they grasped;

but when they recovered their speech, it is not to be imagined what tender things they expressed to each other, wondering what strange fate had brought them again together. They soon informed each other of their fortunes and equally bewailed their fate, but at the same time they mutually protested that even fetters and slavery were soft and easy and would be supported with joy and pleasure, while they could be so happy to possess each other and to be 10 able to make good their vows. Cæsar swore he disdained the empire of the world, while he could behold his Imoinda; and she despised grandeur and pomp, those vanities of her sex, when she could gaze on Oroonoko. He adored the very cottage where she resided and said that little inch of the world would give him more happiness than all the universe could do; and she vowed it was a palace, while adorned with the presence of Oroonoko.

Trefry was infinitely pleased with this novel and 20 found this Clemene was the fair mistress of whom Cæsar had before spoke and was not a little satisfied, that heaven was so kind to the Prince as to sweeten his misfortunes by so lucky an accident; and leaving the lovers to themselves, was impatient to come down to Parham House, which was on the same plantation, to give me an account of what had happened. I was as impatient to make these lovers a visit, having already made a friendship with Cæsar and from his own mouth learned what I have related; which was 30 confirmed by his Frenchman, who was set on shore to seek his fortune and of whom they could not make a slave, because a Christian; and he came daily to Parham Hill to see and pay his respects to his pupil Prince. So that concerning and interesting myself in all that related to Cæsar, whom I had assured of liberty as soon as the Governor arrived, I hasted presently to the place where these lovers were and was infinitely glad to find this beautiful young slave (who had already gained all our esteems, for her modesty and extraordinary prettiness) to be the same I had heard Cæsar speak so much of. One may imagine, then, we paid her a treble respect; and though from her being carved in fine flowers and birds all over her body, we took her to be of quality before, yet when we knew Clemene was Imoinda, we could not enough admire her.

10 I had forgot to tell you that those who are nobly born of that country are so delicately cut and raised all over the fore-part of the trunk of their bodies that it looks as if it were japanned, the works being raised like high point round the edges of the flowers. Some are only carved with a little flower or bird, at the sides of the temples, as was Cæsar; and those who are so carved over the body resemble our ancient Picts that are figured in the chronicles, but these carvings are more delicate.

20 From that happy day, Cæsar took Clemene for his wife, to the general joy of all people; and there was as much magnificence as the country could afford at the celebration of this wedding: and in a very short time after she conceived with child, which made Cæsar even adore her, knowing he was the last of his great race. This new accident made him more impatient of liberty, and he was every day treating with Trefry for his and Clemene's liberty, and offered either gold or a vast quantity of slaves, which 30 should be paid before they let him go, provided he could have any security that he should go when his ransom was paid. They fed him from day to day with promises and delayed him till the Lord-Governor should come; so that he began to suspect them of falsehood and that they would delay him till the time of his wife's delivery and make a slave of that too; for all the breed is theirs to whom the parents

belong. This thought made him very uneasy, and his sullenness gave them some jealousies of him; so that I was obliged, by some persons who feared a mutiny (which is very fatal sometimes in those colonies that abound so with slaves, that they exceed the whites in vast numbers), to discourse with Cæsar and to give him all the satisfaction I possibly could. They knew he and Clemene were scarce an hour in a day from my lodgings, that they ate with 10 me, and that I obliged them in all things I was capable of. I entertained him with the lives of the Romans and great men, which charmed him to my company; and her, with teaching her all the pretty works that I was mistress of, and telling her stories of nuns, and endeavouring to bring her to the knowledge of the true God. But of all discourses, Cæsar liked that the worst and would never be reconciled to our notions of the trinity, of which he ever made a jest; it was a riddle he said would turn his brain 20 to conceive, and one could not make him understand what faith was. However, these conversations failed not altogether so well to divert him, that he liked the company of us women much above the men, for he could not drink, and he is but an ill companion in that country that cannot. So that obliging him to love us very well, we had all the liberty of speech with him, especially myself, whom he called his *Great Mistress*; and indeed my word would go a great way with him. For these reasons I had opportunity to 30 take notice of him, that he was not well pleased of late, as he used to be, was more retired and thoughtful; and told him, I took it ill he should suspect we would break our words with him and not permit both him and Clemene to return to his own kingdom, which was not so long a way, but when he was once on his voyage, he would quickly arrive there. He made me some answers that showed a doubt in him,

which made me ask him what advantage it would be to doubt? It would but give us a fear of him and possibly compel us to treat him so as I should be very loth to behold; that is, it might occasion his confinement. Perhaps this was not so luckily spoke of me, for I perceived he resented that word, which I strove to soften again in vain; however, he assured me that whatsoever resolutions he should take, he would act nothing upon the white people; and as for
10 myself, and those upon that plantation where he was, he would sooner forfeit his eternal liberty and life itself than lift his hand against his greatest enemy on that place. He besought me to suffer no fears upon his account, for he could do nothing that honour should not dictate, but he accused himself for having suffered slavery so long; yet he charged that weakness on love alone, who was capable of making him neglect even glory itself, and for which now he reproaches himself every moment of
20 the day. Much more to this effect he spoke, with an air impatient enough to make me know he would not be long in bondage; and though he suffered only the name of a slave and had nothing of the toil and labour of one, yet that was sufficient to render him uneasy; and he had been too long idle, who used to be always in action, and in arms. He had a spirit all rough and fierce, and that could not be tamed to lazy rest; and though all endeavours were used to exercise himself in such actions and sports as this world
30 afforded, as running, wrestling, pitching the bar, hunting and fishing, chasing and killing tigers of a monstrous size, which this continent affords in abundance, and wonderful snakes, such as Alexander is reported to have encountered at the river of Amazons and which Cæsar took great delight to overcome; yet these were not actions great enough

for his large soul, which was still panting after more renowned actions.

Before I parted that day with him, I got, with much ado, a promise from him to rest yet a little longer with patience and wait the coming of the Lord-Governor, who was every day expected on our shore. He assured me he would, and this promise he desired me to know was given perfectly in complaisance to me, in whom he had an entire confidence.

10 After this, I neither thought it convenient to trust him much out of our view, nor did the country, who feared him; but with one accord it was advised to treat him fairly and oblige him to remain within such a compass, and that he should be permitted, as seldom as could be, to go up to the plantations of the negroes; or, if he did, to be accompanied by some that should be rather, in appearance, attendants than spies. This care was for some time taken, and Cæsar looked upon it as a mark of extraordinary respect

20 and was glad his discontent had obliged them to be more observant to him; he received new assurance from the overseer, which was confirmed to him by the opinion of all the gentlemen of the country, who made their court to him. During this time that we had his company more frequently than hitherto we had had, it may not be unpleasant to relate to you the diversions we entertained him with, or rather he us.

My stay was to be short in that country; because

30 my father died at sea and never arrived to possess the honour designed him (which was Lieutenant-General of six-and-thirty islands, besides the continent of Surinam) nor the advantages he hoped to reap by them; so that, though we were obliged to continue on our voyage, we did not intend to stay upon the place. Though, in a word, I must say thus much of it: that certainly had his late Majesty, of

sacred memory, but seen and known what a vast and charming world he had been master of in that continent, he would never have parted so easily with it to the Dutch. It is a continent whose vast extent was never yet known and may contain more noble earth than all the universe beside; for, they say, it reaches from east to west one way as far as China and another to Peru. It affords all things both for beauty and use; it is there eternal spring, always the very months of April, May, and June; the shades are perpetual, the trees bearing at once all degrees of leaves and fruit, from blooming buds to ripe autumn; groves of oranges, lemons, citrons, figs, nutmegs, and noble aromatics continually bearing their fragrances; the trees appearing all like nosegays, adorned with flowers of different kinds; some are all white, some purple, some scarlet, some blue, some yellow; bearing at the same time ripe fruit, and blooming young, or producing every day new. The very wood of all these trees has an intrinsic value, above common timber; for they are, when cut, of different colours, glorious to behold, and bear a price considerable, to inlay withal. Besides this, they yield rich balm and gums; so that we make our candles of such an aromatic substance as does not only give a sufficient light, but as they burn, they cast their perfumes all about. Cedar is the common firing, and all the houses are built with it. The very meat we eat, when set on the table, if it be native—I mean of the country—perfumes the whole room; especially a little beast called an Armadillo, a thing which I can liken to nothing so well as a rhinoceros; it is all in white armour, so jointed, that it moves as well in it as if it had nothing on. This beast is about the bigness of a pig of six weeks old. But it were endless to give an account of all the divers wonderful and strange things that country affords and which he took a great delight to go in search of, though those adventures are oftentimes fatal and at least dangerous. But while we had Cæsar in our company on these designs, we feared no harm, nor suffered any.

As soon as I came into the country, the best house in it was presented me, called St. John's Hill. It stood on a vast rock of white marble, at the foot of which the river ran a vast depth down and not to be descended on that side; the little waves still dashing
10 and washing the foot of this rock, made the softest murmurs and purlings in the world; and the opposite bank was adorned with such vast quantities of different flowers eternally blowing, and every day and hour new, fenced behind them with lofty trees of a thousand rare forms and colours, that the prospect was the most raving that fancy can create. On the edge of this white rock, towards the river, was a walk or grove of orange and lemon trees about half the length of the Mall here, whose flowery and fruit-
20 bearing branches met at the top and hindered the sun, whose rays are very fierce there, from entering a beam into the grove; and the cool air that came from the river made it not only fit to entertain people in, at all the hottest hours of the day, but refresh the sweet blossoms and made it always sweet and charming; and sure, the whole globe of the world cannot show so delightful a place as this grove was; not all the gardens of boasted Italy can produce a shade to outvie this, which nature has joined with art to
30 render so exceeding fine; and it is a marvel to see how such vast trees, as big as English oaks, could take footing on so solid a rock and in so little earth as covered that rock. But all things by nature there are rare, delightful, and wonderful. But to our sports!

Sometimes we would go surprising and in search of young tigers in their dens, watching when the old ones went forth to forage for prey; and oftentimes we have been in great danger and have fled apace for our lives, when surprised by the dams. But once, above all other times, we went on this design, and Cæsar was with us; who had no sooner stolen a young tiger from her nest, but going off, we encountered the dam, bearing a buttock of a cow, which he had torn off with his mighty paw, and going with it towards his den. We had only four women, 10 Cæsar, and an English gentleman, brother to Harry Martin the great Oliverian; we found there was no escaping this enraged and ravenous beast. However, we women fled as fast as we could from it; but our heels had not saved our lives, if Cæsar had not laid down his cub, when he found the tiger quit her prey to make the more speed towards him; and taking Mr. Martin's sword, desired him to stand aside or follow the ladies. He obeyed him; and Cæsar met this monstrous beast of mighty size and vast limbs, 20 who came with open jaws upon him; and fixing his awful stern eyes full upon those of the beast and putting himself into a very steady and good aiming posture of defence, ran his sword quite through his breast, down to his very heart, home to the hilt of the sword. The dying beast stretched forth her paw, and going to grasp his thigh, surprised with death in that very moment, did him no other harm than fixing her long nails in his flesh very deep, feebly wounded him, but could not grasp the flesh to tear 30 off any. When he had done this, he hollowed us to return; which, after some assurance of his victory, we did, and found him lugging out the sword from the bosom of the tiger, who was laid in her blood on the ground. He took up the cub, and with an unconcern that had nothing of the joy or gladness of a victory, he came and laid the whelp at my feet. We all extremely wondered at his daring and at the bigness of the beast, which was about the height of a heifer but of mighty great and strong limbs.

Another time, being in the woods, he killed a tiger that had long infested that part and borne away abundance of sheep and oxen and other things that were for the support of those to whom they belonged. Abundance of people assailed this beast, some affirming they had shot her with several bullets quite through the body at several times, and some swear-
10 ing they shot her through the very heart and they believed she was a devil, rather than a mortal thing. Cæsar had often said he had a mind to encounter this monster and spoke with several gentlemen who had attempted her; one crying, "I shot her with so many poisoned arrows," another with his gun in this part of her, and another in that; so that he, remarking all the places where she was shot, fancied still he should overcome her by giving her another sort of a wound than any had yet done; and one day said,
20 at the table, "What trophies and garlands, ladies, will you make me, if I bring you home the heart of this ravenous beast that eats up all your lambs and pigs?" We all promised he should be rewarded at our hands. So taking a bow, which he chose out of a great many, he went up into the wood, with two gentlemen, where he imagined this devourer to be. They had not passed very far into it when they heard her voice, growling and grumbling, as if she were pleased with something she was doing. When they
30 came in view, they found her nuzzling in the belly of a new ravished sheep, which she had torn open; and seeing herself approached, she took fast hold of her prey with her fore-paws and set a very fierce raging look on Cæsar, without offering to approach him, for fear at the same time of loosing what she had in possession. So that Cæsar remained a good while, only taking aim and getting an opportunity

to shoot her where he designed. It was some time before he could accomplish it, and to wound her, and not kill her, would but have enraged her the more and endangered him. He had a quiver of arrows at his side, so that if one failed, he could be supplied. At last, retiring a little, he gave her opportunity to eat, for he found she was ravenous and fell to as soon as she saw him retire, being more eager of her prey than of doing new mis-
10 chiefs; when he going softly to one side of her and hiding his person behind certain herbage that grew high and thick, he took so good aim that, as he intended, he shot her just into the eye, and the arrow was sent with so good a will and so sure a hand that it stuck in her brain and made her caper and become mad for a moment or two; but being seconded by another arrow, she fell dead upon the prey. Cæsar cut him open with a knife, to see where those wounds were that had been reported
20 to him, and why she did not die of them. But I shall now relate a thing that, possibly, will find no credit among men, because it is a notion commonly received with us that nothing can receive a wound in the heart and live. But when the heart of this courageous animal was taken out, there were seven bullets of lead in it and the wounds seamed up with great scars, and she lived with the bullets a great while, for it was long since they were shot. This heart the conqueror brought up to us, and it was
30 a very great curiosity, which all the country came to see; and which gave Cæsar occasion of many fine discourses of accidents in war and strange escapes.

At other times he would go a-fishing; and discoursing on that diversion, he found we had in that country a very strange fish, called a Numb-Eel (an eel of which I have eaten), that while it is alive, it has a quality so cold that those who are angling, though with a line of ever so great a length, with a rod at the end of it, it shall in the same minute the bait is touched by this eel, seize him or her that holds the rod with a numbness that shall deprive them of sense for a while; and some have fallen into the water, and others dropped, as dead, on the banks of the rivers where they stood, as soon as this fish touches the bait. Cæsar used to 10 laugh at this and believed it impossible a man could lose his force at the touch of a fish and could not understand that philosophy, that a cold quality should be of that nature; however, he had a great curiosity to try whether it would have the same effect on him it had on others and often tried, but in vain. At last, the sought-for fish came to the bait, as he stood angling on the bank; and instead of throwing away the rod or giving it a sudden twitch out of the water, whereby he might 20 have caught both the eel and have dismissed the rod before it could have too much power over him, for experiment-sake he grasped it but the harder and, fainting, fell into the river; and being still possessed of the rod, the tide carried him, senseless as he was, a great way, till an Indian boat took him up, and perceived, when they touched him, a numbness seize them, and by that knew the rod was in his hand; which with a paddle (that is a short oar) they struck away and snatched it into the boat, eel and all. If 30 Cæsar were almost dead with the effect of this fish, he was more so with that of the water, where he had remained the space of going a league, and they found they had much ado to bring him back to life; but at last they did and brought him home, where he was in a few hours well recovered and refreshed and not a little ashamed to find he should be overcome by an eel and that all the people, who heard his defiance, would laugh at him. But we cheered him up; and he being convinced, we had the eel at supper, which was a quarter of an ell about and most delicate meat and was of the more value, since it cost so dear as almost the life of so gallant a man.

About this time we were in many mortal fears, about some disputes the English had with the Indians; so that we could scarce trust ourselves, 10 without great numbers, to go to any Indian towns or place where they abode, for fear they should fall upon us, as they did immediately after my coming away; and the place being in the possession of the Dutch, they used them not so civilly as the English; so that they cut in pieces all they could take, getting into houses and hanging up the mother and all her children about her, and cut a footman I left behind me, all in joints and nailed him to trees.

This feud began while I was there, so that I lost 20 half the satisfaction I proposed, in not seeing and visiting the Indian towns. But one day, bemoaning of our misfortunes on this account, Cæsar told us we need not fear, for if we had a mind to go, he would undertake to be our guard. Some would, but most would not venture. About eighteen of us resolved and took barge, and, after eight days, arrived near an Indian town. But approaching it, the hearts of some of our company failed; and they would not venture on shore; so we polled who would and who 30 would not. For my part, I said, if Cæsar would, I would go. He resolved; so did my brother and my woman, a maid of good courage. Now none of us speaking the language of the people and imagining we should have a half diversion in gazing only and not knowing what they said, we took a fisherman that lived at the mouth of the river, who had been a long inhabitant there, and obliged him to go with us.

But because he was known to the Indians as trading among them and being, by long living there, become a perfect Indian in colour, we, who resolved to surprise them by making them see something they never had seen (that is, white people), resolved only myself, my brother, and woman should go. So Cæsar, the fisherman, and the rest, hiding behind some thick reeds and flowers that grew on the banks, let us pass on towards the town, which was on the bank of the river all along. A little distant from the houses or huts, we saw some dancing, others busied in fetching and carrying of water from the river. They had no sooner spied us, but they set up a loud cry that frighted us at first; we thought it had been for those that should kill us, but it seems it was of wonder and amazement. They were all naked, and we were dressed, so as is most commode for the hot countries, very glittering and rich; so that we appeared extremely fine; my own hair was cut short, and I had a taffety cap, with black feathers on my head; my brother was in a stuff-suit, with silver loops and buttons and abundance of green ribbon. This was all infinitely surprising to them; and because we saw them stand still till we approached them, we took heart and advanced, came up to them, and offered them our hands; which they took and looked on us round about, calling still for more company; who came swarming out, all wondering and crying out *Tepeeme*; taking their hair up in their hands, and spreading it wide to those they called out to; as if they would say (as indeed it signified) *Numberless wonders* or not to be recounted, no more than to number the hair of their heads. By degrees they grew more bold, and from gazing upon us round, they touched us, laying their hands upon all the features of our faces, feeling our breasts and arms, taking up one petticoat, then wondering to see another, admiring our shoes and stockings, but more our garters, which we gave them, and they tied about their legs, being laced with silver lace at the ends, for they much esteem any shining things. In fine, we suffered them to survey us as they pleased, and we thought they never would have done admiring us. When Cæsar and the rest saw we were received with such wonder, they came up to us; and finding the Indian trader whom they knew (for it is by these 10 fishermen, called Indian traders, we hold a commerce with them; for they love not to go far from home, and we never go to them), when they saw him therefore, they set up a new joy, and cried in their language, "Oh, here's our Tiguamy, and we shall know whether these things can speak." So advancing to him, some of them gave him their hands, and cried, "Amora Tiguamy"; which is as much as, *How do you do?* or, *Welcome, friend*; and all, with one din, began to gabble to him and asked if we had 20 sense and wit? If we could talk of affairs of life and war, as they could do? If we could hunt, swim, and do a thousand things they use? He answered them we could. Then they invited us into their houses and dressed venison and buffalo for us; and going out, gathered a leaf of a tree, called a *Sarumbo* leaf, of six yards long, and spread it on the ground for a table-cloth; and cutting another in pieces instead of plates, set us on little low Indian stools, which they cut out of one entire piece of wood and 30 paint in a sort of Japan-work. They serve every one their mess on these pieces of leaves; and it was very good, but too high-seasoned with pepper. When we had eaten, my brother and I took out our flutes and played to them, which gave them new wonder; and I soon perceived, by an admiration that is natural to these people and by the extreme ignorance and simplicity of them, it were not difficult to establish any

unknown or extravagant religion among them and to impose any notions or fictions upon them. For seeing a kinsman of mine set some paper afire with a burning-glass, a trick they had never before seen, they were like to have adored him for a god and begged he would give them the characters or figures of his name, that they might oppose it against winds and storms; which he did, and they held it up in those seasons and fancied it had a charm to conquer
10 them and kept it like a holy relic. They are very superstitious and called him the Great Peeie, that is, *Prophet*. They showed us their Indian Peeie, a youth of about sixteen years old, as handsome as nature could make a man. They consecrate a beautiful youth from his infancy, and all arts are used to complete him in the finest manner, both in beauty and shape. He is bred to all the little arts and cunning they are capable of; to all the legerdemain tricks and sleight of hand whereby he imposes upon
20 the rabble and is both a doctor in physic and divinity; and by these tricks makes the sick believe he sometimes eases their pains, by drawing from the afflicted part little serpents, or odd flies, or worms, or any strange thing; and though they have besides undoubted good remedies for almost all their diseases, they cure the patient more by fancy than by medicines and make themselves feared, loved, and reverenced. This young Peeie had a very young wife, who seeing my brother kiss her, came running and
30 kissed me. After this they kissed one another and made it a very great jest, it being so novel; and new admiration and laughing went round the multitude, that they never will forget that ceremony, never before used or known. Cæsar had a mind to see and talk with their war-captains, and we were conducted to one of their houses, where we beheld several of the great captains, who had been at

council. But so frightful a vision it was to see them, no fancy can create; no such dreams can represent so dreadful a spectacle. For my part, I took them for hobgoblins or fiends, rather than men. But however their shapes appeared, their souls were very humane and noble; but some wanted their noses, some their lips, some both noses and lips, some their ears, and others cut through each cheek, with long slashes, through which their teeth appeared. They had sev-
10 eral other formidable wounds and scars, or other dismemberings. They had *Comitias* or little aprons before them, and girdles of cotton, with their knives naked stuck in it; a bow at their backs, and a quiver of arrows on their thighs; and most had feathers on their heads of divers colours. They cried "Amora Tiguamy" to us at our entrance and were pleased we said as much to them. They seated us and gave us drink of the best sort and wondered as much as the others had done before to see us. Cæsar was mar-
20 velling as much at their faces, wondering how they should be all so wounded in war; he was impatient to know how they all came by those frightful marks of rage or malice, rather than wounds got in noble battle. They told us, by our interpreter, that when any war was waging, two men, chosen out by some old captain, whose fighting was past and who could only teach the theory of war,—these two men were to stand in competition for the generalship, or great war-captain; and being brought before the old
30 judges, now past labour, they are asked what they dare do to show they are worthy to lead an army. When he who is first asked, making no reply, cuts off his nose and throws it contemptibly on the ground; and the other does something to himself that he thinks surpasses him and perhaps deprives himself of lips and an eye. So they slash on till one gives out, and many have died in this debate. And

it is by a passive valour they show and prove their activity,—a sort of courage too brutal to be applauded by our black hero; nevertheless he expressed his esteem of them.

In this voyage Cæsar begat so good an understanding between the Indians and the English that there were no more fears or heart-burnings during our stay, but we had a perfect, open, and free trade with them. Many things remarkable and worthy reciting, 10 we met with in this short voyage; because Cæsar made it his business to search out and provide for our entertainment, especially to please his dearly adored Imoinda, who was a sharer in all our adventures; we being resolved to make her chains as easy as we could and to compliment the Prince in that manner that most obliged him.

As we were coming up again, we met with some Indians of strange aspects; that is, of a larger size, and other sort of features than those of our country. 20 Our Indian slaves, that rowed us, asked them some questions; but they could not understand us, but showed us a long cotton string with several knots on it and told us, they had been coming from the mountains so many moons as there were knots; they were habited in skins of a strange beast and brought along with them bags of gold-dust; which, as well as they could give us to understand, came streaming in little small channels down the high mountains, when the rains fell; and offered to be the convoy to 30 anybody or persons that would go to the mountains. We carried these men up to Parham, where they were kept till the Lord-Governor came. And because all the country was mad to be going on this golden adventure, the Governor, by his letters, commanded (for they sent some of the gold to him) that a guard should be set at the mouth of the river of Amazons (a river so called, almost as broad as the river of Thames) and prohibited all people from going up that river, it conducting to those mountains of gold. But we going off for England before the project was further prosecuted and the Governor being drowned in a hurricane, either the design died or the Dutch have the advantage of it. And it is to be bemoaned what his Majesty lost, by losing that part of America.

Though this digression is a little from my story, 10 however, since it contains some proofs of the curiosity and daring of this great man, I was content to omit nothing of his character.

It was thus for some time we diverted him; but now Imoinda began to show she was with child and did nothing but sigh and weep for the captivity of her lord, herself, and the infant yet unborn, and believed, if it were so hard to gain the liberty of two, it would be more difficult to get that for three. Her griefs were so many darts in the great heart of 20 Cæsar, and taking his opportunity, one Sunday, when all the whites were overtaken in drink, as there were abundance of several trades and slaves for four years that inhabited among the negro houses; and Sunday being their day of debauch (otherwise they were a sort of spies upon Cæsar), he went, pretending out of goodness to them, to feast among them, and sent all his music and ordered a great treat for the whole gang, about three hundred negroes, and about a hundred and fifty were able to bear arms, 30 such as they had, which were sufficient to do execution, with spirits accordingly. For the English had none but rusty swords that no strength could draw from a scabbard, except the people of particular quality, who took care to oil them and keep them in good order. The guns also, unless here and there one of those newly carried from England, would do no good or harm; for it is the nature of that country to rust and eat up iron or any metals but gold and silver. And they are very unexpert at the bow, which the negroes and Indians are perfect masters of.

Cæsar, having singled out these men from the women and children, made a harangue to them of the miseries and ignominies of slavery; counting up all their toils and sufferings under such loads, burdens, and drudgeries as were fitter for beasts than men,—senseless brutes, than human souls. He 10 told them it was not for days, months, or years, but for eternity; there was no end to be of their misfortunes. They suffered not like men, who might find a glory and fortitude in oppression; but like dogs, that loved the whip and bell and fawned the more they were beaten; that they had lost the divine quality of men and were become insensible asses, fit only to bear. Nay, worse; an ass, or dog, or horse, having done his duty, could lie down in retreat and rise to work again, and while he did his duty, en- 20 dured no stripes; but men, villainous, senseless men, such as they, toiled on all the tedious week till Black Friday; and then, whether they worked or not, whether they were faulty or meriting, they, promiscuously, the innocent with the guilty, suffered the infamous whip, the sordid stripes, from their fellow-slaves, till their blood trickled from all parts of their body; blood whose every drop ought to be revenged with a life of some of those tyrants that impose it. "And why," said he, "my dear friends and fellow- 30 sufferers, should we be slaves to an unknown people? Have they vanquished us nobly in fight? Have they won us in honourable battle? And are we by the chance of war become their slaves? This would not anger a noble heart; this would not animate a soldier's soul. No, but we are bought and sold like apes or monkeys, to be the sport of women, fools and cowards; and the support of rogues and runagates, that have abandoned their own countries for rapine, murders, theft, and villainies. Do you not hear every day how they upbraid each other with infamy of life, below the wildest savages? And shall we render obedience to such a degenerate race, who have no one human virtue left, to distinguish them from the vilest creatures? Will you, I say, suffer the lash from such hands?" They all replied with one accord, "No, no, no; Cæsar has spoke like 10 a great captain, like a great king."

After this he would have proceeded, but was interrupted by a tall negro, of some more quality than the rest (his name was Tuscan); who bowing at the feet of Cæsar, cried, "My lord, we have listened with joy and attention to what you have said, and, were we only men, would follow so great a leader through the world. But O! consider we are husbands and parents too, and have things more dear to us than life: our wives and children, unfit 20 for travel in these unpassable woods, mountains, and bogs. We have not only difficult lands to overcome, but rivers to wade and mountains to encounter, ravenous beasts of prey."

To this Cæsar replied that honour was the first principle in nature, that was to be obeyed; but as no man would pretend to that, without all the acts of virtue, compassion, charity, love, justice, and reason, he found it not inconsistent with that to take equal care of their wives and children as they would of 30 themselves; and that he did not design, when he led them to freedom, and glorious liberty, that they should leave that better part of themselves to perish by the hand of the tyrant's whip. But if there were a woman among them so degenerate from love and virtue to choose slavery before the pursuit of her husband, and with the hazard of her life, to share with him in his fortunes; that such a one ought to be abandoned and left as a prey to the common enemy.

To which they all agreed—and bowed. After this, he spoke of the impassable woods and rivers and convinced them, the more danger, the more glory. He told them that he had heard of one Hannibal, a great captain, had cut his way through mountains of solid rocks; and should a few shrubs oppose them, which they could fire before them? No, it was
10 a trifling excuse to men resolved to die or overcome. As for bogs, they are with a little labour filled and hardened; and the rivers could be no obstacle, since they swam by nature, at least by custom, from the first hour of their birth. That when the children were weary, they must carry them by turns, and the woods and their own industry would afford them food. To this they all assented with joy.

Tuscan then demanded what he would do. He said he would travel towards the sea, plant a new
20 colony, and defend it by their valour; and when they could find a ship, either driven by stress of weather or guided by providence that way, they would seize it and make it a prize, till it had transported them to their own countries; at least they should be made free in his kingdom and be esteemed as his fellow-sufferers and men that had the courage and the bravery to attempt, at least, for liberty; and if they died in the attempt, it would be more brave than to live in perpetual slavery.

30 They bowed and kissed his feet at this resolution, and with one accord vowed to follow him to death; and that night was appointed to begin their march. They made it known to their wives and directed them to tie their hammocks about their shoulders and under their arms, like a scarf, and to lead their children that could go and carry those that could not. The wives, who pay an entire obedience to

their husbands, obeyed and stayed for them where they were appointed. The men stayed but to furnish themselves with what defensive arms they could get; and all met at the rendezvous, where Cæsar made a new encouraging speech to them and led them out.

But as they could not march far that night, on Monday early when the overseers went to call them all together to go to work, they were extremely surprised to find not one upon the place, but all fled 10 with what baggage they had. You may imagine this news was not only suddenly spread all over the plantation, but soon reached the neighbouring ones; and we had by noon about six hundred men, they call the Militia of the country, that came to assist us in the pursuit of the fugitives. But never did one see so comical an army march forth to war. The men of any fashion would not concern themselves, though it were almost the common cause; for such revoltings are very ill examples and have very fatal 20 consequences oftentimes in many colonies. But they had a respect for Cæsar, and all hands were against the Parhamites (as they called those of Parham Plantation) because they did not in the first place love the Lord-Governor; and secondly, they would have it that Cæsar was ill-used and baffled with; and it is not impossible but some of the best in the country was of his council in this flight and depriving us of all the slaves; so that they of the better sort would not meddle in the matter. The Deputy- 30 Governor, of whom I have had no great occasion to speak, and who was the most fawning fair-tongued fellow in the world and one that pretended the most friendship to Cæsar, was now the only violent man against him; and though he had nothing and so need fear nothing, yet talked and looked bigger than any man. He was a fellow whose character is not fit to be mentioned with the worst of the slaves. This

fellow would lead his army forth to meet Cæsar or rather to pursue him. Most of their arms were of those sort of cruel whips they call *Cat with nine tails*; some had rusty useless guns for show; others old basket-hilts, whose blades had never seen the light in this age; and others had long staffs and clubs. Mr. Trefry went along, rather to be a mediator than a conqueror in such a battle; for he foresaw and knew, if by fighting they put the negroes into
10 despair, they were a sort of sullen fellows that would drown or kill themselves before they would yield; and he advised that fair means was best. But Byam was one that abounded in his own wit, and would take his own measures.

It was not hard to find these fugitives; for as they fled, they were forced to fire and cut the woods before them; so that night or day they pursued them by the light they made and by the path they had cleared. But as soon as Cæsar found he was pur-
20 sued, he put himself in a posture of defence, placing all the women and children in the rear; and himself, with Tuscan by his side or next to him, all promising to die or conquer. Encouraged thus, they never stood to parley, but fell on pell-mell upon the English, and killed some, and wounded a good many; they having recourse to their whips as the best of their weapons. And as they observed no order, they perplexed the enemy so sorely with lashing them in the eyes; and the women and children seeing their
30 husbands so treated, being of fearful and cowardly dispositions, and hearing the English cry out, "Yield, and live! Yield, and be pardoned!" they all run in amongst their husbands and fathers and hung about them, crying out, "Yield! Yield! and leave Cæsar to their revenge," that by degrees the slaves abandoned Cæsar, and left him only Tuscan and his heroic Imoinda, who grown big as she was, did

nevertheless press near her lord, having a bow and a quiver full of poisoned arrows, which she managed with such dexterity, that she wounded several and shot the Governor into the shoulder; of which wound he had liked to have died, but that an Indian woman, his mistress, sucked the wound and cleansed it from the venom. But however, he stirred not from the place till he had parleyed with Cæsar, who, he found, was resolved to die fighting and would not be taken;
10 no more would Tuscan or Imoinda. But he, more thirsting after revenge of another sort than that of depriving him of life, now made use of all his art of talking and dissembling, and besought Cæsar to yield himself upon terms which he himself should propose and should be sacredly assented to and kept by him. He told him it was not that he any longer feared him or could believe the force of two men, and a young heroine could overcome all them, with all the slaves now on their side also; but it was the
20 vast esteem he had for his person, the desire he had to serve so gallant a man and to hinder himself from the reproach hereafter of having been the occasion of the death of a Prince whose valour and magnanimity deserved the empire of the world. He protested to him he looked upon his action as gallant and brave, however tending to the prejudice of his lord and master, who would by it have lost so considerable a number of slaves; that this flight of his should be looked on as a heat of youth and a rash-
30 ness of a too forward courage and an unconsidered impatience of liberty and no more; and that he laboured in vain to accomplish that which they would effectually perform as soon as any ship arrived that would touch on his coast. "So that if you will be pleased," continued he, "to surrender yourself, all imaginable respect shall be paid you; and yourself, your wife and child, if it be here born, shall depart

free out of our land." But Cæsar would hear of no composition; though Byam urged, if he pursued and went on in his design, he would inevitably perish, either by great snakes, wild beasts or hunger; and he ought to have regard to his wife, whose condition required ease, and not the fatigues of tedious travel, where she could not be secured from being devoured. But Cæsar told him there was no faith in the white men or the gods they adored; who instructed them
10 in principles so false that honest men could not live amongst them; though no people professed so much, none performed so little; that he knew what he had to do when he dealt with men of honour, but with them a man ought to be eternally on his guard and never to eat and drink with Christians, without his weapon of defence in his hand, and, for his own security, never to credit one word they spoke. As for the rashness and inconsiderateness of his action, he would confess the Governor is in the right;
20 and that he was ashamed of what he had done, in endeavouring to make those free, who were by nature slaves, poor wretched rogues, fit to be used as Christians' tools,—dogs, treacherous and cowardly, fit for such masters; and they wanted only but to be whipped into the knowledge of the Christian gods, to be the vilest of all creeping things, to learn to worship such deities as had not power to make them just, brave, or honest. In fine, after a thousand things of this nature not fit here to be recited, he told Byam
30 he had rather die than live upon the same earth with such dogs. But Trefry and Byam pleaded and protested together so much, that Trefry believing the Governor to mean what he said and speaking very cordially himself, generously put himself into Cæsar's hands, and took him aside, and persuaded him, even with tears, to live, by surrendering himself, and to name his conditions. Cæsar was over-

come by his wit and reason and in consideration of Imoinda; and demanding what he desired and that it should be ratified by their hands in writing, because he had perceived that was the common way of contract between man and man amongst the whites, all this was performed, and Tuscan's pardon was put in, and they surrendered to the Governor, who walked peaceably down into the plantation with them, after giving order to bury their dead. Cæsar
10 was very much toiled with the bustle of the day, for he had fought like a fury; and what mischief was done, he and Tuscan performed alone and gave their enemies a fatal proof that they durst do anything and feared no mortal force.

But they were no sooner arrived at the place where all the slaves receive their punishments of whipping, but they laid hands on Cæsar and Tuscan, faint with heat and toil; and surprising them, bound them to two several stakes, and whipped them in a most
20 deplorable and inhuman manner, rending the very flesh from their bones, especially Cæsar, who was not perceived to make any moan or to alter his face, only to roll his eyes on the faithless Governor and those he believed guilty, with fierceness and indignation; and to complete his rage, he saw every one of those slaves who but a few days before adored him as something more than mortal, now had a whip to give him some lashes, while he strove not to break his fetters; though if he had, it were impossible; but he
30 pronounced a woe and revenge from his eyes, that darted fire that was at once both awful and terrible to behold.

When they thought they were sufficiently revenged on him, they untied him, almost fainting with loss of blood from a thousand wounds all over his body, from which they had rent his clothes, and led him bleeding and naked as he was, and loaded him all

over with irons; and then rubbed his wounds, to complete their cruelty, with Indian pepper, which had like to have made him raving mad; and, in this condition made him so fast to the ground that he could not stir, if his pains and wounds would have given him leave. They spared Imoinda and did not let her see this barbarity committed towards her lord, but carried her down to Parham and shut her up; which was not in kindness to her, but for fear
10 she should die with the sight or miscarry, and then they should lose a young slave and perhaps the mother.

You must know that when the news was brought on Monday morning that Cæsar had betaken himself to the woods and carried with him all the negroes, we were possessed with extreme fear, which no persuasions could dissipate, that he would secure himself till night and then would come down and cut all our throats. This apprehension made all the
20 females of us fly down the river, to be secured; and while we were away, they acted this cruelty; for I suppose I had authority and interest enough there, had I suspected any such thing, to have prevented it; but we had not gone many leagues, but the news overtook us that Cæsar was taken and whipped like a common slave. We met on the river with Colonel Martin, a man of great gallantry, wit, and goodness, and whom I have celebrated in a character of my new comedy, by his own name, in memory of so
30 brave a man. He was wise and eloquent and, from the fineness of his parts, bore a great sway over the hearts of all the colony. He was a friend to Cæsar and resented this false dealing with him very much. We carried him back to Parham, thinking to have made an accommodation; when he came, the first news we heard was that the Governor was dead of a wound Imoinda had given him, but it was not

so well. But it seems he would have the pleasure of beholding the revenge he took on Cæsar, and before the cruel ceremony was finished, he dropped down; and then they perceived the wound he had on his shoulder was by a venomed arrow, which, as I said, his Indian mistress healed, by sucking the wound.

We were no sooner arrived, but we went up to the plantation to see Cæsar, whom we found in a very
10 miserable and unexpressible condition; and I have a thousand times admired how he lived in so much tormenting pain. We said all things to him that trouble, pity, and good-nature could suggest, protesting our innocency of the fact and our abhorrence of such cruelties, making a thousand professions and services to him and begging as many pardons for the offenders, till we said so much that he believed we had no hand in his ill-treatment; but told us he could never pardon Byam; as for Trefry, he con-
20 fessed he saw his grief and sorrow for his suffering, which he could not hinder, but was like to have been beaten down by the very slaves, for speaking in his defence. But for Byam, who was their leader, their head—and should, by his justice and honour, have been an example to them—for him, he wished to live to take a dire revenge of him, and said, "It had been well for him, if he had sacrificed me, instead of giving me the contemptible whip." He refused to talk much, but begging us to give him
30 our hands, he took them and protested never to lift up his to do us any harm. He had a great respect for Colonel Martin and always took his counsel like that of a parent, and assured him he would obey him in anything, but his revenge on Byam. "Therefore," said he, "for his own safety, let him speedily despatch me; for if I could despatch myself, I would not, till that justice were done to my injured person

and the contempt of a soldier. No, I would not kill myself, even after a whipping, but will be content to live with that infamy and be pointed at by every grinning slave, till I have completed my revenge; and then you shall see that Oroonoko scorns to live with the indignity that was put on Cæsar." All we could do could get no more words from him; and we took care to have him put immediately into a healing bath, to rid him of his pepper, and ordered a chirurgeon to anoint him with healing balm, which he suffered, and in some time he began to be able to walk and eat. We failed not to visit him every day and to that end had him brought to an apartment at Parham.

The Governor was no sooner recovered and had heard of the menaces of Cæsar, but he called his Council, who (not to disgrace them, or burlesque the Government there) consisted of such notorious villains as Newgate never transported and, possibly, originally were such who understood neither the laws of God or man, and had no sort of principles to make them worthy the name of men; but at the very council-table would contradict and fight with one another and swear so bloodily that it was terrible to hear and see them. (Some of them were afterwards hanged, when the Dutch took possession of the place, others sent off in chains.) But calling these special rulers of the nation together and requiring their counsel in this weighty affair, they all concluded that (damn them) it might be their own cases; and that Cæsar ought to be made an example to all the negroes, to fright them from daring to threaten their betters, their lords and masters; and at this rate no man was safe from his own slaves; and concluded, *nemine contradicente*, that Cæsar should be hanged.

Trefry then thought it time to use his authority and told Byam his command did not extend to his lord's plantation; and that Parham was as much exempt from the law as White Hall; and that they ought no more to touch the servants of the Lord —— (who there represented the King's person) than they could those about the King himself; and that Parham was a sanctuary; and though his lord were absent in person, his power was still in being there, which he had entrusted with him, as far as the dominions of his particular plantations reached and all 10 that belonged to it; the rest of the country, as Byam was lieutenant to his lord, he might exercise his tyranny upon. Trefry had others as powerful, or more, that interested themselves in Cæsar's life and absolutely said he should be defended. So turning the Governor and his wise Council out of doors (for they sat at Parham House), we set a guard upon our lodging-place and would admit none but those we called friends to us and Cæsar.

The Governor having remained wounded at Par- 20 ham till his recovery was completed, Cæsar did not know but he was still there, and indeed for the most part, his time was spent there; for he was one that loved to live at other people's expense, and if he were a day absent, he was ten present there and used to play, and walk, and hunt, and fish with Cæsar. So that Cæsar did not at all doubt, if he once recovered strength, but he should find an opportunity of being revenged on him, though, after such a revenge, he could not hope to live; for if he escaped the fury of 30 the English mobile, who perhaps would have been glad of the occasion to have killed him, he was resolved not to survive his whipping; yet he had some tender hours, a repenting softness, which he called his fits of cowardice, wherein he struggled with love for the victory of his heart, which took part with his charming Imoinda there; but, for the most part, his time was passed in melancholy thoughts and black designs. He considered, if he should do this deed and die either in the attempt or after it, he left his lovely Imoinda a prey or at best a slave to the enraged multitude; his great heart could not endure that thought. "Perhaps," said he, "she may be first ravished by every brute, exposed first to their nasty lusts, and then a shameful death." No, he could not live a moment under that apprehension, too insupportable to be borne. These were his thoughts and his silent arguments with his heart, as he told us afterwards. So that now resolving not only to kill Byam, but all those he thought had enraged him, pleasing his great heart with the fancied slaughter he should make over the whole face of the plantation, he first resolved on a deed (that however horrid it first appeared to us all) when we had heard his reasons, we thought it brave and just. Being able to walk and, as he believed, fit for the execution of his great design, he begged Trefry to trust him into the air, believing a walk would do him good; which was granted him; and taking Imoinda with him, as he used to do in his more happy and calmer days, he led her up into a wood, where (after with a thousand sighs and long gazing silently on her face, while tears gushed, in spite of him, from his eyes) he told her his design, first of killing her and then his enemies and next himself, and the impossibility of escaping, and therefore he told her the necessity of dying. He found the heroic wife faster pleading for death than he was to propose it, when she found his fixed resolution; and, on her knees, besought him not to leave her a prey to his enemies. He, grieved to death, yet pleased at her noble resolution, took her up and, embracing of her with all the passion and languishment of a dying lover, drew his knife to kill this treasure of his soul, this pleasure of his eyes; while tears trickled down his cheeks, hers were

smiling with joy she should die by so noble a hand and be sent into her own country (for that is their notion of the next world) by him she so tenderly loved and so truly adored in this. For wives have a respect for their husbands equal to what any other people pay a deity; and when a man finds any occasion to quit his wife, if he love her, she dies by his hand; if not, he sells her or suffers some other to kill her. It being thus, you may believe the deed
10 was soon resolved on; and it is not to be doubted, but the parting, the eternal leave-taking of two such lovers, so greatly born, so sensible, so beautiful, so young, and so fond, must be very moving, as the relation of it was to me afterward.

All that love could say in such cases being ended and all the intermitting irresolutions being adjusted, the lovely, young and adored victim lays herself down before the sacrificer; while he, with a hand resolved and a heart-breaking within, gave the fatal
20 stroke, first cutting her throat and then severing her yet smiling face from that delicate body, pregnant as it was with the fruits of tenderest love. As soon as he had done, he laid the body decently on leaves and flowers, of which he made a bed, and concealed it under the same cover-lid of nature; only her face he left yet bare to look on. But when he found she was dead and past all retrieve, never more to bless him with her eyes and soft language, his grief swelled up to rage; he tore, he raved, he roared like
30 some monster of the wood, calling on the loved name of Imoinda. A thousand times he turned the fatal knife that did the deed toward his own heart, with a resolution to go immediately after her; but dire revenge, which was now a thousand times more fierce in his soul than before, prevents him; and he would cry out, "No, since I have sacrificed Imoinda to my revenge, shall I lose that glory which I have pur-

chased so dear, as at the price of the fairest, dearest, softest creature that ever nature made? No, no!" Then at her name grief would get the ascendant of rage, and he would lie down by her side and water her face with showers of tears, which never were wont to fall from those eyes; and however bent he was on his intended slaughter, he had not power to stir from the sight of this dear object, now more beloved and more adored than ever.

10 He remained in this deploring condition for two days and never rose from the ground where he had made her sad sacrifice; at last rousing from her side and accusing himself with living too long now Imoinda was dead and that the deaths of those barbarous enemies were deferred too long, he resolved now to finish the great work; but offering to rise, he found his strength so decayed that he reeled to and fro, like boughs assailed by contrary winds; so that he was forced to lie down again and try to 20 summon all his courage to his aid. He found his brains turned round, and his eyes were dizzy, and objects appeared not the same to him they were wont to do; his breath was short, and all his limbs surprised with a faintness he had never felt before. He had not eaten in two days, which was one occasion of his feebleness, but excess of grief was the greatest; yet still he hoped he should recover vigour to act his design and lay expecting it yet six days longer, still mourning over the dead idol of his 30 heart, and striving every day to rise, but could not.

In all this time you may believe we were in no little affliction for Cæsar and his wife; some were of opinion he was escaped, never to return; others thought some accident had happened to him. But however, we failed not to send out a hundred people several ways, to search for him. A party of about forty went that way he took, among whom was

Tuscan, who was perfectly reconciled to Byam. They had not gone very far into the wood, but they smelt an unusual smell, as of a dead body; for stinks must be very noisome that can be distinguished among such a quantity of natural sweets, as every inch of that land produces; so that they concluded they should find him dead or somebody that was so; they passed on towards it, as loathsome as it was, and made such rustling among the leaves that lie
10 thick on the ground by continual falling, that Cæsar heard he was approached; and though he had, during the space of these eight days, endeavoured to rise but found he wanted strength, yet, looking up and seeing his pursuers, he rose and reeled to a neighbouring tree, against which he fixed his back; and being within a dozen yards of those that advanced and saw him, he called out to them and bid them approach no nearer, if they would be safe. So that they stool still, and hardly believing their eyes
20 that would persuade them that it was Cæsar that spoke to them, so much he was altered, they asked him what he had done with his wife, for they smelt a stink that almost struck them dead. He, pointing to the dead body, sighing, cried, "Behold her there." They put off the flowers that covered her, with their sticks, and found she was killed, and cried out, "Oh, monster that hast murdered thy wife." Then asking him why he did so cruel a deed, he replied he had no leisure to answer impertinent questions.
30 "You may go back," continued he, "and tell the faithless Governor he may thank fortune that I am breathing my last, and that my arm is too feeble to obey my heart, in what it had designed him." But his tongue faltering and trembling, he could scarce end what he was saying. The English taking advantage by his weakness, cried, "Let us take him alive by all means." He heard them; and, as if he had

revived from a fainting or a dream, he cried out, "No, gentlemen, you are deceived; you will find no more Cæsars to be whipped; no more find a faith in me. Feeble as you think me, I have strength yet left to secure me from a second indignity." They swore all anew, and he only shook his head and beheld them with scorn. Then they cried out, "Who will venture on this single man? Will nobody?" They stood all silent, while Cæsar replied, "Fatal will 10 be the attempt of the first adventurer, let him assure himself," and, at that word, held up his knife in a menacing posture. "Look ye, ye faithless crew," said he, "'tis not life I seek, nor am I afraid of dying," and, at that word, cut a piece of flesh from his own throat and threw it at them; "yet still I would live if I could, till I had perfected my revenge. But, oh! it cannot be; I feel life gliding from my eyes and heart; and if I make not haste, I shall yet fall a victim to the shameful whip." At that, 20 he ripped up his own belly and took his bowels and pulled them out, with what strength he could; while some, on their knees imploring, besought him to hold his hand. But when they saw him tottering, they cried out, "Will none venture on him?" A bold Englishman cried, "Yes, if he were the Devil," (taking courage when he saw him almost dead) and swearing a horrid oath for his farewell to the world, he rushed on. Cæsar with his armed hand, met him so fairly, as stuck him to the heart, and he fell dead 30 at his feet. Tuscan seeing that, cried out, "I love thee, O Cæsar! and therefore will not let thee die, if possible"; and running to him, took him in his arms; but, at the same time, warding a blow that Cæsar made at his bosom, he received it quite through his arm; and Cæsar having not the strength to pluck the knife forth, though he attempted it, Tuscan neither pulled it out himself nor suffered it to be

pulled out, but came down with it sticking in his arm; and the reason he gave for it was because the air should not get into the wound. They put their hands across and carried Cæsar between six of them, fainted as he was, and they thought dead or just dying; and they brought him to Parham and laid him on a couch and had the chirurgeon immediately to him, who dressed his wounds and sewed up his belly and used means to bring him to life, which they
10 effected. We ran all to see him! and, if before we thought him so beautiful a sight, he was now so altered, that his face was like a death's-head blacked over, nothing but teeth and eye-holes. For some days we suffered nobody to speak to him, but caused cordials to be poured down his throat; which sustained his life, and in six or seven days he recovered his senses. For, you must know, that wounds are almost to a miracle cured in the Indies, unless wounds in the legs, which they rarely ever cure.

20 When he was well enough to speak, we talked to him and asked him some questions about his wife and the reasons why he killed her; and he then told us what I have related of that resolution and of his parting, and he besought us we would let him die and was extremely afflicted to think it was possible he might live. He assured us, if we did not despatch him, he would prove very fatal to a great many. We said all we could to make him live and gave him new assurances; but he begged we would not think
30 so poorly of him, or of his love to Imoinda, to imagine we could flatter him to life again. But the chirurgeon assured him he could not live, and therefore he need not fear. We were all, but Cæsar, afflicted at this news, and the sight was ghastly. His discourse was sad; and the earthy smell about him so strong that I was persuaded to leave the place for some time, being myself but sickly and very apt to

fall into fits of dangerous illness upon any extraordinary melancholy. The servants and Trefry and the chirurgeons, promised all to take what possible care they could of the life of Cæsar; and I, taking boat, went with other company to Colonel Martin's, about three days' journey down the river. But I was no sooner gone, than the Governor taking Trefry, about some pretended earnest business, a day's journey up the river, having communicated his design to one
10 Banister, a wild Irishman, one of the Council, a fellow of absolute barbarity, and fit to execute any villainy, but was rich; he came up to Parham and forcibly took Cæsar and had him carried to the same post where he was whipped; and causing him to be tied to it, and a great fire made before him, he told him he should die like a dog, as he was. Cæsar replied, this was the first piece of bravery that ever Banister did, and he never spoke sense till he pronounced that word; and if he would keep it, he
20 would declare, in the other world, that he was the only man, of all the whites, that ever he heard speak truth. And turning to the men that had bound him, he said, "My friends, am I to die, or to be whipt?" And they cried, "Whipt! no, you shall not escape so well." And then he replied, smiling, "A blessing on thee"; and assured them they need not tie him, for he would stand fixed like a rock and endure death so as should encourage them to die. "But if you whip me," said he, "be sure you tie me fast."

30 He had learned to take tobacco; and when he was assured he should die, he desired they would give him a pipe in his mouth, ready lighted; which they did. And the executioner came, and first cut off his members, and threw them into the fire; after that, with an ill-favoured knife, they cut off his ears and his nose and burned them; he still smoked on, as if nothing had touched him; then they hacked off one

of his arms, and still he bore up and held his pipe; but at the cutting off the other arm, his head sunk, and his pipe dropped, and he gave up the ghost, without a groan or a reproach. My mother and sister were by him all the while, but not suffered to save him; so rude and wild were the rabble and so inhuman were the justices who stood by to see the execution, who after paid dearly enough for their insolence. They cut Cæsar into quarters and sent
10 them to several of the chief plantations; one quarter was sent to Colonel Martin, who refused it and swore, he had rather see the quarters of Banister and the Governor himself, than those of Cæsar, on his plantations; and that he could govern his negroes, without terrifying and grieving them with frightful spectacles of a mangled king.

Thus died this great man, worthy of a better fate and a more sublime wit than mine to write his praise. Yet, I hope, the reputation of my pen is consider-
20 able enough to make his glorious name to survive to all ages, with that of the brave, the beautiful, and the constant Imoinda.

NOTES, COMMENTS, AND TOPICS FOR DISCUSSIONS AND REPORTS

SELECTED READING LIST FOR THE WHOLE FIELD OF ENGLISH FICTION BEFORE 1700

Ernest A. Baker, *The History of the English Novel:* Vol. 1, *The Age of Romance; from the Beginnings to the Renaissance*, London, 1924; vol. 2, *The Elizabethan Age and After*, London, 1929 (other volumes to appear); is the fullest account. Jean J. Jusserand, *The English Novel in the Time of Shakespeare*, London, 1903, is delightfully written. Charlotte E. Morgan, *The Rise of the Novel of Manners* (1600–1740), New York, 1911, is very useful for the seventeenth century. Sir Walter Raleigh, *The English Novel; a Short Sketch of Its History from the Earliest Times to the Appearance of Waverley*, London, 1925, and Wilbur L. Cross, *The Development of the English Novel*, New York, 1926, though covering a larger field and so devoting less space to the novel before 1700, are helpful. George Saintsbury, *The English Novel*, London, 1927, similarly devotes only a limited space to this period. Moreover, R. E. Prothero, Baron Ernle, *The Light Reading of Our Ancestors*, London and New York, 1927, gives a more popular account of the novel from the Greek romances to Scott. In the same way, J. C. Dunlop, *A History of Prose Fiction*, revised by H. Wilson, 2 vols., London, 1911, and F. M. Warren, *A History of the Novel Previous to the Seventeenth Century*, New York, 1908, treat the fiction of different countries and periods; Dunlop, again, is useful in giving many plots. Good works for special aspects of the English novel are S. L. Wolff, *The Greek Romances in Elizabethan Prose Fiction*, New York, 1912; J. G. Underhill, *Spanish Literature in the England of the Tudors*, New York, 1899; F. W. Chandler, *The Literature of Roguery*, 2 vols., Boston, 1907; and A. A. Tieje, *The Theory of Characterization in Prose Fiction Prior to* 1740, *Minnesota Studies in Language and Literature*, no. 5, 1916.

SIR THOMAS MALORY, LE MORTE DARTHUR

The selection given in this volume comprises Book XVIII, chapters 9–20, inclusive, and Book XXI, chapters 1–9. The first edition was printed in folio by Caxton in 1485, and remains only in an imperfect copy in the Althorp Collection in England, and a perfect copy in the Morgan Collection in New York. Our text is based on the exact transliteration of Caxton's published by H. Oskar Sommer, London, 1889–91. A good modern edition is issued by Macmillan in their Library of English Classics.

SELECTED READING LIST: The best biography and general review of scholarly problems arising from Malory's life is *Sir Thomas Malory, His Turbulent Career*, by Edward Hicks, Cambridge, 1928. *Sir Thomas Malory*, by E. K. Chambers, Oxford, 1922, is also useful. The background of the romances is treated in *Chivalry in English Literature*, by W. H. Schofield, Cambridge, 1912, and in *Le Morte Darthur of Sir Thomas Malory and Its Sources* by Vida Scudder, New York, 1917. Sources are discussed in Vol. III of Sommer's edition. An altercation on the sources of Book XXI between Sommer and J. Douglas Bruce may be followed in *Anglia* 23, 67; 29, 529; 30, 209. The most recent treatment of sources is *Malory* by Eugène Vinaver, Oxford, 1930 (a volume which appeared while this book was in press).

SUITABLE TOPICS FOR CLASS DISCUSSIONS OR REPORTS.
Malory's handling of dramatic situations.
Ideals of knighthood in Malory.
Style.
Poetic elements in his plots.
Comparison of these narratives with Tennyson's *Idylls* ("Lancelot and Elaine"; "Passing of Arthur").

19.—16. *a great wallop.* In full gallop.
26.—22. *bobaunce.* Boasting.
27.—3. *enchafe.* Make warm.
31.—8. *button.* Any small rounded body. (Used often in anatomy and surgery.)
34.—9. *mal engin.* Evil machination.
36.—7. *wood wroth.* Fiercely angry.
36.—18. *receive her Creator.* Take the Eucharist.
39.—28. *yede.* Went.
42.—2. *sonds.* Messages.
43.—3. *carracks.* Large ships of burden; galleons.
43.—11. *let.* Hinder, prevent.
44.—6. *cedle.* A written paper.
45.—22. *pight.* Pitched.
46.—14. *chaflet.* Platform.
48.—32. *foining.* Thrusting.

50.—12. *bur.* Bound iron ring on spear just behind place for hand.

50.—36. *rede.* Advice.

52.—17. *the waters wap and the waves wan.* The waters surging and the waves growing dark.

53.—30. *holts hoar.* Gray trees.

53.—36. *flemed.* Put to flight.

54.—7. *besants.* Gold coins first struck at Byzantium, varying from a sovereign to half a sovereign in value.

55.—13. *Hic jacet* etc. Here lies Arthur, king in the past and king in the future.

57.—1. *spered.* Inquired.

58.—14. *boot.* Advantage, profit.

LORD BERNERS, HUON OF BORDEAUX

The English *Huon of Bordeaux* was first published probably in 1534 by Wynkyn de Worde, an edition whereof but a single copy now exists,—in the library of Earl Crawford. From this copy was printed the Early English Text Society edition, from which in turn this text is drawn. The passage begins in chapter XXI and runs through chapter XXIV.

SELECTED READING LIST. The Early English Text Society Edition, edited by Sidney Lee, London, 1882–7, has the complete text and much useful information. The article in the *Dictionary of National Biography* by the same writer is likewise helpful.

SUITABLE TOPICS FOR CLASS DISCUSSIONS OR REPORTS.

Suspense in *Huon*.

The picture of knighthood in *Huon*, compared with that in Malory.

The style, compared with Malory.

61.—9. *faerie.* The fairy people.

66.—17. *let.* Hinder.

JOHN LYLY, EUPHUES

The selection here given comprises Vol. I pp. 196–206 of *The Complete Works of John Lyly*, collected and edited by R. Warwick Bond, Oxford, 1902. To arrive at his text Bond collated all extant early editions of Lyly.

SELECTED READING LIST. A good edition of *Euphues* is that by Morris W. Croll and Harry Clemons, Dutton, 1916. The best lives are Bond's in the introduction to his *Com-*

plete Works of John Lyly; *John Lyly* by J. D. Wilson, Cambridge, 1905, and especially, *John Lyly, contributions à l'histoire de la renaissance en Angleterre*, by Albert Feuillerat, Cambridge, 1910. The last named advances the idea that the plot of *Euphues* was suggested by actual events, a theory discussed and discredited by S. L. Wolff, "The Humanist as Man of Letters," *Sewanee Review*, 1928, p. 342 ff.

SUITABLE TOPICS FOR CLASS DISCUSSIONS OR REPORTS.

The ideal of the gentleman in *Euphues*.
Woman, her role in life and the good qualities desired for her.
Lyly's style, with examples of his various devices.
Qualities in *Euphues* appealing to woman readers of its time.
Source of *Euphues*' popularity.

71.—35. *fere.* Companion.
76.—29. *list.* Desire.
77.—32. *estridge.* Ostrich.
78.—35. *black ox.* Old age.
82.—16. *convince me of fleeting.* Convict me of wavering.

SIR PHILIP SIDNEY, THE ARCADIA

The original version or so-called "old Arcadia," of five books, was not printed in Elizabethan times. The first printed edition of the *Arcadia* (1590) is Sidney's augmentation of the novel, containing two books and a fragment of the third. The second edition (1593) has all the 1590 text; thereafter, the fragmentary Book III of the 1590 edition is completed by the whole of Book III of the "old Arcadia"; finally, all of Books IV and V from the "old Arcadia" are added as separate books. This very rare second edition is the basis of all future ones. Our text is drawn from a copy of the third edition (1598); the two passages being the beginning and one from Book II (found p. 191 ff. in Baker's modern edition).

SELECTED READING LIST. A scholarly edition of the *Arcadia* is found in Sidney's complete works, edited by Albert Feuillerat, 4 vols., Cambridge, England, 1912–1926. (Volume I has the text of the 1590 edition; volume II, what was added in the 1593 edition; volume IV, the "old Arcadia" as originally written.) A handy edition in one volume is by E. A. Baker, London, 1907.

The edition of the *Arcadia* by H. Oskar Sommer, London, 1891, has thorough introductory matter about different editions. Bertram Dobell, *Quarterly Review*, vol. 211, p. 74 ff., is a discussion of the "old Arcadia" by its discoverer. M. W.

Wallace, *The Life of Sir Philip Sidney*, Cambridge, England, 1915, is a good biography. E. A. Greenlaw, *Sidney's "Arcadia" as an Example of Elizabethan Allegory*, in *Kittredge Anniversary Papers*, Boston, 1913, is a helpful discussion of the moral and political significance of the work. Friedrich Brie, *Sidney's "Arcadia"*, Strassburg, 1918, is a fuller discussion in German of these and other aspects. A good account of the influence of Greek romances on the *Arcadia* is S. L. Wolff, *The Greek Romances in Elizabethan Prose Fiction*, New York, 1912. (Pages 262–307 give a detailed analysis of the plot.) T. P. Harrison, *A Source of Sidney's "Arcadia,"* in *University of Texas Studies in English*, No. 6, 1926, is useful for Spanish influences. W. W. Greg, *Pastoral Poetry and Pastoral Drama*, London, 1906, treats the influence of the *Arcadia* on the drama.

SUITABLE TOPICS FOR CLASS DISCUSSIONS OR REPORTS.

Ideals of manhood in the *Arcadia* (compare Malory or Lyly).
The descriptions.
The style, with examples of the various devices.
Reasons for the *Arcadia's* popularity.

The Greek romances influencing the *Arcadia* are Heliodorus' *Ethiopica* and Achilles Tatius' *Clitophon and Leucippe*. For the travels of a lover and his lady in Greek romances, Sidney substitutes the travels of two man friends, one of whom is captured by pirates, as is the lady in Greek romances. In particular, the episode of Musidorus' being frightened from helping Pyrocles by a galley of pirates in the first selection is paralleled by one in Achilles Tatius, where the Governor of Pharos with Clitophon sets out to rescue Leucippe but is frightened away by a pirate galley. The grandiose framework of the novel resembles that of Heliodorus.

In the opening passage of the *Diana* which inspired the early pages of the first selection, the shepherd Sireno comes to the banks of the River Ezla and laments his love for Diana, among other things apostrophizing Memory.

90.—21. *running at base*. The game of prisoner's base.
102.—20. *make-bate*. A breeder of strife.

THOMAS LODGE, ROSALYNDE

This text is based on the reprint of the first (1590) edition of *Rosalynde* (whereof but one copy now exists) in the *Complete Works of Thomas Lodge*, edited by E. Gosse and printed for the Hunterian Club (4 vols., Glasgow, 1878–1883). To insure accuracy, we have checked this text by the Elston Press (New Rochelle, New York, 1902) reprint of the second (1592) edition of *Rosalynde* (a reprint in which this edition has been collated with the third edition of 1598).

Selected Reading List. The above mentioned complete edition of Lodge, besides giving the text, provides a memoir of Lodge by E. Gosse (reprinted in that writer's *Seventeenth Century Studies*, London, 1883). The article on Lodge in the *Dictionary of National Biography* is by Sidney Lee. W. W. Greg's edition of *Rosalynde*, New York, 1907, has helpful prefatory remarks. *The Tale of Gamelyn* is in volume four of Skeat's large edition of Chaucer. A discussion of the sources of Lodge's lyrics (in *Rosalynde* and elsewhere) is found in A. H. Bullen, *Poems Chiefly Lyrical from Romances and Prose Tracts of the Elizabethan Age*, London, 1890, introduction, p. X ff.; Sidney Lee, *Elizabethan Sonnets*, 2 vols., 1904, I, pp. LXIV–LXXV; L. E. Kastner, in the *Athenaeum*, Oct. 22, 1904, pp. 552–3.

Neither in *Rosalynde* nor elsewhere does this book try to rectify misquotations of Latin authors by Elizabethans.

Suitable Topics for Class Discussions or Reports.

The characters of Rosalynde and Alinda.

Traits in man appealing to Lodge.

The sylvan background.

Shepherds,—their reality and appeal (compare with those in the Arcadia).

The style (compare with that of the preceding authors).

The good qualities of the songs.

The effect produced by the songs in the book.

Shakespeare's borrowings from Lodge and the difference in his treatment.

A comparison of the names of Lodge's characters with those in *As You Like It*.

Lodge's borrowings from the *Tale of Gamelyn* and differences in his treatment.

106.—10. *salem ingenii*. Shrewdness of nature.

108.—28. *Phaeton*. Apollo's son, who met his death by trying to drive his father's sun chariot.

Icarus. Daedalus' son, who flew too near the sun on his wings of wax, melted them, and fell.

108.—32. *medium tenere tutissimum*. To hold the middle course most safely.

109.—19. *Hyperborei*. Dwellers far in the north who lived in unbroken ease and happiness.

112.—23. *natura naturans*. Creative nature.

112.—26. *Naturam expellas* etc. You may drive out nature with violence, but it will constantly return.

113.—11. *Avicen.* Avicenna, 980–1037, the most celebrated Arabian physician and philosopher.

114.—4. *parole.* Given orally.

114.—11. *Non sapit* etc. He knows not who knows not for his own advantage.

114.—13. *checkmate.* Equal in a contest.

114.—14. *Nimia familiaritas* etc. Too much familiarity breeds contempt.

114.—22. *Galen.* Born about 130 A.D. Famous Greek physician.

114.—23. *riflest with gold.* Gamble for gold.

115.—25. *dumps.* A reverie.

115.—26. *your heart on your half penny.* Have a particular object in view.

115.—33. *cates.* Choice viands.

116.—11. *coy.* Of disdainful manner.

116.—16. *cooling card.* Apparently a term of some unknown game; applied figuratively to anything which cools a person's passion.

116.—34. *Amantium ira* etc. The anger of lovers serves for the renewal of love.

117.—11. *pad hidden in the straw.* Lurking danger (pad = toad).

117.—29. *Quis nisi* etc. Who but the mad man rejects gold when it is offered?

118.—29. *vailed.* Lowered.

118.—31. *bezo les labres.* A kiss on the lips.

119.—25. *Luna kissed the shepherd.* Luna, the moon goddess, loved the shepherd Endymion.

119.—32. *amorets.* Looks inspiring love.

120.—13. *Achelous.* A river god who contended with Hercules for Deianira, but was conquered.

127.—31. *Quaerenda pecunia* etc. Wealth should be sought first and, after money, virtue.

128.—3. *Si nihil* etc. If you have brought nothing, you will be put out, Homer.

130.—24. *rase.* Erase.

132.—34. *implaister.* Plaster.

133.—3. *Consulenti* etc. The man who gives advice doesn't have the headache.

133.—13. *orient.* Precious.

133.—28. *Solamen* etc. It is a comfort for the unhappy to have had comrades in misfortune.

134.—3. *Olim haec* etc. Hereafter we shall take pleasure in recalling these experiences.

134.—34. *black ox.* Adversity.

137.—3. *First shall the heavens* etc. This is taken from Desportes' poem beginning "On verra défaillir tous les astres aux cieux."

137.—34. *Demophoon and Phyllis.* Thinking herself deserted by her lover Demophoon, Phyllis killed herself and was turned into a tree which put forth leaves when he came back and embraced it.

138.—21. *Flora and Tellus.* Flora, the goddess of flowers. Tellus, the goddess of the earth.

138.—32. *Dryades and Hamadryades.* Nymphs of the forests and trees.

139.—7. *greet.* Lament.

140.—15. *arede.* Advice.

142.—22. *fry.* Young fish.

143.—5 ff. *In amore* etc. In love are contained all these faults: truces, hatred, war, peace again; if you wish all these uncertainties to be made certain by reason, you will get no further than if you tried to go insane with reason.

145.—15. *Satis est* etc. What satisfies is enough.

146.—34. *Phoebe sate* etc. This poem is parodied in *Tarlton's News out of Purgatory*, 1590, where it is put in the mouth of Ronsard, from whom Lodge borrowed much.

148.—22. *set up her rest.* To take up permanent abode (figure from gambling).

150.—4. *sicco pede.* With dry foot, i.e. without heed.

150.—16. *while.* Until.

150.—28. *stopped their ears with Ulysses.* Ulysses filled the ears of his men with wax so that they might not hear the Sirens' song and be lured to their death.

151.—9. *rampired up.* Fortified.

152.—6. *losels.* Ne'er-do-wells.

152.—17. *prease.* A crowd.

158.—21. *herehault.* Herald.

160.—20. *recorded.* Warbled.

162.—19. *Ovid and Julia.* Corinna, heroine of some of the *Amores*, erotic poems by Ovid (Roman poet, 43 B.C.—17 A.D.) was sometimes identified with Augustus' daughter, Julia.

163.—14. *Daphne.* Pursued by Apollo, Daphne escaped by turning into a laurel tree.

163.—16. *Ixion.* Ixion loved Juno, but she deceived him with a cloud fashioned in her likeness.

163.—27. *pole-footed.* Club footed.

165.—21. *Periit* etc. He perished from being desperately in love.

168.—28. *Iris.* Personification of rainbow and messenger of gods.

169.—17. *peccavi.* I have sinned.

170.—34. *Oenone.* Nymph of Mount Ida, married to Paris before his elopement with Helen.

171.—10. *Leda.* Wooed by Jupiter in form of a swan. *Danae.* Wooed by Jupiter in a golden shower.

171.—34. *bains.* Bathes.

172.—9. *Rosader en esperance.* Rosader in hope.

172.—21. *amo.* I love.

173.—2. *amorets.* Love poems.

173.—12. *flew to the fist.* Hawking term since hawks were carried on the fist.

173.—26. *Ariadne.* Jupiter made her immortal and set her bridal crown among the stars after she was deserted by her lover Theseus.

175.—37. *suspect.* Suspicion.

176.—3. *Petrarch.* Italian poet, 1304–1374. Lover of Laura. *Tasso.* Italian poet, 1544–1595.

176.—6. *fair.* Beauty.

176.—28. *junkets.* Any dainty sweetmeat.

179.—4. *nill.* Will not.

180.—1. *Tithon's dear.* Aurora, goddess of dawn and wife of Tithonus.

180.—15. *jump.* Coincide.

180.—24. *Zeuxis.* Greek painter of the fifth century, B.C., who painted grapes to look so natural that birds pecked at them.

181.—21. *mazer.* Bowl, drinking cup.

182.—20. *divine.* A diviner.

184.—10. *ambages.* Roundabout proceedings.

192.—3. *bill.* Halberd.

192.—11. *Lupus est* etc. There's a wolf in the story.

193.—24. *Ne Hercules* etc. Not even Hercules against two.

196.—25. *Callisto.* Attendant of Diana loved by Jupiter.

196.—34. *giglot.* A lewd woman.

200.—6. *Virtus, fama* etc. For all things—virtue, fame, honor, both divine things and human things, wait upon fair riches; the man who has laid hand on these will be famous, brave, just, wise, and even a king, and whatever he wishes.

200.—25. *strakes.* Stripes.

202.—30. *Polypheme.* One-eyed Cyclops, lover of Galatea.

203.—14. *Hélas, tyran* etc. Alas, thou most rigorous tyrant, bridle thy violence. What availeth thee so great an effort? It is too fiery for my poor heart. Save therefrom but a spark, and then try thy best to stir that proud maid who refuses to behold in what flames I burn for her. O Love, do but effect this end, and bring down her haughtiness. Her heart should not be made of ice although her bosom is of snow.—This poem is taken from Desportes' *Amours de Diane.*

207.—13. *Narcissus.* Youth sentenced by the gods to love no one but himself.

207.—34. *Adonis.* Beautiful youth, beloved of Venus, who perished from a wound got in the chase.

211.—15. *If it be true* etc. Taken from Desportes' sonnet, "S'il est vray que le ciel ait sa course éternelle."

211.—33. *Et florida pungunt.* Even flowers have thorns.

212.—7 ff. *Otia si tollas* etc. If you take away leisure, the bow of Cupid loses its power, and his torches lie despised and without light.

213.—32. *Circe.* An enchantress who turned men into swine by giving them a magic drink.

213.—36. *Piscator* etc. The fisherman knows bites.

216.—15. *uncouth.* Unknown.

217.—28. *magis aegrotare* etc. Rather ail in mind than body.

218.—14. *standish.* Inkstand.

219.—23. *My boat doth pass the straits* etc. Taken from Desportes' "Ma nef passe au détroit d'une mer courroucée."

222.—18. *Bellerophon.* King Proetus sent Bellerophon to Iobates with a tablet in cipher ordering that he be killed on his arrival.

222.—30. *Achilles' lance.* Telephus, wounded by Achilles' lance, could be cured only by applying rust scraped from the same weapon.

223.—11. *censure.* Judicial sentence.

224.—12. *fetch.* Trick.

224.—13. *malgrado.* In spite of.

224.—36. *Clytia.* Ocean nymph who was loved by Apollo and was turned into heliotrope when he deserted her.

226.—3. *Festina lente.* Make haste slowly.

232.—33. *Wanton wag of Troy.* Paris.

238.—17. *handselled.* Inaugurated.

238.—23. *amort.* Spiritless.

239.—31. *smicker.* Handsome.

240.—9. *kit.* Light woman.

THOMAS NASHE, THE UNFORTUNATE TRAVELLER

This selection comprises Chapters I, V, XII, and XVII of *The Unfortunate Traveller.* The text is that of the first edition, London, 1594.

SELECTED READING LIST. The best modern edition of Nashe is his *Complete Works*, edited by Ronald B. McKerrow, 5 vols., London, 1904–1910. Another useful edition is that edited by H. F. B. Brett-Smith, Oxford, 1920. Both have biographical introductions. *The Unfortunate Traveller* is reprinted in the volume of the Everyman Library entitled *Elizabethan and Jacobean Novels*. For background and sources, consult also *The Literature of Roguery* by Frank Wadleigh Chandler, Boston, 1907.

SUITABLE TOPICS FOR CLASS DISCUSSIONS OR REPORTS.

The character of the hero.

Nashe's sense of character compared with that of the previous authors.

His handling of scenes and his sense of the dramatic.

His personality as evident in his novel.

Realism,—how strong and how true to life.

244.—5. *Turnay and Terwin.* Tournay and Thérouanne, cities in Flanders captured in 1513 by the English under Henry VIII.

244.—12. *Coelum* etc. We seek heaven by means of folly.

245.—7. *Paulo* etc. Let us sing somewhat greater things.

245.—12. *slur a die.* Slip the die out of the box so that it does not turn.

245.—13. *pantoufle.* Slipper (a common oath).

245.—16. *Aliquid* etc. Anything lies hid that is not manifest.

246.—3. *Lord of Misrule.* The man chosen to preside over the Christmas revels in a great house.

246.—5. *welt.* Ornamentation.

246.—9. *Tendit* etc. Virtue aims at the stars.

246.—11. *aqua coelestis.* Heavenly water.

246.—31. *Three Cups.* Probably the name of a room.

247.—16. *by the great.* In large quantities.

249.—15. *hugger-mugger.* Secretly.

250.—25. *Epimenides.* Cretan of the sixth century B.C. who was supposed to have slept for fifty-seven years in a cave near Cnossus.

251.—8. *snudge.* Miser.

251.—23. *beaver's stones.* Testicles.

252.—11. *Mary-bones.* Marrow bones, i.e. the knees (jocular).

252.—3. *beadsmanry.* Position as pensioner charged with duty of praying for benefactor. *outbrothership.* Position of a brother living outside a fraternity.

252.—34. *distrain for impost of cider.* Seize to make up for tax not paid.

253.—18. *Middleborough.* Middelburg in the Low Countries.

253.—20. *Howard, Earl of Surrey.* English poet, born about 1517, beheaded 1547.

253.—33. *Vatis* etc. The English equivalent follows in the text, as in some other cases.

255.—23. *Hampton Court.* Royal palace on the Thames built by Cardinal Wolsey and surrendered to Henry VIII in 1526.

257.—6. *Hinc illae* etc. Hence come these tears.

257.—23. *Erasmus.* Dutch classical and theological scholar, 1465–1536, and author of *In Praise of Folly.*

257.—24. *More.* Sir Thomas More, 1478–1535, English statesman and author of *Utopia*, a sketch of an ideal state.

258.—29. *zany.* Attendant.

261.—15. *Maecenas.* Roman patron of arts (died 8 B.C.), who suffered for years from insomnia.

263.—11. *weasand.* Throat.

264.—25. *Hecuba.* Wife of Priam, King of Troy, who saw her children killed and her city destroyed and who finally committed suicide in captivity.

264.—37. *Cephalus.* Cephalus killed his wife Procris by mistake when she unexpectedly ran toward him while he was hunting.

265.—1. *Oedipus.* Oedipus was exposed in infancy by his father Laius to whom it had been prophesied that his son would kill him and marry his wife Jocasta. Rescued and preserved to manhood, Oedipus unwittingly fulfilled the prophecy.

266.—7. *Agamemnon.* Leader of the Greek forces at Troy. During his absence from home, Aegistheus corrupted his wife.

272.—4. *lazar.* Leper.

272.—5. *spittle.* Hospital.

275.—21. *Julian.* Julian the Apostate, Emperor of Rome, 361–363. Originally a Christian, he became pagan on ascending the throne but made an edict of toleration for all religions.

275.—23. Compare Hamlet's action in not killing Claudius while he was at prayer.

277.—22. *scruzed.* Squeezed.

THOMAS DELONEY, JACK OF NEWBURY

The text is drawn from the excellent edition by Francis Oscar Mann,—*The Works of Thomas Deloney, edited from the earliest extant editions and broadsides*, Oxford, 1912. Beginning in the early part of chapter VIII, the selection runs through chapter X.

SELECTED READING LIST. The aforementioned edition provides, not only the best text, but a most valuable introduction and notes with full accounts of Deloney's life and works. The first part of Deloney's *Gentle Craft* has been edited with introduction and notes by W. J. Halliday, Oxford, 1928. Abel Chevalley, *Thomas Deloney, le roman des métiers au temps de Shakespeare*, Paris, 1926, studies Deloney in relation to the economic history of the times.

SUITABLE TOPICS FOR CLASS DISCUSSIONS AND REPORTS.

The sense of character,—especially as compared with Nashe's.

The dialogue, compared with that of preceding novelists, especially Nashe.

The management of scenes (compare with Nashe).

The author's personality (compare with Nashe).

Traits that would appeal to the working classes.

282.—13. *stain.* Eclipse by superior beauty.

283.—14. *points.* Particles.

284.—1. *orts.* Fragments of food left from meal.

285.—16. *quotha.* "Said he" (used contemptuously in repeating other person's words).

286.—12. *bucks.* Tubs to steep clothes in lye and the clothes put through the process.

287.—18. *point.* Cord for attaching hose to doublet.

291.—1. *powdered beef.* Salted or pickled beef.

292.—21. *codlings.* Young apples.

292.—25. *sir-reverence.* With apologies to you.

293.—22. *che.* Dialect for I (ich).

295.—3. *cucking stool.* Chair to punish scolds and others. The offender was fastened into it, jeered at, and often ducked in a pond or river.

OVERBURY AND EARLE, CHARACTERS

The text here given of Overbury's *Affected Traveller* and *An Elder Brother* is that of the third edition of *A Wife Now a Widow*, London, 1614. *A Fair and Happy Milkmaid* is taken from its first appearance in the seventh edition of the same volume, London, 1616. For Earle we have used the sixth edition (augmented) of his *Microcosmography*, London, 1633.

SELECTED READING LIST. Modern editions of the characters are: Overbury, *Miscellaneous Works in Prose and Verse*, edited by E. F. Rimbault, London, 1890; Earle, *Microcosmography*, edited by A. S. West, Cambridge, 1897. Both volumes have useful introductions. *A Cabinet of Characters*, selected by Gwendolen Murphy, London, 1925, is a good collection from various authors. Two excellent articles are those by E. C. Baldwin, *The Relation of the English Character to Its Greek Prototype*, *Publications of the Modern Language Association*, 18, p. 412 ff., and *The Relation of the Seventeenth Century Character to the Periodical Essay*, *Publications of the Modern Language Association*, 19, p. 75 ff.

SUITABLE TOPICS FOR CLASS DISCUSSIONS OR REPORTS.

Realistic touches in the characters.

Style.

A comparison of Overbury and Earle: in insight into character; in style; in people or qualities they admire.

A comparison of characters by these two men with those of Addison and Steele. (How are the latter two nearer the novel?)

298.—7. *jointure.* The part of the estate left to the wife on her husband's death.

298.—17. *commonwealth's men.* Men devoted to the interests of the commonwealth; therefore, good citizens.

298.—28. *insinuation.* Stealing into favor.

298.—29. *comprehend.* Describe summarily.

300.—15. *happy.* Lucky.

302.—34. *drawer.* Waiter.

303.—20. *bewray* etc. A coarse pun on *bewray*, "to disclose," and *beray*, "to befoul."

303.—33. *St. Mary's.* St. Mary the Virgin, official university church of Oxford.

304.—6. *conceited.* Fantastic. *at large.* Fully.

304.—12. *Bellarmine.* Italian cardinal and Jesuit theologian, 1542–1621.

304.—21. *commendation.* Recommendation.

304.—32. *town-precisian.* One who is rigidly precise in rules. Used for a Puritan.

305.—14. The butler kept accounts of food and drink sold by him to the students.

305.—16. *Gallobelgicus.* Latin periodical, first issued in 1598 at Cologne.

305.—22. *vails.* Profits.

305.—24. *Keckermann.* Scientist and philosopher of Dantzig, 1573–1609.

306.—1. *manchet.* Finest wheaten bread.

306.—7. *pair.* A pack. *Post and pair.* An old game of cards.

EARL OF ORRERY, PARTHENISSA

This selection comprises pages 6–10 of the edition of *Parthenissa that most Famed Romance,* which appeared in London in 1676.

Selected Reading List. There is no modern edition of *Parthenissa,* but its plot is given in *The History of Prose Fiction* by J. C. Dunlop, London, 1911; vol. II, 563–566. The only modern life of Lord Orrery is that in the *Dictionary of National Biography.*

Suitable Topics for Class Discussions and Reports.

Extravagances in plot and character.
Extravagances in style.
Elements which might appeal to literarily minded people after the Restoration.

APHRA BEHN, OROONOKO

This text follows an original edition of 1688, containing three of Mrs. Behn's novels,—*Three Histories.*

Selected Reading List. *The Works of Aphra Behn,* edited by Montague Summers, 6 vols., London, 1915, afford a good text, with a helpful memoir in the first volume. A convenient edition of Aphra Behn's prose fiction in one volume is E. A. Baker's *The Novels of Mrs. Aphra Behn,* London, 1905. Ernest Bernbaum, *Mrs. Behn's Biography a Fiction, Publications of the Modern Language Association,* vol. 28, destroys earlier mythical details of her life, and the same author's *Mrs. Behn's "Oroonoko," Kittredge Anniversary Papers,* Boston, 1913, discusses the possibility of her trip to Surinam and reaches an adverse decision.[1] V. Sackville-West, *Aphra Behn the Incomparable Astrea,* London, 1927, is a less valuable biography.

Suitable Topics for Class Discussions and Reports.

The management of action and suspense.
The depiction of character.

[1] The discussion of this question is continued in two articles in Dutch by H. D. Benjamins in *De West-Indische Gids,* February, 1921, and February, 1927. The author contends that Mrs. Behn *may* have gone to Surinam.

The realism and effectiveness of the background.

The realism,—compared with that of *Parthenissa*; of Nashe; of Deloney.

Passages reflecting the extravagance of the French romance.

The state of society in Corymantien.

The degree of sympathy shown for the unfortunate.

318.—36. *King's Theater and dress of the Indian Queen. The Indian Queen* was a tragedy by Dryden and Sir Robert Howard, produced with great splendor in 1664.

357.—6. *Surinam.* Dutch Guiana. Settled by the English in 1652 and acquired by the Dutch in 1667 in exchange for their North American colonies.

371.—19. *The Mall.* Broad promenade in St. James Park, London.

372.—12 ff. From this point on Mrs. Behn uses masculine and feminine pronouns indiscriminately in referring to the tiger.

393.—19. *Newgate.* Great prison in London.

393.—35. *nemini contradicente.* With no one disagreeing.

394.—2. *White Hall.* Royal palace in London.

394.—30. *mobile.* Common people, mob.